ABUSES AND EXCUSES

How To Hold Bad Nursing Homes Accountable

Jeffrey Powless

Boatdock Publishing, LLC

INDIANAPOLIS, INDIANA

Boatdock Publishing, LLC
P.O. Box 36723
Indianapolis, IN 46236
www.boatdockpublishing.com

Ordering Information:
Quantity sales. Special discounts are available on quantity purchases by corporations, associations, and others. For details, contact Boatdock Publishing, L.L.C. at the address above.

Library of Congress Cataloguing-in Publication Data
Powless, Jeffrey.
Abuses and Excuses: How To Hold Bad Nursing Homes Accountable
Includes bibliographical references.
1. Nursing homes – United States. 2. Nursing Homes – Neglect and Abuse – United States. 3. Nursing Homes – Laws and Legislation.

Abuses and Excuses: How To Hold Bad Nursing Homes Accountable / Powless, J. -- 1st edition. 418 p., soft cover
United States of America

ISBN: 978-0-9990270-0-4

AUTHOR'S NOTE

There are various episodes and vignettes throughout this book that are based upon actual cases in which I have served as lead counsel. However, these episodes and vignettes, while based upon actual cases, are composites and have had the names of all litigants, witnesses, and counsel, and other identifying details, changed. Accordingly, any similarity between the fictionalized names and other particulars in this book and the real names is strictly coincidental.

PUBLISHER'S NOTE

This publication is designed to provide accurate and authoritative information regarding the subject matter covered. It is sold and/or distributed however, with the understanding that the publication, distribution, and reading of this book does not create any attorney-client relationship between the reader and the author and/or publisher, and that neither the publisher nor the author are engaged in rendering any legal, or other professional service or advice. If legal advice or other expert assistance is required by the reader, the direct services of a competent professional person should be sought.

The publisher, editors, and authors must disclaim any liability, in whole or in part, arising from the information in this book. The reader is hereby urged to verify any reference material prior to any reliance thereupon. Since this book deals with legal, medical, and other technical information, the reader is urged to consult with an appropriate licensed professional prior to taking any action that might involve any interpretation or application of any laws or other information within the realm of a licensed professional practice. It is also further expressly understood that by reading this book, the reader acknowledges that no attorney-client relationship is hereby created and the reader is responsible for verifying the information contained herein to the extent reader relies thereupon.

ACKNOWLEDGEMENTS

I often hear people use the term *individual achievement*. I'm not sure that I can think of many, or frankly, perhaps any, true examples of a so-called "individual achievement." I know for certain that this book is *not* an individual achievement.

Aside from having the good fortune of being born in the United States during the 20th century, and thus being afforded the freedom, technology infrastructure, and resources to write and publish a book on any topic of my choosing, I am fortunate to have had the assistance and support of so many others in preparing me for, and assisting me with, the writing of this book.

To begin with, I thank my wife Tricia and my wonderful children, Justin, Clark, and Brooke. They provide inspiration, support and motivation for everything I do, and allowed me to borrow time from our activities together to complete this project. In addition, Tricia was enormously helpful in taking care of the many things that must be done in order to transform a raw manuscript into an actual book that can reach the public, and hopefully make an actual difference.

I thank Debbie Curtis, my researcher, editor, and writing coach, who guided and motivated me during the many months it took to complete this book. Without her tremendous talents, insight, and humor to help power this project, this book may never have come together, and certainly would not have come together as well.

I thank my parents, Jane and Ron, who have provided me with a lifetime of love and support. Nothing that I have accomplished, including the writing of this book, would have been possible without them.

I thank those with whom I work — Bethany, Jackie, Toni, Robyn, Eli, Justin and Rebecca — for bringing their talents, dedication, and hard work to bear each day to collectively further our clients' mission of standing up to the nursing home industry and demanding answers and accountability. Special thanks to Bethany for using her extraordinary skills and diligence to keep me organized throughout this project.

Finally, I thank all of my clients and the attorneys I've worked for and with over the years who have given me the valuable opportunities and experiences which have shaped my thinking, skills, and approach to being an advocate and lawyer for those in need. I've learned valuable lessons from each and every one of you, and for that I am forever grateful.

I hope this book will achieve the goal of helping others in their time of need. To whatever extent this book may do that, it is truly the achievement of many.

This book is dedicated to all of the residents/patients, families, nursing home patient advocates, ombudsmen, state surveyors, law enforcement, legislators, devoted nursing home employees, trial attorneys (including their staff), and juries willing to stand up to this powerful industry to help make a difference.

CONTENTS

In order to escape accountability for his crimes, the perpetrator does everything in his power to promote forgetting. If secrecy fails, the perpetrator attacks the credibility of his victim. If he cannot silence her absolutely, he tries to make sure no one listens.

— **Judith Lewis Herman**

BEGIN HERE: MAKING A DIFFERENCE

The book you're about to read may change the way you view the nursing home industry forever.

The first thing to understand is that a nursing home is a *business*, that someone is profiting from this business, and that the nursing home's bottom line is very much the focus of those who own and operate the facility. Second, the nursing home industry is just that — an *industry*. And it's big business, generating estimated annual revenues of more than $200 billion in the U.S. alone (National Health Policy Forum, 2014).

The primary mission of for-profit nursing home corporations is to generate profit for their shareholders. In 2014, nearly 70% (69.8%) of U.S. nursing homes were for-profit, according to the Centers for Medicare and Medicaid Services (CMS) (CMS, 2015). Even many so-called "non-profits" funnel substantial funds to profit-driven companies owned by individuals related or somehow connected to the "non-profit" company in exchange for handsome fees for "management" or "consulting" services. The bottom line is that it is the goal of almost all nursing homes to create a profit for someone, somewhere.

Perhaps it should be no surprise, then, that a closer look reveals that this industry thrives by putting profits over *people* — the patients they're obligated to protect and care for, the most vulnerable members of society. This seemingly relentless drive to increase profits at the expense of patients can manifest in so many ways, influencing practically every aspect of patient care. To save money, management knowingly — and even intentionally — understaff facilities with employees who are poorly screened, poorly trained, poorly paid, poorly supported, and poorly supervised. They ignore or conceal suspected and known abuse and neglect in order to avoid regulatory scrutiny of their operations, negative publicity and, of course, liability. They exert their considerable economic and political power to enact laws that insulate them from accountability for allowing, enabling, and perpetrating neglect and abuse. They conceal evidence, blame patients, blame families, and generate excuse after excuse in an effort to deflect responsibility for the harm that inevitably results from their financial greed and misconduct.

And they do it all while callously and purposefully turning a blind eye toward the inevitable and clearly foreseeable harm to the patients they're *paid* to help and care for.

A society is judged by how it treats its weakest members. This truth has been stated many times in many ways over the years by religious leaders, scholars, and others, but the core principle remains the same: those responsible for caring for the sick, the vulnerable, and the elderly have choices as to how they execute this responsibility. And those choices should not be guided by moral ambiguity.

Unfortunately, the manner in which our nursing home patients are being treated says a lot about the priorities of today's powerful, profit-driven nursing home industry. We know the patient neglect-abuse problem exists and persists, despite industry claims that the quality of care is improving. In fact, decades of research from a wide variety of credible sources confirms that nursing home abuse and neglect occurs, on any given day, with shocking frequency.

In the U.S. today, the corporations comprising the nursing home industry compete for the business of taking care of more than 1.4 million patients. And since the aging Baby Boomer generation is expected to increase demand for long-term residential nursing care, the persistent pattern of abuse and neglect that will be revealed in this book will, in all likelihood, only grow worse due to the industry's ever-increasing obsession with maximizing profits.

Chances are, you're reading this book because a loved one has suffered at the hands of the nursing home industry, or is at risk of doing so. Perhaps you're already aware that the nursing home industry is troubled and feel compelled to arm yourself with knowledge and tools in case they're needed. But perhaps you fear that reporting maltreatment will trigger retaliation. Perhaps you still want to believe that the nursing home staff is providing the high quality care they promised, even though you suspect that something is just not right. Or perhaps you simply don't know where to begin.

With so much misinformation out there, finding your way through this wilderness can be daunting, confusing, and even frightening. After all, the stakes are so high, the issues often so complex, and you may be forced to confront a brazen and powerful industry that too often cannot be trusted.

That's why I wrote this book. You've heard the old adage, "knowledge is power." And it's absolutely true — certainly when dealing with the nursing home industry.

I wrote this book because I've become passionate about helping victims hold the nursing home industry accountable for the abuse and neglect they inflict, day after day, year after year, in so many of our nation's nursing homes. I believe it's essential for patients, families, and anyone else who has concerns about nursing home care to understand the powerful forces that exert influence over these vulnerable patients' health and well-being and become educated about the rights and remedies that can help protect patients from becoming victims of abuse and neglect. My goal is to help you avoid the pitfalls and land mines, and help empower you to make a difference.

In this book, you'll learn the steps that patients, families, nursing home employees, and others can take to hold the nursing home industry accountable, and ultimately, case by case, significantly improve the quality of nursing home care everywhere. My goal is to share strategies for holding nursing homes accountable with as many patients, families, and concerned citizens as I can. Collectively, we can (and will) make a difference.

Over the years, my law firm has been privileged to work with some extraordinary patients, families, and eldercare advocates to do just that. Because of our clients' principled commitment to exposing the abuse and neglect they've suffered in hopes that others may avoid such a fate, we've learned that those responsible for bad nursing homes do take notice — and can be held accountable — if you force them to.

By the time you finish this book, you'll be empowered to take the right steps to help ensure that your loved one receives the quality care that he or she deserves.

If you've ever wondered…

- Is nursing home abuse and neglect prevalent, or is it just my nursing home?
- What are the signs of neglect and abuse?
- How can I research a nursing home before choosing one?
- How do I know if what happened to my loved one was caused by abuse or neglect?
- Do I have a right to obtain a patient's nursing home medical records?
- Are there any advocates who can help solve problems before a patient gets hurt?
- How do I go about having my complaint about abuse or neglect investigated by independent state investigators?
- How do I know if I can or should pursue a civil lawsuit against a nursing home?
- Should I contact law enforcement about suspected abuse or neglect?

…you'll learn the answers to these questions, and many more, in the pages that follow.

Abuses and Excuses reveals the firsthand knowledge, experiences, and insights of an attorney who has spent years in the trenches investigating nursing home neglect and abuse. You'll learn what *really* goes on behind the scenes in nursing homes, and how to battle the industry culture of cover-up to find answers and accountability. The tools and strategies you'll learn in these pages are not just theories that only work sometimes and only for some people. They're actionable steps that you can begin taking *immediately* to help any patient who has suffered — or is at risk of suffering — mistreatment in any nursing home facility in this country.

I believe nursing home neglect and abuse is one of the largest, most dangerous, and preventable health threats in the United States today. If you think I'm exaggerating or overstating the case, please read the chapters that follow, consider the facts, and decide for yourself. Hopefully, *Abuses and Excuses* will be both a journey of empowerment and a road map to guide patients and families to the accountability and justice they deserve.

PART I: THE PERFECT STORM

"A particularly bad or critical state of affairs,
arising from a combination of negative
circumstances and factors that, in confluence,
result in an event of unusual magnitude."

1

WHY BOTHER?

In matters of truth and justice, there is no difference
between large and small problems, for issues concerning
the treatment of people are all the same.

— Albert Einstein

Some skeptics ask: "Why bother suing nursing homes? Their patients are already old and sick. It's not as if they have a great quality of life anyway."

Here is but one of many reasons we should "bother..."

Charles was born in 1923, a few years before the Great Depression. When he was 11 years old, his father died and his family lost their home. He, his mother and sisters had to rely on hard work and the mercy of relatives and friends to make ends meet. Charles spent virtually all of his time after school working to help meet the family's needs.

At age 14, Charles met Florence, a sensitive, beautiful, vibrant classmate with whom he instantly connected. They became fast friends. After graduating high school together in 1941, they couldn't bear being apart and began dating. They eventually married in April 1942.

World War II began, and Charles joined the Army Air Corps. After leaving military service, Charles and Florence had their first child. They would have three other children in the coming years, who would later spoil them with many grandchildren and great-grandchildren.

Charles worked during the daytime and attended law school at night on the GI Bill. Soon after earning his law license, however, Charles — with Florence' blessing — felt called to enter the clergy. Charles completed his theological training and spent the remainder of his work life as an ordained minister. Florence served as a volunteer in Charles' churches, helping with the choir, missionary groups, teaching Sunday School, and participating in other activities.

Charles and Florence were virtually inseparable throughout their adult life together. They enjoyed nearly every meal together, a ritual that continued on through retirement.

But in 2010, Florence' health began to decline. She fell at home and broke her hip, which limited her mobility. She also developed a problem with swallowing and needed a feeding tube to help her meet her nutritional requirements.

Charles was a diligent caregiver. He assumed full responsibility for helping Florence take care of herself at home and was trained to provide care related to her feeding tube. He told people that he viewed this not as a burden but as a blessing. "It brought us even closer together because we spend all of our time in each other's company."

While Florence was no longer physically capable of taking the long walks she had always so enjoyed, she and Charles spent much of their time together on long strolls down memory lane. As always, they were content just being together.

In June of 2014, Charles injured his back while attending to their bird feeder and was temporarily unable to help Florence with her daily routine. He grew concerned that Florence might need immediate assistance and he'd be unable to promptly and adequately assist her. So they made the difficult decision that while Charles recovered from his back injury, Florence would be admitted, temporarily, to a nearby nursing home to ensure her safety and well-being. As difficult as it was for both Charles and Florence to contemplate being apart, they knew they'd be together again once Charles' back pain subsided. And despite his pain, Charles could visit Florence at the nursing home.

The nursing home offered assurances that they were fully equipped to take care of Florence, promoting the fact that they were staffed 24/7 with professional nursing caregivers who would make sure Florence received the attention and care she needed.

But just ten days later, the unexpected happened...

Charles was awakened by a telephone call in the middle of the night from a nursing home employee who bluntly stated: "We're informing you that your wife just died." Charles was so overwhelmed by shock and grief that he couldn't process the news. This shock would linger.

Charles did recover from his back injury. But sometime later, after Florence' funeral, Charles — still in the grip of sadness and grief — became determined to find out what happened to Florence on the night she died. According to the death certificate, she died of "aspiration pneumonia."

How could she have died so suddenly and unexpectedly? Had Florence's needs been neglected by the nursing home staff?

Charles requested copies of Florence' medical records from the nursing home, and believing that the matter warranted further investigation, requested that the Indiana State Department of Health (ISDH) investigate. The ISDH investigation found that the nursing home failed to comply with state and federal nursing home regulations and failed to provide necessary care and services to Florence.

The ISDH required the nursing home to prepare a plan for correcting these deficiencies, but the facility was not required to pay any monetary penalty or fine of any kind. This is not uncommon, unfortunately, even when nursing homes are found to have committed serious care violations.

Charles asked our law firm to investigate. After reviewing documents related to the case and deposing Florence' physician, who was called on the night she died, Charles learned the following details:

- To prevent choking, the nursing home should have elevated the head of Florence' bed to 30 degrees as the doctor ordered, but nursing home records indicate that the staff didn't;

- The nursing home staff should have routinely checked and attended to Florence' feeding tube to prevent choking or other injury, but nursing home records indicate that the nursing staff didn't;

- The nursing staff should have administered oxygen to Florence when they knew she had vomited, was having trouble breathing, and her blood oxygen saturation levels dropped below 90%, but nursing home records indicate that the nursing staff didn't administer oxygen;

- Even though the nursing home staff knew Florence was having difficulty breathing, was not getting enough oxygen, and was declining toward death, they never even called 911 or requested an ambulance;

- Nursing home records indicate that no one checked Florence' vital signs for at least 40 minutes as her condition deteriorated prior to her death;

- A nursing home staff member later claimed that Florence' doctor refused to order her transport to the hospital; however, no such conversation or phone call was ever documented in Florence' nursing home medical record; and,

- Although a physician's order stated that Florence should be resuscitated if needed, nursing staff never attempted to resuscitate her.

The bottom line is that this horrible tragedy of errors was preventable. Of course, Charles was never told of these multiple, blatant care failures by any nursing home representative. It is only because Charles chose to obtain records, investigate, and prosecute this matter with the help of counsel that these horrific facts came to light.

Charles invested more than 70 years in his wonderful, lifelong relationship with Florence. Certainly their relationship and good fortune should not have been stolen from them that day, that way. Charles knows his efforts would not bring Florence back, of course. But they would secure some degree of accountability that would hopefully serve to help protect others. This was reason enough for Charles, who wanted to make a difference in order to honor his wife, who was wrongfully taken from him.

So, why bother? Because life is precious. Because no one has the right to decide that someone else's life is not important enough to matter. And because no one should be mistreated like too many nursing home patients are mistreated every day in this country.

SCOPE OF THE PROBLEM

All nursing homes that receive Medicare funding (i.e., virtually all of them) explicitly agree and promise to help every resident "attain or maintain the highest practicable physical, mental and psychosocial well–being." Yet, most of us have had a family member or other loved one who resided in a nursing home and suffered a far different experience. Far too many of us have heard achingly similar tales about the most vulnerable among us suffering abuse and neglect at the hands of the very people to whom their care was entrusted. It has become startlingly clear that the nursing home industry is failing to protect its residents from abuse and neglect.

Elder mistreatment has a devastating impact on its victims, robbing them of dignity, quality of life and hope. For decades now, the industry has been plagued by reports of abuse and neglect — study after study reveals the extent and severity of this shameful problem. Nursing home abuse and neglect is also, as you'll soon see, underreported, underestimated, and under-recognized.

In other words, the problem is even worse than we think.

Most nursing home residents are vulnerable due to their decreased ability for self-care and chronic illnesses that limit their physical and cognitive functioning. Many are either unable to report abuse and neglect, or are fearful that such reporting will lead to retaliation, especially if they're dependent on — and at the mercy of — nursing facility staff for virtually every aspect of their daily existence: bedding, food, medical treatments, hygiene needs, and mobility. In fact, research suggests that the 2.5 million residents in long-term nursing care facilities, which are presumably staffed by health care professionals, are at much higher risk for abuse and neglect than older adults who live at home (Hawkes, 2003).

Who's At Risk?

By the end of 2014, just over 1.4 million residents were living in nursing homes in the U.S. Nearly two-thirds (65.6%) are women (CMS Annual Nursing Home Data Compendium, 2015). Around 1 million live in residential care facilities, variously referred to as *personal care homes, adult congregate living facilities, domiciliary care homes, adult care homes, homes for the aged*, and *assisted living facilities* (Hawkes et al, 2003).

But ultimately, it could be any of us.

National Mortality Followback Survey researchers estimate that more than two-fifths (43%) of us who turned 65 in 1990 or later will enter a nursing home at some point before we die, and 55% of those will reside in a nursing facility for at least one year. The probability of living in a nursing home increases dramatically with age, of course — rising from 17% for those aged 65 to 74 to 60% for people aged 85 to 94. And because women live longer than men, their risk of a nursing home stay over their lifetimes is higher (52% versus 33%) (NMFS, 1993).

> **Researchers estimate that 43% of adults who turned 65 in 1990 or later will enter a nursing home.**

So while only around 2.5 million people living in a residential long-term care facility may be at risk for abuse and neglect on any given day, far more of us may be at risk when we count those of us who will experience shorter-term stays in nursing homes.

The federal government has long been aware of the nursing home abuse-neglect problem. Beginning with the widely publicized late-1970s Congressional hearings on the mistreatment of the elderly, policy makers and practitioners have sought ways to protect golden-agers from abuse. Congressional passage of the Omnibus Budget Reconciliation Act (OBRA) of 1987 (OBRA 1987. Pub L. No. 100-203), in fact, implemented the most sweeping reforms to nursing home regulation since the passage of Medicaid and Medicare, addressing many areas of resident care and quality of life. The Act explicitly stated that "residents had the right to be free from verbal, sexual, physical, and mental abuse, including corporal punishment and involuntary seclusion," (42 CFR Ch. IV (10-1-98 Edition) §483.13 (b)) and limited the use of physical restraints and inappropriate use of psychotropic medications.

Yet a 2001 Congressional report found that over 30% of U.S. nursing homes (5,283 in 2003) had been cited for nearly 9,000 abuse violations that, in a two-year period, had the potential to cause harm to residents (U.S. House of Representatives, Waxman, 2001). Over one-third of those abuse violations were severe enough to cause actual harm to residents or place them in immediate jeopardy of death or serious injury. Nearly 10% of all nursing homes (1,601) were cited for abuse violations that caused actual harm, or worse, to residents.

The state inspection reports and citations reviewed describe many instances of appalling physical, sexual, and verbal abuse of residents. Some nursing homes were cited because a staff member committed acts of physical or sexual abuse against the residents under his or her care. Others were cited because they failed to protect vulnerable residents from violent residents who beat or sexually assaulted them. After all, isn't it ultimately the staff's responsibility to protect vulnerable residents from resident perpetrators of abuse?

It's important to note that over 40% — more than 3,800 — of these abuse violations were discovered only after a formal complaint was filed.

So, yes, we're paying more attention to nursing home industry abuse and neglect now. But we still aren't fully addressing the shameful problem that those responsible — and sometimes the neglected and abused themselves — want to conceal.

What Constitutes Abuse?

While there's no universal agreement as to exactly what constitutes neglect and abuse, definitions used by various government agencies are very similar. *Abuse* is generally considered to be the willful infliction of injury, unreasonable confinements, intimidation, or punishment that results in physical harm, pain, or mental anguish. Importantly, this includes isolation and the deprivation of goods or services that are necessary to attain or maintain a patient's physical, mental, and psychosocial well-being. Abuse may take the form of physical abuse, sexual abuse, and emotional or psychological abuse.

For example, *physical abuse* includes: acts of violence such as striking (with or without an object), hitting, beating, pushing, shoving, shaking, slapping, kicking, pinching, burning, inappropriate use of drugs and physical restraints, force-feeding, or physical punishment of any kind.

Sexual abuse is defined as non-consensual sexual contact of any kind with another person, including sexual contact with any person incapable of giving consent. It includes, for example: unwanted touching, all types of sexual assault or battery, such as rape, sodomy, coerced nudity, and sexually explicit photographing.

Emotional or psychological abuse is defined as the infliction of anguish, pain, or distress through verbal or nonverbal acts. It includes, for example: verbal assaults, insults, threats, intimidation, humiliation, and harassment. In addition, treating an older person like an infant; isolating an elderly person from his/her family, friends, or regular activities; giving an older person the "silent treatment;" and enforced social isolation are examples of emotional/psychological abuse.

Neglect is defined as the refusal or failure to fulfill any part of a person's obligations or duties to an elder. It may include the failure to provide goods and services necessary to avoid physical harm, mental anguish, or mental illness. Typically, this may involve a refusal or failure to provide an elderly person with life necessities such as food, water, clothing, shelter, personal hygiene, medicine, comfort, personal safety, and other essentials included in an implied or agreed-upon responsibility to an elder. Neglect may also include failure of a person who has fiduciary responsibilities to provide care for an elder (e.g., pay for necessary home care services), or the failure on the part of an in-home service provider to provide necessary care.

We'll take a closer look at some examples of the injuries and harms that can result from various forms of abuse and neglect in the *Harms* section of this book.

HOW WIDESPREAD IS THE PROBLEM?
A LOOK AT THE NUMBERS.

> **MYTH:** Neglect and abuse in nursing homes is a relatively rare occurrence.
>
> **REALITY:** In a study of 2,000 nursing home residents, 44% said they'd been abused, and 95% said they'd been neglected, or seen another resident neglected (Broyles, 2000).

How is nursing home neglect and abuse reported? Generally, by residents and their family members, nursing home staff, healthcare practitioners, long-term care ombudsmen, (officials appointed to investigate individual complaints against nursing facilities), state investigators/surveyors, and other sources, such as nurse aide registries. Each of these sources of information confirm that the U.S. nursing home industry is allowing neglect and abuse to not only occur, but to occur with alarming frequency. In fact, the statistics are profoundly disturbing.

Reports By Patients and Family

In focus group interviews, surveys, and individual interviews conducted by the Atlanta Ombudsmen, a startling 95% of Georgia nursing home residents interviewed reported that they had experienced neglect or witnessed other residents being neglected (Atlanta Long-Term Care Ombudsman Program, 2000). Appalling instances of abuse and neglect included: residents being left for hours or even days in clothing and bedding that was wet or soiled with feces; not being turned and positioned, causing pressure ulcers which, improperly treated, led to sepsis and death; ignoring residents' call lights without providing assistance; residents scalded after being placed in too-hot tubs of water; not receiving enough help at mealtimes, thus, not getting enough to eat or drink, resulting, in some cases, in death from malnutrition and dehydration.

This survey found that 44% of residents reported that they had been abused; 48% reported that they had been treated roughly; for example…

They throw me like a sack of feed ... [and] that leaves marks on my breast.

— Georgia Nursing Home Resident

Thirty-eight percent of the residents reported that they had witnessed abuse of other residents, and 44% said they had seen other residents being treated roughly. For example, one resident reported:

My roommate — they throw him in the bed. They handle him any kind of way. He can't take up for himself.

— Georgia Nursing Home Resident

Reports By Nursing Home Employees

Oh, yeah. I've seen abuse. Things like rough handling, pinching, pulling too hard on a resident to make them do what you want. Slapping, that too. People get so tired, working mandatory overtime, short-staffed. It's not an excuse, but it makes it so hard for them to respond right.

— Certified Nursing Aide (CNA) from South Carolina
(Hawes et al., 2003)

The results of studies that interview nursing home staff about committing or witnessing resident abuse and neglect suggest the problem may be even more widespread and severe than reports by residents and their families.

Highlights of key studies include:

- One 2010 study found that over 50% of nursing home staff actually *admitted* to mistreating (e.g. physical violence, mental abuse, neglect) older patients within a one-year period. Two thirds of those incidents involved neglect (Ben Natan & Lowenstein, 2010).

- A study of Certified Nursing Assistants (CNAs) found that 17% of CNAs had pushed, grabbed, or shoved a nursing home resident. Fifty-one percent yelled at a resident and 23% had insulted or sworn at a resident (Pillemer & Hudson, 1993).

- Investigative surveys of CNAs found that an overwhelming 81% of them had observed — and 40 percent had *committed* — at least one incident of psychological or emotional abuse during a 12-month period. Psychological abuse included yelling in anger (observed by 70%), insulting or swearing at a resident (observed by 50%), inappropriate isolation, threatening to hit or throw an object, or denying food or privileges (Pillemer & Moore, 1989).

- A 2000 CNA focus group study of 31 nursing facilities (MacDonald, 2000) supported the Pillemer and Moore findings, reporting widespread verbal abuse by staff:

  ○ 58% of the CNAs observed instances of yelling at a resident in anger;

  ○ 36% observed swearing at a resident;

  ○ 11% witnessed staff threatening to hit or throw something at a resident.

  ○ 25% of CNAs also witnessed rough treatment of residents, including staff isolating a resident beyond what was needed to manage his/her behavior; 21 percent witnessed restraint of a resident beyond what was necessary;

  ○ 11% observed a resident being denied food as punishment.

  ○ 21% witnessed a resident being pushed, grabbed, shoved, or pinched in anger;

  ○ 12% witnessed staff slapping a resident;

  ○ 7% witnessed a resident being kicked or hit with a fist;

  ○ 3% saw staff throw something at a resident;

  ○ 1% saw a resident being hit with an object.

In any other domestic environment in our society, we would comfortably classify such treatment of any child, any human — even our pets, for that matter — as abuse, behavior that warrants immediate intervention by law enforcement and perhaps a social services agency. Why, then, is it so hard to ensure that the same standards and remedies are applied to residents in nursing homes, many of whom are as utterly helpless to defend themselves as newborn babies?

Reporting By State Surveyors / Investigators
State and Federal Citations for Abuse and Neglect

> **MYTH:** Most adverse events that cause injuries or deaths in nursing homes are inevitable or unnavoidable.
>
> **REALITY:** Most such adverse events are "clearly or likely preventable." (According to the Inspector General of the DHHS)

Nursing facilities that participate in the Medicare and/or Medicaid programs are subjected to an unannounced survey each year, conducted by state survey agencies, typically located in the state's department of health. They follow a survey protocol developed, tested, and validated by the federal government. But as you'll soon see, this survey process has flaws. For example, nursing home staff know approximately when these surveys will take place and can take measures in the interim to remedy or improve problems, if only temporarily, in order to avoid being cited for substandard care.

Nonetheless, this publicly-conducted survey is the only objective, independent assessment of a nursing facility's quality of care, other than in instances when the investigators are called upon to report a specific complaint that has been made about a facility. So, while surveys are incapable of detecting *all* abuse and neglect, they can still shed additional light on the scope of the abuse-neglect problem. And, to be clear, the surveys have demonstrated that U.S. nursing homes have failed time and again to even meet the minimum regulatory standards required to ensure adequate care to the patients.

For example, a U.S. House of Representatives Report found that 1 in 3 nursing homes were cited for violations of federal standards from 1999-2001 that had the potential to cause harm or had caused actual harm. Nearly 1 of 10 nursing homes had violations that caused residents harm, serious injury, or placed them in jeopardy of death (U.S. House of Representatives,

Waxman, 2001). And we know that elder mistreatment is, in fact, strongly associated with increased mortality rates (Gibbs, 2004).

A 2001 U.S. House of Representatives Report included these key statistics on abuse violations over a two-year study period:

- Over 30% of U.S. nursing homes (5,283) were cited for an abuse violation.

- Overall, 1,327 nursing homes were cited for more than one abuse violation. A total of 305 homes were cited for three or more abuse violations, and 192 nursing homes were cited for five or more abuse violations.

- Over 2,500 of the abuse violations were serious enough to cause actual harm to residents or to place residents in immediate jeopardy of death or serious injury. Nearly 10% of U.S. nursing homes (1,601) were cited for abuse violations that caused actual harm to residents or worse.

More recently, a 2014 report by the Inspector General of the Department of Health and Human Services (Levinson, OIG, 2014) confirmed a shocking number of preventable injuries and deaths due to neglect, finding that one third-of nursing home residents in a Medicare-nursing home stay suffered an adverse event or other harm in the month of August 2011, and that most of the events were "clearly or likely preventable."

Key highlights of this 2014 OIG report include:

- Physician reviewers found that 59% of the adverse events and incidents of temporary harm were preventable, attributing much of the preventable harm to "substandard treatment, inadequate resident monitoring, and failure or delay of necessary care." Preventable events included: 66% of medication events; 57% of resident care events; 52% of infection events.

- Few staffing deficiencies were cited and, in many cases, even the most serious deficiencies — those identified as causing residents "immediate jeopardy" — were never sanctioned in any way.

- In a one-month period, an estimated 1.5 percent of Medicare nursing home residents (1,538 people) experienced adverse events that contributed to their deaths. For most of them, death was "likely not an expected outcome."

- ◦ These adverse events were related to:
- ◦ Medication (37%)
- ◦ Resident care (37%)
- ◦ Infection (26%), including aspiration pneumonia and other respiratory infections (10%)
- Temporary events under the same three categories included:
  - ◦ Medication (43%)
  - ◦ Resident care (40%), including pressure ulcers (19%)
  - ◦ Infections (17%)

In 2014, the Centers for Medicare & Medicaid Services (CMS) also reported deficiencies (Annual Nursing Home Data Compendium, Centers for Medicare & Medicaid Services, (CMS, 2015):

- U.S. nursing homes were cited for 5.7 health deficiencies each, on average, per state, totaling 89,148 citations (i.e., 5.7 x 15,640).
- 95.1% of the Health Deficiencies cited had potential for "more than minimal harm" involved "actual harm," or involved "immediate jeopardy to resident health or safety."

THE BOTTOM LINE

So what's the take-away? The bottom line is two-fold…

First, patients, families, nursing home employees, and state surveyors *all* report that nursing home neglect and abuse is a decades-old problem that continues to this day with shocking frequency and tragic results. As alarming as the statistics are, they actually reflect only a portion of the problem for reasons that will be discussed in more detail later.

To add insult to injury, over 50% of the residents who experienced harm were hospitalized for treatment, costing Medicare (thus, U.S. taxpayers) an estimated $208 million in the month of August 2011 alone. Thus, not so indirectly, we are all forced to help subsidize the financial burden of the nursing home industry's neglect and abuse. And this cost is on top of the Medicare and Medicaid payments that we, as taxpayers, pay the nursing home industry in exchange for promising to properly care for their patients in the first place.

But second, and importantly, there *is* hope. Despite the staggering enormity of the abuse-neglect problem, there are steps that you can take to hold bad nursing homes accountable. This book will show you how.

In the chapters that follow, you'll learn how to research nursing homes, identify troubled facilities, and spot the warning signs of abuse or neglect. You'll also learn how to take definitive steps to help ensure that a nursing home is providing proper care — and if they aren't, how to hold them accountable.

2

TIP OF THE ICEBERG

All we know is still infinitely less than all that remains unknown.

— William Harvey

Most scientists say that only around 10 percent of the typical iceberg is visible above the ocean waterline. But as we now know, it was that other 90 percent, submerged deep beneath the surface, that sank the Titanic.

If you spot the tip of an iceberg, you know there's more. There's always more. It's always worse than it seems.

So, as disturbing as the reports, studies and statistics in Chapter 1 are, we have every reason to believe that they're only the tip of the iceberg that is the *true* hulking presence of abuse and neglect within the U.S. nursing home industry. How can that be? We know that the abuse-neglect problem is widespread across the industry… why is it so difficult to pinpoint exactly how pervasive it is?

The answer lies within the data sources, in the abilities and motivations of those from whom reports of abuse and neglect are gathered. Data obtained from patients, families, nursing home employees, state surveyors, ombudsmen, and other officials is prone to underestimating the true extent of the problem. In fact, there is persuasive evidence that underreporting of abuse and neglect occurs with alarming frequency [at every level] and always has. Let's explore the reasons…

UNDERREPORTING BY PATIENTS AND FAMILY MEMBERS

The first problem is that many patients, unfortunately, are unable to report neglect and abuse due to cognitive or physical limitations that impact their ability to clearly communicate. Whether this incapacity is due to dementia, speech or language difficulties, or any other impairment, many patients simply cannot make their own needs known, much less clearly articulate instances of abuse and neglect that may have occurred with no other witnesses around.

Studies that gather reports of neglect and abuse by patients and family members reveal a variety of other reasons for underreporting. Focus group interviews, surveys, and individual interviews conducted by Atlanta Ombudsmen found that some residents and family members were reluctant to complain, evidently feeling that there were other mechanisms for resolving problems, such as speaking with the administrator or working through the resident and family councils.

Others feared that a formal complaint might generate retaliation by the facility against the resident. This fear is understandable, but it appears to account for roughly half of underreporting. For example, 44% of the residents who had witnessed abuse of other residents didn't report it, and 50% of those individuals didn't report the abuse because they feared retaliation. In addition, 38% of these residents didn't file formal complaints because they believed the process to be futile, stating that complaining "wouldn't do any good" (Atlanta Long-Term Care Ombudsman Program, 2000).

50% of patients and families who witness abuse of another patient choose not to report it out of fear of retaliation by the nursing home staff.

Now, it's also important to bear in mind that families whose loved one has been injured due to neglect or abuse are typically immersed, unexpectedly, in an extraordinarily stressful situation, one that dramatically impacts their own lives. They must focus on caring for their loved one and resolving the abuse-neglect problem while attempting to maintain some semblance of control over their own work and home responsibilities. This reality was reflected in another study, in which some families reported that they didn't file formal complaints because all their energy was focused on getting adequate medical care by moving the abused loved one to the hospital, then finding a new nursing home for him/her following acute care discharge (Bowers et al, 2001).

The ripple effect of nursing home industry abuse and neglect can be devastating.

Another problem is that family members may hesitate to report abuse or neglect because they may not be able to *prove* that clearly suspicious injuries were the result of neglect or abuse. Focus groups and interviews with residents and family have revealed families finding their loved ones with bruises and abrasions, unexplained falls (some of which caused fractures), and residents suffering for days with broken bones before the family or resident's physician were even notified (Hawes et al., 2001). For example…

> *Have I seen abuse? No, not directly. But I've come in and found my mom battered and bruised. I mean, her whole face was bruised and swollen, the backs of her hands and arms were bruised, as if she tried to protect herself.*

> — Daughter of a Texas Resident

Another complicating factor which may account for the underestimation of the abuse-neglect problem is that there have been relatively few studies of elder abuse, compared to child abuse (National Center on Elder Abuse, 1998; Kleinschmidt et al, 1997; Lachs and Pillemer, 1995). Unfortunately, there doesn't seem to be as much passion for studying abuse of individuals who are aging out of our society. But there is some evidence to suggest that elder abuse in residential long-term care facilities may, in fact, be nearly as widespread as child abuse (National Center on Elder Abuse, 1998; Kleinschmidt et al, 1997).

Yet, even with all the limitations attached to the reporting of abuse and neglect by patients and families, studies clearly indicate that the problem exists, and that the scope of the problem is significant.

What can you do about it?

Because some patients are unable to report abuse and neglect themselves, others must do it for them. You shouldn't feel that you must have *proof* to report abuse or neglect — you should report abuse or neglect if you *suspect* it. It's not the responsibility of the patient or the family to secure evidence to prove a case of neglect or abuse. It's up to state investigators and other authorities to interview witnesses, review evidence available to them by virtue of their positions, and determine if sufficient proof exists to hold the nursing home accountable. While fear of retaliation is always a concern, keep in mind that reports to state investigators can be made anonymously, and investigators can take steps to keep the identity of the complainant confidential.

> **MYTH:** One should not report abuse or neglect unless they have absolute proof.
>
> **REALITY:** Anyone can, and should, report suspected nursing home abuse and neglect because of the potential patient harm. It is the job of the professional investigators to obtain and evaluate the evidence.

Reporting suspected abuse and neglect is one of the essential first steps to holding nursing homes accountable for their actions, and one of the crucial means by which others can learn of problems associated with a particular facility and/or corporate nursing home chain. In the *Empowerment* section of this book, you'll learn how to properly report suspected abuse and neglect and get results.

UNDERREPORTING BY HEALTHCARE PROFESSIONALS AND NURSING HOME EMPLOYEES

Healthcare providers, too, have been found to underreport neglect and abuse — even healthcare providers who were not personally involved in a particular instance of abuse or neglect. When a nursing home patient is abused or neglected and suffers an injury or harm that cannot be ignored, they're typically seen by a physician either in the nursing home, an emergency room, or in an outpatient setting. But some evidence suggests that physicians "rarely or never" report suspected cases of elder abuse in nursing facility settings (e.g., U.S. Department of Health and Human Services, OIG, 1990b).

Other studies report similar findings with respect to staff in hospitals. Several studies have found that hospital and emergency department (ED) personnel, such as physicians and nurses, are often unfamiliar with mandatory elder abuse reporting laws (Blakely & Dolon, 1991); Clark-Daniels et al, 1990; Wolf, 1988).

Another study found that only 27% of emergency physicians had established protocols for identifying and addressing suspected cases of elder abuse (McNamara et al, 1992). The reality is, few cases of elder abuse are ever reported to authorities (Pillemer & Finkelhor, 1988) by the very health care professionals who are in a position to detect abuse and neglect.

MYTH: We can rely on doctors and other healthcare professionals to report abuse and neglect.

REALITY: Studies show doctors and other healthcare providers grossly under-report evidence of elder abuse and neglect.

A Florida study of emergency department (ED) nurses found that 83% reported seeing what they believed to be evidence of abuse of elderly individuals admitted to an emergency room for treatment, but only 36% actually reported this suspected abuse (Reynolds & Stanton, 1983).

Studies that involved interviews with Indiana and Michigan ED nurses, home health agency nurses, nurses in acute care (i.e., medical or surgical units) or long-term psychiatric facilities revealed observations of appalling abuse, including instances of severe injuries, such as skull fractures, sexual assault, bites, and severe bruising (Pettee, 1997). Yet, even though 73% of the nurses observed suspected abuse, only 36% reported it! Surprisingly, the majority of nurses (59% in Indiana; 66% in Michigan) were unaware of laws on elder abuse. And many (43% in Indiana; 15% in Michigan) were unaware of state mandatory reporting requirements.

The motivation, for nursing home employees, to *not* report abuse and neglect are obvious. Obviously, nursing home employees who actually engage in neglectful or abusive conduct are unlikely to report themselves. Some are either grossly incompetent or stubbornly ignorant and fail to either recognize or acknowledge wrongdoing. Fear of losing their jobs, and possibly their licenses, is motivation enough to deter many nurses and nurse aides.

But tragically, the reluctance to report neglect and abuse extends to nursing home employees who were not even personally involved in a particular instance of neglect or abuse. This happens for several reasons. First, there's often a camaraderie among staff who spend long hours together in the trenches. Relationships form and those relationships may prevent some from reporting the neglectful or abusive acts of their co-workers.

Second, nursing home employees often feel pressured by management (whether spoken or unspoken) to maintain a code of silence, which provokes in these employees a fear of retribution if they dare to report neglect and abuse that will bring in state investigators who may levy fines or establish legal liability for the harm that has befallen the neglected or abused patient.

It's no secret within the industry that, too often, nursing home management expects the staff to be "team players," to "look out for each other," and to protect the reputation of the facility, even if at the expense of truth and accountability.

By way of example, facility management often willfully suppress reports and complaints by employees to authorities, as is illustrated here…

> It's kind of a nurse/nursing aide understanding that if you talk to the state surveyors or anybody — it's called "singing like a canary." You know, you're basically telling them maybe things you shouldn't tell them. Even though they need to be said, technically, you probably shouldn't tell them because you're going to get in trouble for it if they [facility management] find out you've told them.
>
> — Deposition of nursing home employee

Many patients and families tend to believe that doctors and other healthcare providers "know best" and that because of their provider-patient relationship and responsibility, they'll make sure any evidence of abuse or neglect is properly reported. Unfortunately, as the evidence in this chapter shows, this is not necessarily true. Thus patients and families assume the responsibility of reporting suspected misconduct.

And as we'll explore next, even data from government agencies and programs also likely fail to accurately reflect the full extent of the neglect and abuse perpetrated in U.S. nursing homes.

UNDERREPORTING BY GOVERNMENT AGENCIES

Underreporting is a reality that has even been recognized by the governmental authorities responsible for reporting the extent of harm from neglect and abuse. For example, the 2014 Inspector General's report (Levinson, OIG, 2014) discussed in Chapter 1 concluded that its study may have underestimated both the number of residents who were harmed and the costs to the Medicare program.

A 2008 study conducted by the U.S. General Accounting Office revealed that state surveys understate problems in licensed facilities: 70% of state surveys miss at least one deficiency and 15% of surveys miss actual harm and immediate jeopardy of a nursing home resident (U.S. Government Accounting Office, 2008).

> **The universal lack of resources, the enormous variation across jurisdictions, and the low priority given to elder abuse and neglect make it difficult to see how significant progress can be made without some federal standards and financial support for investigating, detecting, resolving and preventing elder abuse in residential care (Hawes & Kimbell, 2010).**

Surveys of the state nurse aide registries also suggest that the abuse prevalence data is underreported in OSCAR (Online Survey, Certification and Reporting). OSCAR is a data network maintained by the Centers for Medicare and Medicaid Services (CMS) in cooperation with the state long-term care surveying agencies.

Even when cases of abuse or neglect were substantiated, most states didn't cite the facilities with sanctions. In fact, 63% of the states that could provide data on deficiency citations reported that they cited deficiencies in fewer than 10% of the substantiated cases (Hawes et al, 2001).

Reports By Nurse Aide Registries

It's not that there are no laws in place to protect nursing home residents. There are. For example, federal law requires states to establish a nurse aide registry and investigate any complaints of abuse, neglect, and misappropriation of resident property by any nurse aide who works in a nursing home that participates in the Medicare or Medicaid program. And aides found to have neglected, abused or misappropriated resident property are to be barred from nursing home employment. States are also obligated by federal law to determine whether facility practices or policies caused or contributed to the substantiated abuse, neglect, or misappropriation.

But several studies provide clues as to where the investigation process can go awry. One study that surveyed the state agencies administering the nurse aide registries (Hawes et al, 2001) found that while 40 of the 51 agencies responded, they varied widely in their ability to provide data and in their systems processing, from intake to investigation and resolution. For example, only 14 states provided a detailed breakdown of the types of complaints or allegations. But for the vast majority (79%) of those states providing a breakdown of cases by type, more than 70% of the cases involved allegations of abuse. Fewer than 20% of the cases involved neglect, and less than 10% involved misappropriation.

States also vary in the rate of complaints they received. Due to very limited data systems, only about half of the participating states could provide statistics on the allegations broken down by category — abuse, neglect, or misappropriation. And there was tremendous variation in the rate of reported complaints across the states. For example, the reported number of complaints in the nurse aide registry system varied from 1 per 1,000 nursing home beds to 174 per 1,000 beds, a wide variability that was similarly reported by the U.S. Department of Health and Human Services, (OIG, 1998), which found that the rates of abuse complaints varied from less than 1% to more than 17% of the state's nursing home population.

This variability in reporting, coupled with the inability to classify complaints by type, make it difficult to establish the true prevalence of abuse complaints. Some researchers use a model rate of 10 to 20 complaints per

1000 beds. Imagine this rate applied to 1.8 million beds nationwide... that computes to a nationwide average of 18,000 to 36,000 complaints per year. If 70% of these are abuse complaints (as the above studies indicate), the annual rate would be 12,600 to 25,200 abuse complaints nationwide.

But the truth is, if all states had effective outreach and reporting systems and inclusive definitions of abuse and neglect, the true rate would almost certainly be dramatically higher.

In one state with a test-model education and outreach program, the rate was 54 complaints per 1,000 beds (Hawes et al, 2003). That rate applied nationwide would equate to 97,200 complaints, with more than 54,000 complaints about abuse. In this particular state, a much higher proportion of complaints addressed issues related to neglect (e.g., 56% were about abuse in this state, versus the national average of 70%; 38 percent were about neglect). Also, unlike other states, most of the complaints in this model state were about verbal or psychological abuse rather than physical abuse.

One state with a relatively low rate of abuse and neglect had instituted fingerprinting as part of the criminal background check for CNA applicants. As a result, the state agency reported that the number of applicants who were rejected for employment quadrupled, and that this might account for the drop in complaints.

Underreporting By Nurse Aide Registries

How do reporting agencies view abuse and neglect allegations? One study found that only 39% of the state nurse aide registry directors felt that facilities reported allegations of abuse or neglect "all of the time" (Hawes et al, 2001). Second, the differing perspectives of the nature of abuse complicated results. Some respondents labelled reports of verbal or psychological abuse as "overreporting," as illustrated by this comment from a registry director (Hawes et al, 2001)...

> Oh, there is just tremendous overreporting. You know, things like yelling at or threatening a resident. That's not really abuse, and we don't count it.
>
> — Aide Registry Director

The actual number of abuse and neglect cases reported by the nurse aide registries as *substantiated* appears to be quite small compared to the number of allegations received. This is another reason to believe that data from the nurse aide registries underestimate abuse and neglect, considering the historically low rates at which these agencies actually substantiate allegations.

The norm appears to be that only about one-third of all allegations of abuse and neglect are substantiated. Only 18% of the state agencies had substantiation rates above 60%. About 47% reported substantiation rates of 20 to 39 percent, while 35% had rates between zero and 19% (Hawes et al, 2001).

Why such low substantiation rates?

First, in some states, considerable time had elapsed between the date of the alleged incident and the formal investigation by the state nurse aide registry.

Second, if the only witnesses were the alleged perpetrator and the victim, most state registries simply closed the case, classifying it as either "insufficient evidence" or "unsubstantiated." Many nurse aide registry respondents reported being uncomfortable with this decision to essentially drop cases that were based only on the word of a resident. They attributed this decision to the fact that the penalty for a CNA found to have committed abuse was being barred for life from nursing home employment. Thus, the states felt they were held to such a high burden of proof (e.g., beyond a reasonable doubt) — or would be, if the case were appealed to an administrative law judge — that they would not accept cases viewed as being essentially "he said/she said."

Third, if the facility were unable (or unwilling) to identify the alleged perpetrator of abuse, some states would close the case, classifying the injury as "an incident of unknown origin" and the case as "unsubstantiated," as illustrated below in a case reported by the adult daughter of a resident during a family member focus group (Hawes et al, 2001).

> The DON [Director of Nursing] called me and said my mother had waked up with a bump, a red bump, on her forehead. When I got to the facility that morning, I found her horribly

bruised on her face and [the backs of her] forearms, as you can see in the photograph. She looked as if someone had gone seven rounds with her, except she has advanced Parkinson's. The only movement she can make is to raise her arms like this [indicating she could raise them defensively in front of her face]. The facility said she must have gotten them [the bruises and contusions] falling against her bedrails, but she can't move independently in bed. … So then they said they didn't know how it happened. When I called the state's toll-free number [for the abuse hotline], I was told they couldn't do anything if the facility couldn't identify the perpetrator. … Did anyone suggest I call the police? No, no one.

— Daughter of a resident

Finally, some evidence suggests that if the nursing home terminates the employment of the alleged perpetrator, or if the CNA in question quits after an alleged incident, the case is closed. However, it appears that some of these cases are never marked as "substantiated," nor is the CNA in question ever listed on the registry as barred from nursing home employment (Hawes et al, 2001).

Even directors of the state survey agencies with administrative authority for the nurse aide registries have expressed concern about the low substantiation rates. Most tend to believe that residents and families complained only when something "significant" had occurred.

But the definition of *significance* is in the eye of the beholder. Patients and their families may have a very different perspective of any given incident than the nursing home industry.

Reports By Ombudsmen

In 2013 alone, Long-Term Care Ombudsmen received 135,620 complaints involving nursing home facilities, more than 47,000 of which involved violations of resident rights, including but not limited to, patient abuse, gross neglect, and exploitation.

The Long-Term Care Ombudsman program was established in the early 1970s to "identify, investigate, and resolve individual- and systems-level complaints" that affect residents in nursing homes and residential care facilities (Huber et al, 2001). Their mission is to enhance the lives of residents through advocacy, education, and resolution of resident complaints, including those related to abuse, neglect and exploitation (e.g., financial).

Trained and designated volunteers or professional Long-Term Care Ombudsmen work to resolve complaints made by, or on behalf of, residents of long-term care facilities, which, since 1996, are summarized in the National Ombudsman Reporting System (NORS). They also educate consumers and providers about resident rights, abuse prevention and good care practices, provide regular visits to facilities, promote and participate in abuse prevention task forces and citizen organizations.

Anyone interested in the welfare of residents may use Ombudsman services, including: residents and their families, care facilities and their administrators and employees, and people considering long-term care placement. Ombudsman programs are federally funded through the Older Americans Act. Some programs also receive state funding (Huber et al, 1996).

Underreporting By Ombudsmen

In addition to the underreporting of complaints identified by the Atlanta Ombudsmen mentioned earlier (Atlanta Long-Term Care Ombudsman Program, 2000), other ombudsmen have expressed similar concerns (Administration on Aging, 2000; Tatara, 1990) for reasons such as, for example, residents and family member who do not consent to filing a formal complaint.

One survey found that 36% of the Ombudsmen reported that they viewed their role as resolving complaints with the facility and filing a complaint only if they were unable to resolve the complaint. Another 4% reported that they resolve problems between the resident or family and facility without ever filing a complaint (Hawes & Blevins, 2001), thus, we have no idea as to the basis of those complaints.

"QUALITY OF CARE IS IMPROVING…" OR IS IT?

Despite all the evidence you've just read, the nursing home industry insistently claims that the quality of resident care has improved and they cite data to prove it. How is that possible? Because their claims are largely based upon improvements in self-reported data. It's the old fox-in-the-henhouse tactic that is, as always, suspect.

Let's take a look at how the data underlying nursing home industry claims of improvement is produced…

In a 2013 Quality Report, the American Health Care Association (AHCA, 2013), which is the trade association for multi-state chains and for-profit providers, cited improvements in almost all of the quality measures from 2011 to 2012 and higher "star ratings" in the Centers for Medicare & Medicaid Services' (CMS's) Five-Star Quality Rating System. According to AHCA reports, in the years between 2009 and 2013, the number of five star facilities increased from 11.8% to 19.6% and the number of one-star facilities decreased from 22.5% to 13.5%.

Sounds good (or at least *better*), right? But even if these ratings improvements are true, the overall improvement in the industry's quality of care would only be marginally better. And even if it's true that 19.6% of nursing homes are 5-star-rated, what about the other 80.4% of them? Would you deliberately choose a nursing home with less than a 5-star rating for your loved one?

And worse, the reality is that improved star ratings do not necessarily even reflect improvement in residents' quality of care and quality of life. As you're about to learn, they reflect the self-reported, unaudited claims of improvement by the nursing facilities themselves.

Nursing Home Compare. Since the Clinton Administration, the federal government has maintained a website called Nursing Home Compare that provides information to the public about nursing facilities that participate in Medicare and Medicaid programs. Centers for Medicare & Medicaid Services (CMS) reports state health survey results, staffing levels, and quality measures (QMs). Federal sanctions are imposed against facilities cited with deficiencies that violate federal standards of care. (Nursing Home Compare does not, however, include state-imposed sanctions.)

Problem is, these results are not formally audited by the CMS or any other independent government regulatory agency. Nursing facilities' self-regulation cannot replace independent surveys. In fact, in discussing data sources for Nursing Home Compare, the official Medicare.gov website freely states:

> *All of these data are reported by the nursing homes themselves. Nursing home inspectors review it, but don't formally check it to ensure accuracy. This information changes frequently as residents are discharged and admitted, or residents' conditions change. The information should be interpreted cautiously and used along with information from the Long Term Care Ombudsman's office, the State Survey Agency, or other sources.*

About Those Star Ratings. Nursing Home Compare features a user-friendly Five-Star Quality Rating System, similar to what we're accustomed to in other arenas, such as the film industry and various consumer goods and services. The original mission was noble. The goal was to educate the public, attract public attention to nursing home performance and incentivize nursing homes to improve their performance.

But Abt Associates, contracted by the CMS, analyzed the first three years of star ratings and found that "improved Overall ratings may reflect changes in reporting practices rather than real changes in quality" (Abt Associates, 2013).

Facilities are rated on three types of performance measures:

- **Health Inspections** (measures based on state Health inspections and complaint surveys)
- **Staffing** (measures based on nursing home staffing levels)
- **Quality Measures** (based on 10 of the 19 reported long-stay and short-stay quality measures)

The Five-Star Quality Rating System also include an **Overall** or composite rating that combines these three individual measures. The independent Abt Associates 3-year analysis, however, noted that, by design, the health inspection measure remained constant over the 3-year period. They concluded that the composite score reflected "changes in reporting practices rather than real changes in quality," adding that "the distribution of ratings for health inspections is essentially fixed" (Abt Associates, 2013).

Here's how the health inspection measure is rated:

- Top 10% of facilities in each state receive 5 stars (= "much above average")
- Bottom 20% receive 1 star (= "much below average")
- Middle 70% receive, 2, 3, or 4 stars (at 23.33% each)
  - 2 stars = "below average"
  - 3 stars = "average"
  - 4 stars = "above average"

As for quality measures, nine of the 19 measures reported are not even included in the calculation of the publicly-reported quality measures. Unlike health inspections, where the distribution of ratings remains constant, quality measure ratings are "allowed to shift" (Abt Associates, 2013). The Centers for Medicare & Medicaid Services has expressed concern about "quality measure data integrity," directing facilities to update information on missing discharge assessments (CMS, MDS, 2013). (Federal regulations require discharge assessments to be completed within 14 days of a resident's discharge and to be reported to CMS within 14 days of their completion.)

And that's not all…

Improved star ratings may only reflect a facility's *self-reported* quality measures. Since health survey ratings have remained constant, while both staffing and QMs are "allowed to shift," nursing homes' so-called "improved" star ratings reflect only improved ratings in the self-reported staffing and quality measures.

Why is this so crucial? Because poor-quality facilities can self-report high staffing and quality measures to boost their Overall star ratings. Poor-quality facilities with 1-star health ratings can increase staff and report high quality measures and dramatically improve their Overall star rating.

In 2013, the Center found that facilities with 1-star ratings in health surveys in three geographically diverse states — Georgia, Illinois, and Oregon — had high quality ratings. Similarly, they found that 17 of 47 Special Focus Facilities (SFFs) previously identified as providing the worst care in the country were now reporting quality 4- and 5-star quality measure ratings, thus boosting their Overall score. In a follow up analysis in April, 2014, they found similar disparities: 19 of the facilities had not improved, and 11 of that 19 had Overall ratings that exceeded their health rating.

Here's a recent example... after being on CMS's SFF watch list for 39 months, Southaven Nursing Center in Dallas finally lost its Medicare and Medicaid certification in March 2014. The facility rated 2 stars in health inspections, but 5 stars in quality measures, boosting its Overall rating to 3 stars.

You can see the dangers of inflated ratings. If the nursing home industry claims that it can show you the data to prove that the quality of resident care is improving, can you trust it?

The answer: not entirely. But please bear in mind, that regardless of the flaws in the Nursing Home Compare reporting system, it's a prudent place to start your research. And given that much of the data is self-reported by the nursing homes themselves, if a facility's star-ratings are in fact low, you should certainly beware, investigate further, and consider your options carefully.

Inflated quality ratings and underreporting the true incidence of abuse and neglect creates the atmosphere for a gathering storm, for it is difficult, if not impossible, to remove dangers that lurk in the unknown. But as you'll learn in the next chapter, other key elements can conspire to put any one patient, at any given time, at grave risk.

3

A PERFECT STORM IN THE MAKING

When morality comes up against profit,
it is seldom that profit loses.

— **Shirley Chisholm, U.S. Representative**

Grace was born in Chicago. She understood the value of hard work from an early age, having been raised in the family hardware store, founded by her grandfather, on the south side of Chicago.

After graduating high school, she married and had three sons and a daughter. She raised her family in Chicago, and worked as a companion aide for many years, sharing her sunny personality with others and helping with household tasks. She played guitar and sang at prayer meetings and in nursing homes as a volunteer, often bringing bells and tambourines for the residents to play along. Until the age of 80, Grace drove her car and was independent. She took care of her household and enjoyed visiting with her granddaughters, who called her their "funny, musical grandma."

Then Grace began to struggle in managing her daily living activities, and eventually, she moved into a nursing home facility across the street from her granddaughter's high school. Always one to look out for others, Grace took another patient — a man injured in an auto accident — under her wing while he recovered. She was known for her positive outlook and strong faith. She remained in close touch with her family and friends.

But about a year later, Grace began experiencing classic stroke symptoms: drooling, facial drooping, difficulty swallowing, and right-sided weakness. Although the nursing staff was aware of these warning signs, she was not taken to the hospital and the staff made no effort to obtain help for her. Days went by.

One night, at the 11 p.m. shift change, the oncoming third shift nurse received a report from the second shift nurse that Grace appeared to have suffered a stroke, and that she had informed the director of nursing only to be told that this was "normal" for Grace. The third shift nurse assessed Grace and grew concerned as she recognized clear signs of a stroke. She notified the family, the doctor, and called 911. She later reported that when she notified the director of nursing of Grace's situation, the director became confrontational, saying, "You know our census [number of patients] is only 27, so why would you send her off?" The nurse also reported that the director then tried to justify this comment by telling the nurse that she should have let Grace die at the nursing home where she knew people, instead of at the hospital.

After Grace was finally taken to the hospital, it was determined that she may have been exhibiting signs of stroke for days before she was finally transported to the hospital for evaluation. Tragically, because of that delay, Grace had aspirated and developed aspiration pneumonia because the nursing home staff continued to feed Grace and give her oral medications, even though she was visibly unable to safely swallow pills due to the effects of the stroke. By the time Grace was diagnosed at the hospital, her fate was sealed. She developed sepsis from the pneumonia and died 13 days later, leaving her children and grandchildren behind.

The third shift nurse who obtained help for Grace, despite the wishes of the director of the nursing, was fired shortly thereafter.

By now, you may be asking: "How did we get here? How can this degree of nursing home neglect and abuse be allowed to happen in the United States?" The short answer is: *Greed.* But the greed motive thrives within — and bears fruit for — this industry because of a unique cluster of factors that have for, too long, allowed this industry to operate with near-impunity. These factors converge and collectively enable — if not actually *encourage* — the nursing home industry to chase profits at the expense of patients. Each factor, alone, is dangerous in itself, but together, they conspire to create a perfect storm of, often, life-threatening risk for vulnerable patients. These factors include:

- the staggering amount of dollars at stake
- the vulnerability of the patient-victims, making them easy marks
- the pervasive nursing home industry culture of cover-up and shirking responsibility
- the restrictions and hurdles encountered by those who seek to hold nursing homes accountable

You see each of these elements at work in Grace's story…

Grace was vulnerable, disabled, and at the mercy of the nursing staff to properly care for her. She was an easy mark.

The dollars at stake were the prime motivator for the nursing home's neglect. The director of nursing (DON) at the nursing home was angry with the third shift nurse for calling 911 and having Grace transported to the hospital because they only had 27 beds filled and discharge would mean leaving a bed unfilled and losing a revenue stream. The facility administration was more concerned about keeping Grace in their facility as long as possible so they could continue receiving payments for her "care" than they were about Grace's health and well-being.

The remarkable fact the facility's DON would actually verbalize this callous desire to deny a patient the emergency care she so clearly and desperately needed just to reap more revenue demonstrates the industry culture of shirking responsibility and prioritizing corporate well-being over patients' well-being. It wasn't personal. It was "just business."

But as playwright George Bernard Shaw once said, "The worst sin towards our fellow creatures is not to hate them, but to be indifferent to them: that's the essence of inhumanity."

Because Grace's neglect occurred in a state where insurance companies and healthcare corporations have immense influence over those elected to office, Grace's family will be severely restricted from holding the nursing home fully accountable for her death. See, the state in which Grace lived enacted laws that placed arbitrary "caps" on the amount that clearly negligent defendants have to pay for the harm they create, no matter how egregious the misconduct and no matter how much harm was caused, even when the judge and an impartial jury of citizens all believe a larger judgment against the nursing home corporation (or other defendant) is needed to adequately compensate the victims and help ensure this type of mistreatment doesn't happen to someone else. Since it was the nursing home's neglect that ultimately killed Grace, a wrongful death damage cap law applies to Grace's case, giving the nursing home corporation the comfort of knowing that her elected lawmakers had ensured that the very most they will ever have to pay for killing Grace is $300,000 for the resulting loss of her "love and companionship." In fact, under this particular state's laws, the nursing home is *exempt* from having to pay any compensation for the immense human suffering that Grace herself endured from being denied emergency care when she needed it, precisely and entirely *because the negligence killed her.*

It's worth noting that, in this same state, there's no arbitrary cap on damages that apply when someone's prized farm animals, livestock, or pets are wrongfully killed.

You'll see, as we explore each of these elements in depth, how the elements conspire to devalue the lives of vulnerable, elderly nursing home patients.

DOLLARS AT STAKE

It's an unfortunate reality that, in any industry where there's enough money to be made, companies are often willing to absorb any legal or financial consequences that result from violating consumer protection laws and regulations as long as they can still maximize profit. For many nursing homes, this strategy has become standard operating procedure. And to be sure, there's "enough" money to be made in the nursing home industry. In fact, it's becoming a virtual gold mine.

The U.S. nursing home industry is a multi-billion-dollar enterprise. In 2012, total patient spending (public, out-of-pocket and other private spending) for long-term care was $219.9 billion, or 9.3% of all U.S. personal health care spending. This total is projected to increase to $346 billion in

2040 (National Health Policy Forum, 2014).

> **By 2040, total patient spending on long-term care in the United States is estimated to reach $346 billion.**

As investment strategist Dr. Harold Goldmier stated in his 2015 article "Nursing Home Care Industry Is A Solid Investment," which pointed out the virtues of investing in the nursing home industry: "Profits are staggering, and the nursing home companies have a long list of add-on sales for supplemental services through subsidiaries they control" (Goldmier, 2015).

In fact, one nursing home company alone, Genesis Healthcare, reported generating $5.73 billion in revenues for the year 2016 alone. In Genesis' Fourth Quarter and Fiscal Year End 2016 report, CEO George V. Hager, Jr. stated: "Already in 2017, we have executed a plan to reduce overhead and operating costs by approximately $50 million to counter external business pressures we expect will persist throughout 2017."

And as you'll soon see, it's this mission within the U.S. nursing home industry to "reduce overhead and operating costs" that conspires with other factors to create a breeding ground for neglect and abuse.

To be sure, the industry is predicting a rosy economic future because it can, as Mr. Hager noted in the 2016 Genesis fiscal report, "capitalize on the favorable demographics and longer term supply." (In other words, "capitalize" on an ever-increasing population of aging patients who are candidates for nursing home care.)

In 2015, *Provider* magazine, an insider healthcare industry publication, described the industry's future this way: "Skilled nursing facility companies continue to be big business and are poised to grow exponentially given that in 2011, the first baby boomers turned 65."

Not only are there more Americans turning 65, longevity has increased — more people are living longer. Individuals 85 years and older, the oldest of the elderly, are one of the fastest growing segments of the population.

The industry, growing ever richer, can then wield its enormous wealth to influence lawmakers to create an even more favorable and lucrative environment in which to operate in the future. As if conditions were not already favorable enough to the corporations that operate nursing homes, the industry continues to spend money to vigorously (and often successfully) lobby lawmakers for additional measures intended to further boost profits and protect their turf. For example, in at least one state (Indiana), existing nursing home owners sought to forbid new competitors from entering the market by lobbying for legislation that would enforce a five-year construction moratorium on new nursing homes, even as they acknowledged the surge in their own revenue and profits. The law passed in 2015, but not without revealing a glimpse of what goes on behind the scenes. A state legislator who had privately lobbied to defeat the passage of the moratorium bill resigned his office after it was revealed that at least one of his children had a significant financial stake in a company that built new nursing homes in that state.

On one hand, the nursing home industry purports to passionately support the free market concept, but then, some nursing home corporations turn around and fight to restrict the market by way of new legislation and regulation so that they can make *even more* money. It's not enough for those corporations to get a generous slice of the pie — they want *the whole pie*. The consequence of this unbridled greed is decreased competition in that geographical area, which restricts a patient's ability to choose safer, cleaner, better-staffed nursing homes. Ultimately, it's just another way for these nursing home corporations to insulate their facilities from being held accountable for providing poor care.

You can see how the enormous sums of money at stake for those who gain financially from selling the promise of nursing care to those who need it creates an incentive for those participating in this gold rush to cut corners and place profits over patients.

Cheating the Taxpayer: Fraudulent Billing

Fraud is the daughter of greed.
— Jonathan Gash, The Great California Game

If you pay taxes, you should know that the U.S. Inspector General ("OIG") found that U.S. nursing homes have been submitting inaccurate, medically unnecessary, and even fraudulent billing claims to Medicare for years (Levinson, OIG, 2011). In 2009 alone, *one out of every four* (25%) claims submitted by the U.S. nursing home industry was erroneous, resulting in $1.5 billion worth of unjustified payments from Medicare (i.e., the taxpayers) to nursing home industry coffers.

> **In 2009 alone, 1 out of every 4 billing claims submitted by U.S. nursing homes to Medicare were erroneous, representing $1.5 million in unjustified payments.**

The study found that the nursing homes misreported information about the condition of the patient on 47% of claims for at least one item in the MDS (Minimum Data Set) forms, which are used by nursing homes to assess the patient's condition, functional status, and expected and actual use of services. This information is ultimately factored into payments the nursing home facilities receive from Medicare.

Even more troubling, information from the MDS form is supposed to be used by nursing homes to develop proper care plans to meet patients' specific needs. If 47% of them are incorrect, one has to wonder how many patients have care plans that are also incorrect.

The OIG report found that information misreported by the nursing homes included, for example, such services as therapy (30% of claims inflated the actual amount of therapy provided), special care such as IV medication, tracheostomy care, and pressure ulcers, among others (16.8% of claims). Thus, not only is Medicare (the taxpayers) paying for improper services — they're paying for services (or services *not* performed) that may be detrimental to the patient's health.

Nursing home patients have a right to obtain a copy of all medical records, including the MDS form. In *Chapter 9, Your Right to Medical Records*, we'll discuss this right in-depth and show you exactly how to do it. Having a copy of medical records can be useful for many reasons, from substantiating a claim of neglect or abuse to reviewing them for false information and other red flags that could impact future care.

VULNERABILITY OF THE VICTIMS

Nursing home patients are, almost by definition, vulnerable to neglect and abuse. The patient is often sick, ill, unable to effectively communicate, and entirely at the mercy of the nursing home staff member in their presence. Patients in nursing homes are very frequently alone in the presence of the nursing home staff, in need of assistance or care, and in the presence of a single nursing home employee. This employee is also the person responsible for documenting what actually occurred in the medical record, thus single-handedly controlling what's likely to be some of the most important evidence in any review of the patient's care. There's very little to stop a nursing home employee from engaging in misconduct, other than his or her own conscience. Unfortunately, that is often simply not enough. That's why nursing homes must be diligent in screening, training, and supervising their staff.

Certainly, impairments in physical and cognitive functioning are common among nursing home residents. Impairments, such as neurological events (e.g., dementia) that cause personality changes, memory loss, and communication deficits can trigger challenging behaviors in residents, making them more challenging to manage. Staff members may view aggressive resident behaviors or attempts to resist care as deliberate attempts to be "difficult," or even as attempts to harm staff, which can increase the likelihood that staff will abuse them or "handle them roughly" (Hawes et al, 2003).

Several studies have found that residents with behavioral symptoms such as physical aggressiveness may be at higher risk for staff abuse (Pillemer & Bachman-Prehn, 1991; Hawes et al, 2001). Another study found that Alzheimer's, other dementias, or some form of memory loss or confusion was present at a higher rate among nursing home residents who had been sexually abused than among the average nursing home population (Burgess et al, 2000).

Further complicating matters, patients who suffer from dementia or other cognitive deficits are often unable to clearly communicate their neglect or abuse, which gives their neglectful or abusive caregivers an opportunity to cast doubt upon the accuracy and credibility of those patients' reports. And since it's been projected that there will be 6.2 million people age 85 or over with severe or moderate memory impairment by 2050, this problem will only grow worse (Family Caregiver Alliance, 2016).

Considering the extraordinary profitability of the nursing home industry, why are these corporations failing to ensure that elderly and vulnerable patients are being protected and cared for?

SHIRKING RESPONSIBILITY AND THE CULTURE COVER-UP

The nursing home industry has developed a culture of cutting corners with patients, likely because cutting costs can facilitate enormous profit margins, and because the real victims of such cost-cutting measures are their patients, most of whom are vulnerable and defenseless, thus only too easy to exploit. These shortcuts pervade almost every aspect of care rendered in nursing homes, including staffing levels, supplies, quality assurance, employee training, and even proper employee screening.

The economic incentives to cut corners commonly flow all the way down from top management to facility managers (e.g., the administrator and director of nursing), many of whom receive big bonuses for outperforming financial projections — "coming in under budget." Problem is, the "budget" should be an estimation of the cost of services and supplies necessary to provide reasonable and proper care, not an incentive for staff to shift some of the resources necessary for high-quality care to the corporate savings account. This is the very essence of choosing profits over patients, and it is nothing short of purposeful neglect.

The only reason for choosing to understaff a nursing home is to save money and increase the bottom line. Not surprisingly, then, for-profit corporate owners are more inclined to understaff than the non-profits. The problem for their patients is that low staffing levels are widely considered to be the strongest predictor of poor-quality care.

The Perennial Understaffing Problem

Most nursing homes receiving substantial funding from Medicare and Medicaid in exchange for providing care to their patients — in fact, federal funding is believed to represent roughly 90% of revenue for many nursing homes. In an effort to help ensure that nursing home patients are receiving proper care in return for these payments, both state and federal regulations require that facilities provide adequate staffing, training, and quality assurance oversight to ensure that each patient's individual care needs are met.

A nursing home's first responsibility, in fact, is to ensure that it has a sufficient number of adequately trained and properly screened staff members present to provide the care that the patients need. Yet, reports and testimony by nursing facility staff often echo the same theme: Understaffing facilities results in abuse and neglect. And the profit motive results in understaffing. You can see the vicious cycle.

In order to fill beds and increase revenues, nursing homes sell patients and their families on the promise that, in return for the significant payment the nursing home will receive, the nursing home can be entrusted with the responsibility of protecting the patient and caring for their needs. But it's well-established, industry-wide, that one primary reason so many nursing homes are understaffed is that they simply choose not to hire enough staff to take care of their patients in order to reduce labor cost and thus maximize profitability.

The largest nursing home expense is staffing, so many upper management teams attempt to run their facilities on skeleton crews, which leaves their front-line workers (e.g., Certified Nurse Aides) exhausted, burnt out and struggling to accomplish the impossible (bathing, dressing, toileting, turning and repositioning, etc.) for literally dozens of patients all at once. This ultimately results in high employee turnover and makes it difficult to hire employees willing to work under these conditions. Then nursing home management blames the understaffing problem on a labor shortage, rather than the grueling work lives they've subjected their staff to.

One LPN, when questioned about what shortcuts, due to understaffing, the CNAs were required to take, stated…

Well, the CNAs and myself, and this is, unfortunately...
I mean, we were so busy that maybe a patient wouldn't get
turned every two hours like they were supposed to be. Maybe
it would be every 4, maybe every 5 hours. And I hate to say
that. It truly makes me sick to my stomach.

We would have to leave them in bed or get them up in the
morning and just put them in a wheelchair in their gowns and
robes and bring them to the dining room and, you know, that's
really inappropriate. They should be up and dressed and ready
for their day. And you know, that's how a staffed nursing home
would be. But that wasn't the case here, and at times, it was
noon before they would actually get their baths and get ready
for their day.

— Deposition of nursing home LPN

When asked what happened to other patients when management or
corporate admitted additional high acuity patients whose care required a lot
more time...

They would lose their time, lose possibly getting their shower
for the day, or even possibly getting bathed. You know, maybe
the CNA would have enough time to throw some clothes on
them. They would lose time to maybe sit on the toilet for a few
minutes. To have a good bowel movement, you know. They
would have to be put in briefs, diapers, and then be... have to
sit in them for a while until the aides could get back to them.
There just wasn't enough staff.

— Deposition of nursing home LPN

No doubt, the patients and their families are the primary victims,
but clearly, lower-level nursing home staff are victimized by the industry's
obsession with profits, as well. As if being stressed, overworked, and forced
by circumstances to mistreat patients weren't enough, the median annual
wage of nursing aides and orderlies working in nursing homes is $24,700

and $19,950 to $22,580, respectively (U.S. Bureau of Labor Statistics, 2016-2017). Effectively, the working poor, who are themselves among the most vulnerable in our society, are the ones taking care of elderly, vulnerable patients. Each is being taken advantage of by the nursing home industry.

Who Owns This Place?

All for-profit facilities, driven by the profit motive, are more likely to understaff than non-profit facilities. In fact, several studies have consistently reported lower nurse staffing levels in for-profit nursing homes than non-profit and government-owned nursing homes (CMS, 2000, 2001; Harrington, et al., 1998, 2001, 2003, 2005a, 2005b, 2007; Mueller, et al., 2006).

> **MYTH:** Nursing homes owned by large nursing home chains can be trusted more.
>
> **REALITY:** The number of "serious deficiencies" were 41% higher in facilities managed by large for-profit nursing home chains.

We know that understaffing has a direct, negative impact on the level of care provided to patients. The positive correlation between higher nurse staffing levels and the quality of nursing home care has been demonstrated in study after study (e.g., Aaronson et al., 1994; Bliesmer et al., 1998; Harrington et al., 2000, 2001; Unruh & Wan, 2004).

Because of the enormous profit potential, individual nursing home facilities are being taken over by large, for-profit nursing home chains that proudly tout this "growth industry" in the marketing and investor materials that can be found on their websites.

A study conducted a few years ago by researchers at University of California, San Francisco concluded that consumers considering a nursing home should ask: "Who owns this place?" The study found that among the nation's ten largest for-profit nursing home chains, the quality of care delivered to patients was significantly lower than their non-profit counterparts. The main reason: staffing levels were lower, thus care deficiencies were higher (Harrington et al., 2001).

The study, the first of its kind to focus on staffing and quality at the ten largest nursing home chains, found that total nursing hours were lower in these chain's facilities than any other group. Additionally, the number of "deficiencies" were 36% higher, and "serious deficiencies" were 41% higher for homes managed by the large for-profit nursing home chains. (Deficiencies included, for example, failure to prevent pressure sores, falls, infections, improper nutrition, resident abuse or mistreatment, and poor sanitary conditions.)

Study author Charlene Harrington, RN, PhD noted: "Poor quality of care is endemic of many nursing homes, but we found that the most serious problems occur in the largest for-profit chains." She also noted: "The top ten chains have a strategy of keeping labor costs low to increase profits. They are not making quality a priority."

How many nursing homes are owned by chains? One study found that approximately 57% of nursing facilities are part of a chain (Zinn, et al., 2007). Another study found that the largest nursing home chains controlled approximately 13% of all nursing home beds and operated nearly 2000 nursing homes across the country (Harrington et al., 2008).

From 2003 to 2008, these nursing home chains were found to have fewer nurse staffing hours than non-profit and government nursing homes. Collectively, these chains had the sickest residents, yet their total nursing hours were 30% lower than non-profit and government nursing homes. In fact, the top chains were well below the national average for RN and total nurse staffing, and below the minimum nurse staffing levels recommended by experts, which we'll discuss in more depth below.

The study also found that the four largest for-profit nursing home chains purchased by private equity companies between 2003 and 2008 had more deficiencies after being acquired, demonstrating that poorer quality care resulted from acquisition by private equity companies; that is, the profit motive promotes poorer quality care.

Unfortunately, however, the nursing home industry has been largely successful in many states in blocking the implementation of regulations which would mandate minimum nurse staffing requirements that would improve patient care.

Lack of Minimum Nursing-to-Patient Ratios

Federal Regulations unambiguously require nursing homes to provide "sufficient" nursing staff to address the needs of each and every resident. However, federal nursing home regulations do not mandate *a minimum staff-patient ratio for direct nursing care* (which includes all levels of nursing staff except the director of nursing). One reason is that the level of staffing depends upon not just the number of patients in the facility, but also upon the *acuity* level of the patient population.

> **42 U.S.C. §483.30 Nursing Services:**
>
> The facility must have sufficient nursing staff to provide nursing and related services to attain or maintain the highest practicable physical, mental, and psychosocial well-being of each resident, as determined by resident assessments and individual plans of care.

Acuity has been defined as the measurement of the intensity of nursing care required by a patient; in other words, the concept of acuity recognizes that some patients require more nursing care due to their health conditions than others. An acuity-based staffing system regulates the number of nurses on a shift according to the patients' needs, not according to raw patient numbers.

While acuity levels must always be taken into account, some studies have examined the impact of minimum levels of nurse-patient staffing on care. In 2000, a panel of national experts on staffing and nursing home care quality provided recommendations on minimum standards for nurse staffing levels (Harrington et al., 2000).

The panel recommended the following threshold staffing levels:

- All nursing homes: one full-time RN director of nursing and one RN supervisor on duty at all times (24 hours per day, 7 days per week)
- Facilities with 100+ beds: a full-time RN assistant director of nursing and a full-time RN director of in-service education

- Facilities with less than 100 beds: nursing staff is proportionally adjusted for size
- RN hours per resident day should total 1.15 hours
- LPN hours per resident day should total 0.70 hours
- NA hours per resident day should total 2.70 hours
- Total nursing staff hours: 4.55 per resident per day

Similarly, a ten-year study conducted by the Department of Health and Human Services and reported to Congress in April, 2002 found that, in cases involving long-term stays of 90 days or more, the facility needed to ensure total overall individualized care of *4.1 hours per patient/day* in order to avoid increased quality of care problems. This figure included 2.8 hours of nurse aide individual care and 1.3 hours of nurse individual care (a minimum of .7 RN hours and .55 LPN hours (DHHS, 2001).

While some states have enacted their own nurse-to-patient staffing requirements, many haven't, leaving nursing home operators free to determine whether their staffing levels are "sufficient" or not. But too many nursing home operators exploit this loophole by short-staffing their facilities in order to boost profit margins, and in doing so, neglect the needs of their patients. When nursing home operators are allowed to determine their own staffing needs, they can argue that they provided "sufficient" staffing, regardless of whether the staffing levels are, in actuality, *sufficient*.

> **MYTH:** Nursing homes always have at least one registered nurse on duty.
>
> **REALITY:** Current federal regulations only require nursing homes to have a RN on duty 8 hours per day.

By way of example, in a tragic case involving an Indiana patient who was allowed to develop two advanced pressure sores due to inadequate turning and repositioning by the nursing staff, it was discovered, after a lawsuit was filed, that according to the nursing home's own calculations, the facility allowed for *just 1.95 hours* of nursing care per patient per day. The nursing home administration did not dispute these hours, but instead argued that 1.95 hours of nursing care per patient was sufficient at that time, despite the fact that this level of care equals less than half of the nursing hours deemed necessary by the DHHS study.

Registered Nurses Are M.I.A. Most of the Day

In addition to the number of staff-patient hours allowed by the facility's staffing schedule, the *type* of nursing care is important, as well. Typically, most nursing home care is rendered by certified nursing aides (CNAs), licensed practical nurses (LPNs) (called a licensed vocational nurse or LVN in some states) and registered nurses (RNs). In some states, medications can be administered by either nurses or by a qualified medical assistant (QMA). The nursing staff is typically overseen by a Director of Nursing (DON), who is commonly a registered nurse.

There are tremendous differences between the training, education, skills and responsibilities associated with each of these types of caregivers, and sometimes that can make all the difference in the care a patient receives.

- **A registered nurse** must have graduated from an accredited school of nursing (typically a 2- to 4-year program), successfully pass a state examination, and be licensed by the state in which he or she practices. Registered nurses can be responsible for assessing the patient, making nursing diagnoses, and the planning, implementation and evaluation of the patient's care. RNs must be familiar with the use, dosage, potential hazards, and manner of administration of medications.

- **A licensed practical nurse** must have completed 12-18 months of education (typically culminating in the receipt of a certificate), successfully pass a state examination, and be licensed by the state in which he or she practices. LPNs have less extensive training than RNs, and are expected to report even minor changes in patient care to a RN or other medical professional.

- **A certified nursing assistant** or nursing aide is typically a person who has completed a 50- to 150-hour state-approved training and competency course.

- **A qualified medication aide** is typically a certified nurse aide (CNA) who has completed additional training, annual in-service training, and demonstrated competency while dispensing medications and or applying/administrating treatments under the direct supervision of a RN or a LPN.

Patients are typically admitted to nursing homes because they're unable to live at home alone and require professional nursing care. Yet contrary to common belief, nursing homes of any size — even those with several hundred beds — are not required to have a Registered Nurse (let alone a physician) on duty for more than 8 hours a day! Vulnerable elderly and disabled patients may live in a nursing home 16 hours every day with no access to a RN who can assess and address their medical needs.

Current federal regulations require that a registered nurse be available at the nursing home for *just eight hours a day*. This means that most of the time, the patient's nursing care is delegated to other employees (such as LPNs and CNAs) who don't have the training and experience that a RN does. This is a known danger.

On July 31st, 2014, U.S. Representative Jan Schakowsky of Illinois introduced a bill in Congress to ensure that at least one RN is present 24 hours a day, 7 days a week in all nursing homes that receive Medicare or Medicaid funding. While some states require a RN on site 24/7, many do not. Some states, such as Tennessee, Rhode Island, Hawaii and Connecticut, require a RN on-site for all nursing homes. Other states such as California and New Jersey merely require nursing homes with a certain number of residents to have a RN on site at all times.

So why would federal regulations and some states not require nursing homes to staff at least one RN at all times in a facility full of patients dependent upon nursing care? After all, the benefits of having a RN present in the nursing home are clear. Studies by the National Institutes of Health have found that facilities with higher RN staffing have fewer instances of patients developing life-threatening conditions, such as pressure sores (a.k.a. "bed sores") and urinary tract infections. Studies have even shown that care improves and any increase in staffing costs is offset by a decrease in costs related to the health care complications from a lack of care (e.g., Shekelle, 2013; Institute of Medicine (US) Committee, 1996).

Yet, this cost-benefit reality doesn't seem to motivate many nursing homes to staff properly. This powerful industry doesn't want to pay the rate for registered nurses when they can staff a nursing home more cheaply with other staff members who have not undergone the training registered nurses have.

Lies About Staffing

As if it's not bad enough that nursing homes understaff to increase profits, they often vastly misrepresent their true staffing levels — in fact, let's just call it what it is: *lying*. Given the extent to which nursing homes understaff their facilities, and the obvious and foreseeable harm that can result from understaffing, it's no surprise that nursing homes routinely lie about their staffing levels. And worse, they're often able to get away with it.

> **As many as 80% of nursing homes falsely inflate the staffing levels they report to Medicare for use on the Nursing Home Compare website.**

One key metric displayed on the *Nursing Home Compare* website (discussed in Chapter 2) is the facility's staffing level, which includes the number of RNs, LPNs, and CNAs. A 2014 probe by the Center for Public Integrity, a nonpartisan, nonprofit investigative news organization, found that the staffing data reported to the CMS by nursing homes is dramatically inflated by as many as 80% of those facilities. Incredibly, 25% of nursing homes nationwide reported staffing levels to CMS that were *double* the actual staffing levels reported in their cost reports (financial reports) to Medicare! Such staffing misrepresentations leave families with a false sense of assurance that their family members are being adequately cared for.

Nursing homes with insufficient staffing levels are not a new phenomenon, despite repeated studies showing that the amount of care, especially that provided by RNs, strongly correlates with the overall quality of care a resident receives and subsequently, the patient's health and well-being. To improve industry reporting, and possibly bring real change by exposing facilities' chronic understaffing, the Affordable Care Act mandated that CMS transition by March 2012 from the facilities' self-reported data to an electronic data collection system by which facilities would submit payroll-based, verifiable staffing information about their RNs, LPNs and CNAs. Information about the level of staffing by position and staff turnover would then be published on the Nursing Home Compare website. Nursing home facilities would finally be forced to prove that their staffing levels are what they claim they are.

But sadly, as of this writing, CMS missed that implementation deadline due to fiscal constraints, according to Thomas Hamilton, director of the agency's survey and certification group, and little progress has been made since. One unfortunate result is that the data patients and families may be relying on when choosing a nursing home is unreliable, perhaps even patently false. Another is that families may believe their loved ones are receiving a much higher level of care than they actually are, only to learn "after some avoidable complication or deterioration in their loved ones' condition that the nursing home was understaffed," as the author of the 24/7 RN bill, U.S. Representative Schakowsky, pointed out.

Inadequate Employee Screening

MYTH: Nursing homes screen out convicted criminals during the hiring process.

REALITY: Over 90% of U.S. nursing homes employ one or more convicted criminals.

Federal regulations specifically prohibit any form of patient abuse or neglect. Yet tragically, some form of nursing home abuse, including sexual assault, is inflicted upon patients by nursing home employees each and every day in U.S. nursing homes. In addition, too many nursing home patients dependent upon the nursing home staff for assistance with activities of daily living are neglected, leading to dehydration, malnutrition, and/or pressure sores (often "to the bone") due to the failure by the staff to ensure adequate hydration, nutrition, and adequate turning and repositioning.

One reason that vulnerable patients are neglected and abused is that many nursing homes hire convicted criminals — yes, you read that right: known *criminals*. In some cases, they're not closely examining who they're putting in charge of vulnerable patients; in others, they're hiring people whom they knew, or should have known, were criminals.

A 2011 U.S. Inspector General report revealed that 92% of U.S. nursing homes employ one or more people who have been convicted of at least one crime (Levinson, OIG, 2011). Nearly half of these nursing homes employed *five or more* individuals with at least one criminal conviction. These convictions ranged from personal crimes such as assault and sexual assault to crimes against property, such as theft of personal possessions, medications, or finances.

But perhaps what's most startling is that 84% of these employees' most recent conviction occurred *prior* to beginning employment with these nursing homes! So why didn't background checks reveal their criminal histories?

Because there's currently no national requirement mandating exactly how a nursing home should go about conducting background checks on prospective employees. Currently, only ten states even require nursing homes to search both the FBI criminal background database, along with state databases. This lack of consistency is compounded by the fact that state requirements vary in terms of whose backgrounds must be checked (e.g., direct-care workers only, such as nurses and nurses aides, versus *all* staff, which would include service personnel). The 2014 OIG report found that relying only on state databases leaves crucial gaps in background checks, which enables individuals convicted of crimes in one state to slip through the net and obtain nursing home jobs in other states (Levinson, OIG, 2014).

Congress is aware of this problem. In a recent New York Times report, Senator Herb Kohl, D-Wisconsin, chairman of the Aging Committee, issued this remark:

> *"The current system of background checks is haphazard, inconsistent and full of gaping holes in many states. Predators can easily evade detection during the hiring process, securing jobs that allow them to assault, abuse, and steal from defenseless elders."*

Although most of the convictions were for crimes committed prior to an individual's employment, this study found that, for nearly 16% of employees with criminal backgrounds, the most recent had offenses that occurred *after* the start of their employment. Thus, nursing facilities would have needed to perform ongoing, periodical criminal background checks to discover these convictions. But given the high rate of turnover among nursing home staff, that seems unlikely to happen.

Now, you may be asking, aren't there explicit laws prohibiting nursing homes from hiring criminals? Yes, there certainly are. Federal regulations prohibit Medicare & Medicaid nursing facilities from employing people who have been found guilty of neglecting or mistreating residents by a court of law, or who have a finding of abuse, neglect, or misappropriation of property entered into the State Nurse Registry. Federal regulations also prohibit health care providers (including nursing homes) from billing federal healthcare programs for services performed by these individuals.

Yet, some nursing home corporations continue to flout the rules and employ criminals and, to add insult to injury, bill government-funded programs for the services they provide. In Indiana alone, a total of $988,117.96 in combined state and federal recoveries was obtained through settlements with 36 excluded nursing home providers since early 2008 through the efforts of the Indiana Attorney General's Medicaid Fraud Control Unit. In the largest settlement to date, one nursing home company, American Senior Communities LLC, was forced to pay the State of Indiana and federal government $376,432 to settle allegations that it submitted ineligible bills to Medicaid for work performed by seven employees whom the company knew, or should have known, were ineligible to participate in Medicaid and other federal health care programs.

The Culture of Cover-up

When patients are injured or killed by nursing home neglect and abuse, many nursing home corporations will go to great lengths to avoid responsibility, even if it means deliberately concealing their misconduct from the patient, the patient's family, investigators, and the courts. Throughout this book, you'll read heartbreaking true stories and testimony from actual cases, many of which echo the same theme: a deeply embedded culture of cover-up within the nursing home industry — from the top operators and administrators down to the frontline employees.

To conceal the underlying truth, nursing homes may fail to report incidents of neglect and abuse to investigators and family, once the incidents are discovered. They may simply choose to not document the incident in the patient's medical record, or falsify the record after the fact to indicate that they *did* provide care they were supposed to provide even though they actually didn't, or that they *didn't* do something they weren't supposed to do but actually did.

They may deploy any number of tactics or excuses to explain patient injuries and accidents. They are, in fact, quite adept at deflecting blame and deflecting attention from their own care failures in order to discourage families from taking steps to hold them accountable. Blaming the patient is one of their favorites. It's only too easy, after all, to further exploit a vulnerable patient by casting doubt upon the patient's credibility, especially when the neglect or abuse is committed against patients with mental or physical disabilities who are unable to tell their own stories. And in wrongful death cases, of course, the neglected or abused patients are, obviously, no longer alive to defend themselves.

But there are ways to bring the truth to light, and throughout this book, you'll find specific tips and strategies that will show you what to look for and what steps to take to hold a nursing home accountable.

RESTRICTIONS AND HURDLES

Large corporations, of course, are blinded by greed. The laws under which they operate require it — their shareholders would revolt at anything less.

— Aaron Swartz

When patients and their families attempt to hold nursing home corporations accountable for abuse and neglect, they often face legal obstacles designed to avoid — or at least limit — the nursing home's accountability.

As you'll see throughout this book, some current laws and regulations actually protect bad nursing homes from accountability, thus enabling them to continue neglecting and abusing patients.

Forced or mandatory arbitration is a prime example of one such hurdle. Manuy nursing homes require patients and/or their families to sign binding contracts before admission that contain what's known as a *forced arbitration clause*. This clause effectively says if the nursing home ever abuses or neglects the patient, the patient and his/her family cannot file a lawsuit and have the matter decided by a judge or jury; rather, they must agree to resolve the matter through the private arbitration system. But the problem is, the arbitration system is riddled with conflicts of interest that ultimately ensure that the game is rigged in favor of big business (the nursing home industry) and against the little guy (the patient). Nursing home corporations know that they'll save money and avoid accountability — or at least, be held accountable for a lesser sum of money — if a dispute is resolved by an arbitrator (likely biased) rather than an unbiased judge or jury.

Arbitration proceedings are conducted behind a veil of secrecy by an arbitrator who has a strong financial incentive to rule in favor of the corporation that retained his/her firm to handle the case. Arbitrators don't have to follow precedent and are not bound by the same rules of evidence and procedure as courts. Consumers have limited access to discovery materials, limited rights to appeal, and often incur higher costs than they would in the justice system. We'll discuss the flaws of arbitration in depth in *Chapter 16, Fighting Laws That Protect Bad Nursing Homes: The Arbitration Hurdle.*

Damage caps are another legal strategy that enable nursing home corporations to limit their liability. Many states have passed "cap" laws that *prejudge* and minimize the value that can be placed on the life of a patient and the human suffering caused by nursing home neglect and abuse. Caps limit the amount of restitution nursing homes must pay to compensate abused and/or neglected patients and their families. These laws don't limit the "damage" caused by the wrongdoers; rather, they limit the nursing home's *accountability* for the damage it caused, forcing the patients to bear the burden of all damages in excess of the "accountability cap". This might, for example, include significant unpaid medical bills. As you saw in Grace's case, the most that the nursing home will have to pay for killing her is $300,000 because Grace's neglect occurred in a "cap" state.

Supporters of caps laws claim that caps "combat the high cost of healthcare," but as you'll learn in *Chapter 17, Fighting Laws That Protect Bad Nursing Homes: Arbitrary Caps on Damages,* where we discuss damage caps in depth, nothing could be farther from the truth.

These laws, and other legal maneuvers that we'll discuss in this book, exist because the nursing home industry puts profits over patients and has a powerful influence on legislators. Unfortunately, as this perfect storm would have it, the power and resources of this lucrative industry collide with one of our society's most vulnerable populations.

But the nursing home industry can only get away with this if we let them. The goal of this book is to empower you to stop them.

PART II: THE HARM

If you can, help others;
if you cannot do that,
at least do not harm them.

— Dalai Lhama XIV

4

PRESSURE SORES

An ounce of prevention is worth a pound of cure.

— Benjamin Franklin

Cynthia was 63 years old, a devoted wife who lived on her family farm and took care of her husband who suffered from Alzheimer's disease. One day, Cynthia slipped and fell in the shower, suffering serious injuries. She was admitted to a local nursing home to undergo physical therapy and rehabilitation so that she could return home and continue caring for her husband.

Cynthia had no pressure sores when she was admitted to the nursing home. Due to her immobility and debilitating health conditions, her nursing staff knew she was at increased risk for developing pressure sores unless proper preventive measures were implemented. These necessary precautions should have included routine skin inspections, diligent turning and repositioning, elevating her heels off the mattress, and providing appropriate pressure relief support surfaces for her bed and wheelchair.

Unfortunately, the nursing home failed to implement these basic precautions.

First, Cynthia was allowed to develop a necrotic, painful pressure sore on her coccyx (tailbone) area. To make matters worse, staff continued to position Cynthia directly on this known pressure sore, which not only inhibited healing but actually exacerbated the existing pressure sore. It was not long before the coccyx wound deteriorated into a 7.5-centimeter- by 2.5-centimeter-deep full thickness "Stage IV" pressure sore with yellow drainage (indicating infection) that extended through all layers of her skin and into the muscle and/or bone.

As Cynthia's coccyx wound deteriorated, she was allowed to develop additional pressure wounds on both buttocks, both heels, and her lower right shin. Her medical records indicated that both heel wounds were so advanced that they had become blackened with dead (necrotic) tissue and were considered "unstageable" (effectively, the wound was so severe that it was difficult to even assess exactly how severe it was). These two heel wounds were clearly consistent with the nursing staff's failure to ensure that her heels were elevated using pillows or other elevation devices to avoid constant contact with the bed.

One morning, Cynthia was found to be lethargic, unable to make eye contact, unable to respond to nursing staff. A foul odor emanated from her coccyx wound, which was now draining puss. There was concern that the wound infection could become so severe that it could cause sepsis and damage her internal organs, causing them to fail.

Cynthia was transported to the local hospital emergency room where the multiple advanced pressure sores were diagnosed. She required immediate treatment with antibiotics, which very likely saved her life. Tragically, however, Cynthia was forced to spend the next few years of her life in one hospital or nursing home after another, enduring many painful wound treatments in an effort to fully heal these advanced wounds. The treatment Cynthia required after developing these preventable pressure wounds ultimately cost many hundreds of thousands of dollars, much of which was paid for by Medicare (that is, U.S. taxpayers).

Cynthia was never able to return home to care for her ailing husband, who ultimately had to be admitted to a nursing home himself. After suffering years of extensive, painful wound treatments, Cynthia died in a nursing home.

The healthcare industry has long recognized that patients who are at risk for pressure sores must be positioned on pressure relieving devices while in a bed or wheelchair to protect bodily tissue from excessive, prolonged pressure and ensure sufficient blood flow. Caregivers for bed-bound and chair-bound patients must also ensure proper turning and repositioning: at least every two hours in bed; at least every hour in a wheelchair. They must also conduct frequent patient skin inspections to ensure early detection — and prompt treatment — of skin breakdown. These requirements represent basic, fundamental nursing care.

Cynthia's tragic fate, like that of countless other patients in nursing homes, was avoidable. It all began with a single pressure sore that was *preventable*. Unless health care providers are held accountable for this form of silent neglect, it's difficult to see how the disturbing rate of preventable pressure sores, especially in the elderly, will ever be eliminated.

WHAT ARE PRESSURE SORES?

Pressure sores (also commonly referred to as *bed sores, pressure ulcers* or *decubitus ulcers*) are one of the most common and most dangerous but *preventable* injuries sustained by patients in nursing homes.

A commonly used definition of pressure sore is: *any lesion caused by unrelieved pressure that results in damage to the underlying tissue(s).*

A pressure sore is a localized area of tissue injury that develops when soft tissue is compressed between a bony prominence (any point on the body where the bone is immediately below the skin surface) and an external surface for a prolonged period of time. The external surface may be a mattress, a chair or wheelchair, a medical device (such as a boot, brace, etc.), or even other parts of the body.

In extreme cases, the sore may progress to the death and decay of tissue, known as *gangrene*. Once the tissue dies, bacteria may infect the tissue causing decay.

Pressure sores first appear as intact skin or an open sore, and may be painful. A bed sore may show inflammation, redness, and infection. If a pressure sore becomes infected, the body's response to the infection often results in fever, shaking chills, changes in mental status, and rapid respiratory rate. If the infection progresses, the body can show signs of shock resulting from sepsis, including hypotension, lactic academia, and progressive organ system dysfunction.

Pressure sores can become a very serious problem, leading to significant pain, extended hospital or nursing home stays, and prolonged recovery periods from other health problems. And as with all serious health problems, prevention is of utmost importance.

HOW PRESSURE SORES DEVELOP

> **MYTH:** Most pressure sores are just an unfortunate, "inevitable" byproduct of illness and growing old.
>
> **REALITY:** The vast majority of pressure sores are avoidable when nursing homes take the proper precautions known to prevent them.

The commonly used term "bed sore" can be misleading since some of the most severe pressure sores are not the result of lying in bed, as the name would imply; rather, they may also result from sitting for a prolonged period of time. Pressure sores may develop when patients are allowed to remain in the same position or in contact with some surface for too long — regardless of whether it's a bed, chair, medical device, or otherwise — or if they're not provided with adequate pressure relief surfaces.

The soft tissues of the body, such as skin and muscle, depend upon blood vessels to carry nutrients to the tissues and remove waste products. Pressure sores result when prolonged pressure prevents sufficient blood flow to supply the tissues with nutrients. The resulting pressure sore indicates injury to, or death of, the involved soft tissues.

Pressure sores can result from one period of sustained pressure; however, most pressure sores likely occur as a result of repeated incidents of blood flow interruption without adequate time for recovery. In fact, low pressure endured for long periods of time is believed to be more significant in producing pressure sores than higher pressure for shorter durations.

The location of a pressure sore depends on the position of the patient. For patients who are bed-bound, pressure sores are most likely to form on or around the heels, the hip-bone, the lower back or tailbone. But pressure sores may also develop in a variety of other areas, including the spine, ankles, knees, shoulders, and head, depending on the patient's position.

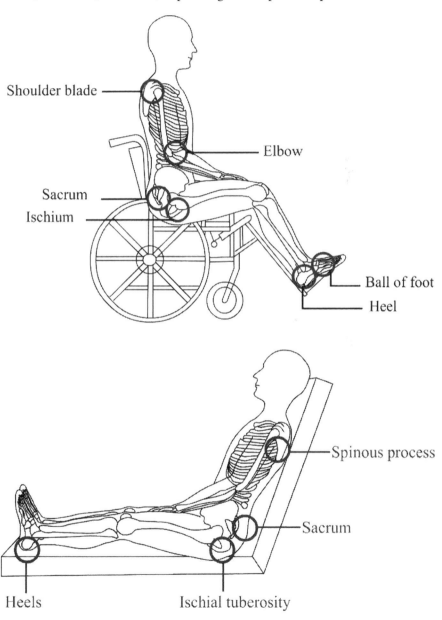

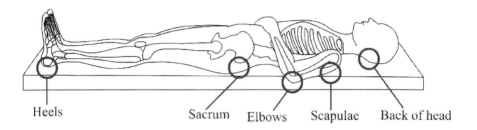

Heels   Sacrum   Elbows   Scapulae   Back of head

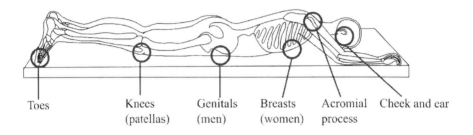

Toes   Knees   Genitals   Breasts   Acromial   Cheek and ear
                  (patellas)   (men)   (women)   process

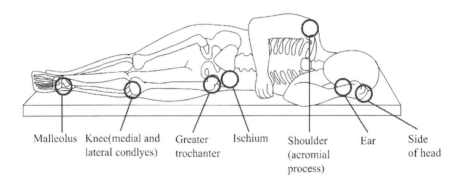

Malleolus   Knee(medial and   Greater   Ischium   Shoulder   Ear   Side
            lateral condlyes) trochanter   (acromial   of head
                                                     process)

DIAGNOSING PRESSURE SORES

Pressure Sore Stages

Caregivers assess a pressure sore's degree of severity by classifying wounds according to *stages*. The staging system developed by the National Pressure Sore Advisory Panel (NPUAP), a leading authority on pressure sores, was presented in April 2016 at a meeting of over 400 professionals. The Staging Task Force and meeting participants reached consensus and validated these definitions through an interactive discussion and voting process.

The pressure staging system is as follows…

Stage I: Non-blanchable erythema of intact skin. Intact skin with a localized area of non-blanchable erythema (reddening), which may appear differently in darkly pigmented skin. Presence of blanchable (loses redness when touched) erythema or changes in sensation, temperature, or firmness may precede visual changes. Color changes do not include purple or maroon discoloration; these may indicate deep tissue pressure injury.

Stage II: Partial-thickness skin loss with exposed dermis. Partial-thickness loss of skin with exposed dermis (thick tissue, "true skin" below the epidermis or outer layer). The wound bed is viable, pink or red, moist, and may also present as an intact or ruptured serum-filled blister. Adipose (fat) is not visible and deeper tissues are not visible. Granulation tissue, slough and eschar (scabbing) are not present. These injuries commonly result from adverse microclimate and shear in the skin over the pelvis and shear in the heel. This stage should not be used to describe moisture-associated skin damage (MASD), including incontinence associated dermatitis (IAD), intertriginous dermatitis (ITD), medical-adhesive-related skin injury (MARSI), or traumatic wounds (skin tears, burns, abrasions).

Stage III: Full-thickness skin loss. Full-thickness loss of skin, in which adipose (fat) is visible in the sore and granulation tissue and epibole (rolled wound edges) are often present. Slough and/or eschar may be visible. The depth of tissue damage varies by anatomical location; areas of significant adiposity can develop deep wounds. Undermining and tunneling may occur. Fascia, muscle, tendon, ligament, cartilage and/or bone are not exposed. If slough or eschar obscures the extent of tissue loss this is an Unstageable Pressure Injury.

Stage IV: Full-thickness skin and tissue loss. Full-thickness skin and tissue loss with exposed or directly palpable fascia, muscle, tendon, ligament, cartilage or bone in the sore. Slough and/or eschar may be visible. Epibole (rolled edges), undermining and/or tunneling often occur. Depth varies by anatomical location. If slough or eschar obscures the extent of tissue loss this is an Unstageable Pressure Injury.

Unstageable Pressure Injury: Obscured full-thickness skin and tissue loss. Full-thickness skin and tissue loss in which the extent of tissue damage within the sore cannot be confirmed because it is obscured by slough or eschar. The wound is a severe or "advanced" pressure sore, but the necrotic tissue covers some or all of the wound, thus caregivers can't yet assess whether it's a Stage III or Stage IV wound. If slough or eschar is removed, a Stage III or Stage IV pressure injury will be revealed. Stable eschar (i.e. dry, adherent, intact without erythema or fluctuant — fluctuating or unstable) on the heel or ischemic limb should not be softened or removed.

Deep Tissue Pressure Injury (DTPI): Persistent non-blanchable deep red, maroon or purple discoloration. Intact or non-intact skin with localized area of persistent non-blanchable deep red, maroon, purple discoloration or epidermal separation revealing a dark wound bed or blood-filled blister. Pain and temperature change often precede skin color changes. Discoloration may appear differently in darkly pigmented skin. This injury results from intense and/or prolonged pressure and shear forces at the bone-muscle interface. The wound may evolve rapidly to reveal the actual extent of tissue injury, or may resolve without tissue loss. If necrotic tissue, subcutaneous tissue, granulation tissue, fascia, muscle or other underlying structures are visible, this indicates a full-thickness pressure injury (Unstageable, Stage III or Stage IV). DTPI is not used to describe vascular, traumatic, neuropathic, or dermatologic conditions.

Additional pressure injury definitions include...

Medical Device Related Pressure Injury. Some patients may develop *medical device-related pressure injuries*, which result from the use of devices designed and applied for diagnostic or therapeutic purposes. The resulting pressure injury generally conforms to the pattern or shape of the device.

Mucosal Membrane Pressure Injury. Mucosal membrane pressure injuries are found on mucous membranes with a history of a medical device in use at the location of the injury. These pressure sores cannot be staged due to the anatomy of the tissue.

WHO'S AT RISK?

Several risk factors are known to significantly increase the likelihood that a patient may develop pressure sores, particularly if proper precautions are not taken. Now, risk factors don't mean that a particular patient will inevitably develop pressure sores. Rather, caregivers are supposed to look for risk factors during the patient assessment and care plan development stage and if those risk factors exist, develop and implement special preventive measures to address or eliminate those risks.

While risk factors may vary with a patient's specific circumstances, here are some of the most common:

- **Confinement to bed, chair, or wheelchair.** Persons confined to beds, chairs, or wheelchairs who are unable to move themselves, can develop pressure-induced injuries in as little as 1-2 hours if the pressure is not relieved.

- **Inability to change positions without help.** (e.g., an individual in a coma, or who is paralyzed or recovering from a hip fracture or other mobility limitation.)

- **Loss of bowel or bladder control.** Sources of moisture on the skin from urine, stool, or perspiration can irritate the skin.

- **Poor nutrition and/or dehydration.** Pressure sores are more likely to form when the skin is not properly nourished.

- **Decreased mental awareness.** An individual with decreased mental awareness may not have the level of sensory perception or ability to act to prevent the development of pressure-induced injury. This lack of mental awareness may arise from medications.

HIDING PRESSURE SORES FROM FAMILIES

Too often, nursing homes hide the existence of pressure sores from the patient's family. In a deposition, the son of a nursing home patient who developed a massive, necrotic pressure sore illustrated how nursing homes often conceal a patient's pressure sores from family members…

> **Question:** *Do you recall when your mother's coccyx area and bottom areas became a problem at [the nursing home]?*

Answer: Nobody ever told me that there was a problem. I found out that after she went — she was sent to the hospital for something. For sepsis, I believe. And the hospital called and told me that she had the pressure sore... the first knowledge I had of it was when she was admitted to the hospital.

Over the years, many families have told similar stories. Often, in fact, it is only after the patient is transferred out of a nursing home to a hospital that the family is told that their loved one was suffering from a massive, deep, pressure sore that extended all the way through the soft tissues to the bone (e,g., "tailbone" or heel bone). To the family's shock, the patient is suffering from an advanced, infected pressure sore that, at the very least, will require extensive, grueling wound treatments for weeks, if not months, and is in fact life-threatening due to the potential for the patient to develop septic shock from the infection. In these cases, because the pressure sore was located over a bony area hidden by clothing (such as the sacral area, buttock, or heels), the family was unaware of the wound.

> **TIP:** Don't assume the nursing home staff will tell you if your loved one has developed a pressure sore. Ask them routinely, at least weekly. You can also request copies of the weekly skin assessments they should be conducting. By taking these affirmative steps, not only are you keeping yourself informed, you're also letting the nursing home know you're paying close attention and do not expect your loved one to develop one of these preventable wounds.

Even when nursing homes do reveal to families that their loved ones have pressure sores (and often, only when they have no other option), they often downplay the significance of these wounds, typically portraying them as insignificant, a very minor condition (which is inaccurate) or "expected" (the "that's what happens to old people when they have to stay in bed" mentality). Family members often say, "I had no idea pressure sores were due to neglect — the nurses just acted like it was expected." In other cases, staff may casually mention in passing something to the effect of: "Oh, by the way, we noticed your father has a small open area on his backside, but we're putting some cream on it and it shouldn't cause any problems." In reality, too often, the patient is actually suffering from a very serious Stage III or Stage IV necrotic wound that puts them at high risk for a life-threatening infection.

Here's the reality: *Every* pressure sore is significant. None can be ignored. If they're not addressed promptly and properly, the consequences can be devastating. As if causing pain and human suffering weren't enough, patients with pressure sores are prone to infection, which can lead to sepsis, septic shock, and death.

And pressure sores are *not* simply to be "expected of old people." In fact, The National Center for Health Statistics found that nursing home residents aged 64 years and under were more likely than older residents to have pressure ulcers (14% and 10%, respectively) (NCHS, Park-Lee & Caffrey, 2004)

Why do nursing homes often fail to tell families about pressure sores, or minimize their significance when they do notify the families? Because pressure sores are almost always preventable if proper precautions are taken, thus, they're considered to be indicative of poor care. The nursing facility would be admitting to likely neglect or, at the very least, inadequate care.

THE PRESSURE SORE: KNOWN INDICATOR OF NEGLECT

Pressure sores have long been established as an indicator of substandard care (Russo et al, 2008). Stages III or IV pressure sores, in fact, were identified by the Centers for Medicare and Medicaid Services (CMS) in its July 2008 letter to Medicaid directors as one of eight preventable conditions.

Pressure sores are known to be a widespread problem in long-term care facilities, with prevalence rates ranging from 2.2% to 23.9% (Institute for Healthcare Improvement, 2007), or from another source: 2% to 28% (NCHS, Park-Lee & Caffrey, 2004). In 2004, more than one in ten nursing home residents had a pressure sore (NCHS, Park-Lee & Caffrey, 2004).

And evidence suggests that the problem may be growing worse. The number of pressure-sore-related hospital stays increased 27.2% from 1993 to 2006, a rate that outpaces the increase in hospitalizations for *all* causes during the same period (Russo et al, 2008).

Blaming the Patient

When nursing homes are unable to hide pressure sores, they often resort to blaming the patient. In an effort to avoid responsibility, nursing homes often argue that its care failures (such as failing to turn and reposition a patient or provide a proper pressure relief mattress) were not the cause of the patient's pressure sore. Instead, they argue, the patient is responsible for the advanced pressure sore because the patient has underlying medical conditions that predispose him/her to developing pressure sores.

When that argument fails, nursing homes often claim that the patient was "noncompliant" and refused to allow them to implement pressure sore preventions. It's not uncommon, for example, for a nursing home to claim that a pressure sore developed because the patient had diabetes or other underlying illnesses and did not want to be turned and repositioned, conditions which inevitably led to the development of pressure sores — *not* the fact that the nursing home failed to ensure a proper turning and repositioning regimen.

These attempts to blame the patient should not be tolerated. Underlying illnesses do not mean a patient *must* develop pressure sores – rather they are *risk factors* that should be recognized and addressed by implementing a proper plan of care. Nursing homes too often make the self-serving claim that a patient is noncompliant with nursing care only *after* they allow the patient to develop an advanced pressure sore. If a patient truly does not want to reposition, it's incumbent upon the nursing staff to identify *why* the patient is hesitant to reposition (e.g., because repositioning causes pain or lack of understanding) and address this underlying issue so that it no longer prevents the patient from complying with the care intervention.

In fact, by definition, a pressure sore cannot be "unavoidable" unless the nursing home ensured that it took every precaution it was supposed to.

The National Pressure Sore Advisory Panel defines avoidable and unavoidable pressure sores as follows:

> **Avoidable** means that the resident developed a pressure sore and that the facility did not do one or more of the following: evaluate the resident's clinical condition and pressure sore risk

factors; define and implement interventions that are consistent with resident needs, resident goals, and recognized standards of practice; monitor and evaluate the impact of the interventions; or revise the interventions as appropriate.

Unavoidable means that the resident developed a pressure sore even though the facility had evaluated the resident's clinical condition and pressure sore risk factors; defined and implemented interventions that are consistent with resident needs, goals, and recognized standards of practice; monitored and evaluated the impact of the interventions; and revised the approaches as appropriate.

These definitions make clear that nursing homes must take responsibility for ensuring the implementation of all available precautions, rather than simply blaming the patient or otherwise claiming that the wound is simply "unavoidable."

The High Cost of Poor Care

What's the cost of negligence that results in pressure sores? The total annual cost for treating pressure sores in the U.S. is a staggering $11 billion (Institute for Healthcare Improvement, 2007).

Since October of 2008, hospitals no longer receive higher Medicare payments related to the pressure sore-specific care of patients who acquire Stages III or IV pressure sores during their inpatient hospital stay. Stages III and IV pressure sores are identified by the Centers for Medicare & Medicaid Services (CMS) as Never Events[1], which are errors in medical care, not unlike operating on the wrong body part or committing a blatant medication error. In other words, Never Events are the fault of the healthcare provider.

This should give you some idea of how widely accepted it is that pressure sores are preventable — the fact that Medicare, in an attempt to disincentivize

---

1   Never Events are defined as: "errors in medical care that are of concern to both the public and health care professionals and providers, clearly identifiable and measurable (and thus feasible to include in a reporting system), and of a nature such that the risk of occurrence is significantly influenced by the policies and procedures of the health care organization."

hospitals from allowing those types of medical errors in the first place, won't pay hospitals for treating injuries that they caused. The federal government is making it clear that taxpayers should not have to pay for treating pressure sores that health care providers cause; rather, the cost should be borne by the health care provider.

While this Medicare/Medicaid Never Event policy applies to hospitals, it does not apply to nursing homes. Clearly it should.

PREVENTION IS THE KEY

It's often said that it's easier to prevent a pressure sore than it is to heal one, once it's been allowed to develop. In fact, the American Medical Director's Association (AMDA) states that "the cornerstone of pressure sore management is prevention" (AMDA, 2008). The AMDA further provides that "early recognition of pressure sores and of any risk factors associated with the development of pressure sores is critical to their successful prevention and management."

Prevention is the key.

Most pressure sores can be prevented. And those that have developed can be treated and prevented from getting worse. Often, the failure of a nursing home to develop and implement a care plan to address a patient's risk for skin breakdown results in the development of pressure sores which would otherwise have been preventable.

Federal nursing home regulations (as well as state regulations), in fact, recognize that pressure sores are almost always preventable. The regulations require nursing homes to "ensure" that a patient "who enters the facility without pressure sores does not develop pressure sores," except in the rare circumstances when they are clinically unavoidable. The regulation also requires nursing homes to "ensure" that a patient with a pressure sore "receives necessary treatment and services to promote healing, prevent infection and prevent new sores from developing."

Federal Regulation §483.25 Quality of Care:

Each resident must receive and the facility must provide the necessary care and services to attain or maintain the highest practicable physical, mental, and psychosocial well-being, in accordance with the comprehensive assessment and plan of care.

Based on the Comprehensive Assessment of a resident, the facility must ensure that- (1) A resident who enters the facility without pressure sores does not develop pressure sores unless the individual's clinical condition demonstrates that they were unavoidable; and (2) A resident having pressure sores receives necessary treatment and services to promote healing, prevent infection and prevent new sores from developing.

Other evidence shows that the vast majority of pressure sores can be avoided. A prevention program implemented in one nursing home that was based on Agency for Health Care Policy and Research (AHCPR) guidelines produced a major drop in the number of pressure sores. Prevalence ranged from 12% to 25% before the project began, declined sharply after implementation, and fell to almost zero in the fourth year of implementation (Tippet, 2009).

Another program provided two heel protectors (costing $56 each) for each resident in a nursing home with 555 patients, resulting in a 95% reduction in new heel pressure sores, which represent approximately 30% of all pressure sores (Lyman, 2009). The net savings fell between $12,400 and $1,048,400 in the three months after implementation. This wide range of savings reflects the varying cost of treating pressure sores according to severity. For the worst pressure sores, the cost can be as high as $70,000. If an estimated average cost of treating pressure sores is used, the facility saved approximately $50,769 (Lyman, 2009).

Clearly, there are reasonably-priced interventions that can prevent the development of pressure sores in nursing homes.

Guidelines for Prevention

To ensure that patients will not develop pressure sores, each patient's individual circumstances must be taken into consideration by the caregiver. Each individual is different, has different risk factors, and thus requires a customized care plan and continued diligence in implementing that care plan.

The following generally represent some of the precautions that nursing home staff should, but too often fail to, undertake:

1. An appropriate, thorough and systematic assessment must be made of the patient's risk for developing a pressure sore;

2. Appropriate periodic reassessment should be made of the patient's risk. Skin inspections should occur with sufficient frequency that skin breakdown can be observed in its early stages so that pressure can be relieved and the skin allowed to heal;

3. The patient should be bathed appropriately;

4. The patient's incontinence should be assessed and treated to assure that moisture on the skin does not contribute to the development of a pressure sore;

5. Appropriate nutrition and hydration must be maintained;

6. Repositioning of the patient should occur with a frequency to assure that the pressure is adequately relieved to avoid breakdown;

7. Use of appropriate support devices should be maintained to relieve pressure from troublesome areas;

8. Postural alignment, distribution of weight, balance and stability, and pressure relief should be considered when positioning patients in chairs or wheelchairs;

9. Appropriate lifting devices and techniques should be used to assure that shear and friction related injuries are avoided;

10. Education should be given to the patient, family, and caregivers on measures to be taken to avoid pressure sores, and those measures should be appropriately documented.

The prevalence of pressure sores in U.S. nursing homes clearly demonstrates that this industry has failed to cultivate a culture of prevention, diligence and vigilance. Every day, their patients are put at risk for developing pressure sores for a variety of reasons... indifference, incompetence, and, of course, the perpetual understaffing problem, which is driven by the profit motive. Many facilities simply fail to employ sufficient staff to turn and reposition all at-risk patients every 1-2 hours as is necessary, given the nursing staff's other responsibilities.

It's a pattern, a pervasive pattern of negligence that also leads to other preventable and — unfortunately, all too common — harms.

TIPS

- Be proactive at or before the time of admission:
  - Research the facility before admission on the Nursing Home Compare website to determine the prevalence of advanced pressure sores within the facility. (https://www.medicare.gov/nursinghomecompare/search.html) (Also see Chapter 12 for more tips about researching facilities.)
  - Visits the Nursing Home Compare website to review the state survey/investigation history of the facility to determine if it has had prior problems with the development and/or treatment of pressure sores. (See Chapter 11 for an in-depth look at state investigations.)
  - At the time of admission, ask the director of nursing what specific care plan interventions will be implemented for the patient to ensure the prevention of new pressure sores. If pressure sores are present at the time of admission, ask what additional interventions will be implemented to ensure the proper treatment and healing of the existing wounds.
- Ask the nursing staff for a copy of the Pressure Sore Risk Assessment (often called a "Braden Assessment") that was done at the time of admission. This assessment uses a scoring system for various factors, and it's not uncommon to see mathematical or other errors, which may result in the development of an incorrect care plan.

- Ask the nursing staff for a copy of the "weekly wound assessments." For any patient considered at risk for the development of pressure sores, there should be at least weekly wound, head-to-toe assessment to identify any new areas of skin breakdown.

- Ask the director of nursing periodically to provide you with a current copy of the nursing care plan pertaining to the issue of pressure sore prevention and treatment. Not only should the facility develop a care plan at the time of admission, they should update it regularly to reflect any changes in the patient's condition.

- If the patient spends a significant amount of time in bed, check to make sure that the patient's heels are elevated off the bed. If not, address the issue with the nursing staff supervisors.

- If you observe the nursing staff failing to turn and reposition a patient in bed (who needs assistance with turning and repositioning) for more than 2 hours, address the issue with the nursing supervisors. It's also a good idea to develop a paper trail documenting that you communicated your concerns to the nursing staff. This can be done by email, fax, or other written communication, which you have the nursing staff sign off on, then provide you with a signed copy.

- If the patient has any wounds that require bandages, look at the bandage to see what date is reflected on the bandage. If the patient is supposed to receive daily wound treatments, but the bandage indicates it's several days old, photograph the bandage and then raise your concern with the nursing supervisor. If the issue is not properly addressed raise the issue with the ombudsman (see Chapter 10), and/or the state investigators (see Chapter 11).

- Periodically discuss the patient's nutritional status with the facility dietician. Make sure that the patient's nutrition is stable, as evidenced by the patient's weight, laboratory values (such as prealbumin), and dietary records. Not receiving proper nutrition can increase the vulnerability to develop pressure sores and prevent the healing of existing pressure sores.

- If the patient has a known pressure sore, make sure the nursing staff is not positioning the patient on that wound. A wound is less likely to heal, and more likely to become progressively worse, if the patient is positioned directly on this known area of skin breakdown. Pressure on a known wound prevents blood, and its nutrients, from reaching affected tissues, which are necessary for healing.

5

FALLS

It's better to look ahead and prepare than to look back and regret.

— Jackie Joyner-Kersee

Evelyn grew up during the Great Depression — one of thirteen siblings. She got married and gave birth to two wonderful children. She and her husband shared a wonderful life together, raising their children, becoming proud, loving grand-parents. She grieved when her husband passed away, but she knew she was fortunate to have her family to keep her young in spirit.

Evelyn eventually developed dementia and had difficulty maintaining balance. The day came when she was no longer safe at home on her own and needed to live in a setting that provided professional nursing care. Her family remained supportive and involved.

When Evelyn was admitted to the nursing home, the facility staff confirmed that she needed to be protected from falls to prevent serious injury. They assured her family that they were prepared to keep her safe. They noted that Evelyn had dementia, a history of falls, an unsteady gait, diminished eyesight and hearing, "poor" safety awareness, was "very unsteady" and had a tendency to fall. They noted that she was sometimes confused, "forgetful", unaware of her inability to stand or ambulate, and unaware of her own personal safety. As time passed, staff noted that Evelyn made "poor" decisions and "cues/supervision" were required.

One day, Evelyn asked nursing staff to wheel her to the designated patient smoking room to smoke a cigarette. The nurse handed her a lit cigarette and walked out, leaving her alone in the room with no supervision. The wheels on Evelyn's wheelchair were not locked to steady her. And most importantly, Evelyn was not positioned so that she could easily reach the ashtray.

As Evelyn's cigarette burned towards her fingers, she reached for the ashtray and tumbled out of the wheelchair face first. As her face hit the hard floor, her glasses shattered. Blood flowed from the wound between her eyes and from a tear in the skin on her arm.

Eventually, the nursing staff found her lying on the floor.

Evelyn complained of neck pain and later began vomiting. She was assessed by a hospital emergency room doctor and found to have multiple broken ribs, a broken left collarbone, a broken nose, and multiple suspected spinal fractures. Because of her age and condition, surgery was not a viable option. She was returned to the nursing home to heal.

By this time, Evelyn required two-person assistance when being transferred from bed to a commode or wheelchair.

One morning, several months later, a nurse aide entered Evelyn's room intending to get her up for breakfast. Evelyn told the aide she didn't feel well enough to get up, which the aide relayed to her supervising nurse. Despite the risk, the nurse chose not to speak with or assess Evelyn; instead, she instructed the aide to get Evelyn out of bed despite Evelyn's wishes.

This decision sealed Evelyn's fate.

In the moments that followed, large bones in both of Evelyn's legs were badly broken. That was clear. What was less clear, is how this happened. According to the nurse's documentation of the event, the nurse aide attempted to transfer Evelyn from her bed to the bedside commode when Evelyn's "knees buckled." According to the nurse aide, she sat Evelyn down on the bedside commode and noticed a "deformity" in her leg. According to both the nurse and nurse aide, Evelyn never fell. They would later blame the leg fractures on osteoporosis.

A nurse called 911; Evelyn was transferred to the hospital. X-rays confirmed a broken right femur and a broken left tibia. She was also diagnosed with pneumonia and a urinary tract infection, which explains why she didn't feel well enough to get up that morning.

She was admitted to the hospital where antibiotics were administered to treat the UTI and pneumonia and Demerol and Phenergan IVP to help alleviate pain, though she continued to grimace and moan in pain.

Evelyn was pronounced dead at 16 minutes after midnight.

Why did Evelyn suffer this trauma? With respect to the first fall, the nursing home staff clearly knew that Evelyn was often confused, prone to making poor safety decisions, and at high risk for falls, which meant that she required nursing supervision, especially when she was taken to the smoking room and given a lit cigarette. For some inexplicable reason, perhaps understaffing, Evelyn was left alone, and unattended, in a room all alone with a burning cigarette. It was clearly foreseeable, and thus preventable, that she could need help and suffer harm without it.

With respect to the incident which snapped the bones in both of Evelyn's legs, Evelyn's family was determined to find out what really happened the day she died. In order to obtain the answer to their many questions about her death, Evelyn's family filed a lawsuit which allowed them to invoke certain procedures to gather facts. In doing so, many months later, the 911 audio recording of the call made by the nursing home staff revealed the truth...

911 TRANSCRIPT:

Caller (nurse): I have a ninety-one-year-old with a possible broken femur.

911: She fall down or something?

Caller: Yeah, I don't know if it broke before she fell or after she fell.

The nursing staff admitted in depositions that only one staff member — instead of two — attempted to transfer Evelyn to the wheelchair, but they concealed the fact that Evelyn fell during the transfer. Despite the nursing staff's assurances that they could and would keep her safe, the staff callously ignored their own care plan requiring the presence of two aides during wheelchair transfer, perhaps because management did not ensure that there was sufficient staff to provide the necessary care. As a result of their negligence, Evelyn died a painful and unnecessary death.

> **MYTH:** Falls are unavoidable and to be expected in nursing homes, just another "inevitable" byproduct of illness and the fragility of growing old.
>
> **REALITY:** Falls *are* to be anticipated, but by taking the proper anticipatory precautions, they can be prevented.

It's a common refrain: An elderly nursing home resident falls and breaks a hip or an arm or a leg. Often the circumstances are mysterious, never fully explained. The family is often told by nursing home staff that it's to be "expected" for elderly people, after all.

But here's the reality: As with pressure sores, the frequency of falls in nursing homes is an indicator of poor care.

Here's what you need to know, in a nutshell:

- Falls and accidents happen too often in nursing homes.
- Falls and accidents can be anticipated and prevented.
- State and federal law requires nursing homes to ensure prudent measures are taken to prevent falls.

FALLS AND ACCIDENTS HAPPEN TOO OFTEN

It's true that falls are the leading cause of injury among adults 65 and older (Findorff et al, 2007). But, importantly, studies have found that elderly patients who live in nursing homes with the presence of around-the-clock professional caregivers suffer approximately *2 to 3 times more falls* than people of the same age living in the community (Rubenstein, 1997; American Geriatrics Society, 2001). Obviously, that higher rate of falls shouldn't be deemed "expected," especially since a primary reason that people are admitted to nursing homes in the first place is that they require 24-hour professional nursing care.

> **Nursing home patients suffer approximately 2 to 3 times more falls than people of the same age living in the community, despite having professional nursing supervision.**

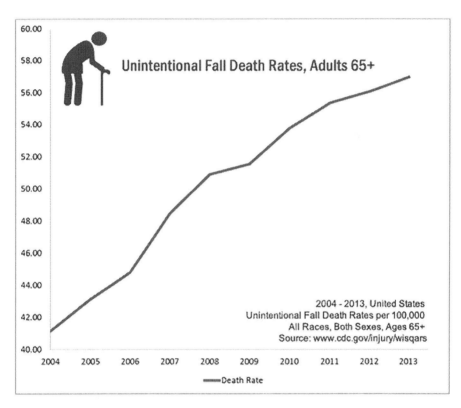

Consider these startling findings from several studies on the issue...

- In the typical 100-bed facility, there are 100 to 200 falls each year, and that doesn't even include the falls that go unreported (Sorensen et al, 2006)

- 75% of nursing home residents will have at least one fall per year and around 25% of those will require medical attention (Sorensen et al, 2006)

- The average nursing home patient falls 2.6 times per year (Rubenstein, 1990)

- Around 1,800 nursing home patients die each year as a result of fall-related injuries (CDC, 2013)

- Patients who can't walk account for approximately 35% of those fall injuries (Thapa et al, 1996)

The Aftermath of the Fall

It's true that some falls don't cause serious injuries, but studies show that one in five falls does cause a serious injury, such as a broken bone (e.g., wrist, arm, ankle, and hip fractures) or a head injury that can make it difficult for the patient to get around, perform everyday activities, or certainly, to live on their own (Alexander et al, 1992; Sterling et al, 2001). Studies of long-term care facilities show that 10% to 25% of falls result in fractures or lacerations (Becker & Rapp, 2010).

> **1 in 5 falls causes a serious injury, such as a broken bone or a head injury.**

Historically, hip fractures have been the most common fall injury. More than 95% of hip fractures are caused by falling (Hayes et all, 1996), usually by falling sideways (Jaeger et al, 1994). But pelvic fractures have been on the rise in recent years (Becker & Rapp, 2010). Both have serious adverse effects on a patient's overall health. Pelvic fractures among nursing home patients are associated with increased mortality rates in the months following the fracture (Rapp et al, 2010) and hip fractures put the patient at increased risk of developing pressure ulcers (Lyman, 2009).

Head injuries can, of course, lead to serious traumatic brain injuries, and can be especially dangerous for patients on blood thinners. Falls, in fact, are the most common cause of traumatic brain injuries (Stevens et al, 2006). Not all traumatic brain injuries are immediately obvious, thus any patient who hits his/her head as a result of a fall should be evaluated by a physician to ensure that there's no serious head injury.

The truth is that many nursing home patients who survive the fall often sustain injuries that cause permanent disability and reduced quality of life (Rubenstein, 1988). And the indignity and emotional trauma of falling should not be discounted either. Many patients who fall ultimately become fearful of falling in the future, even if they weren't injured. This fear can feed anxiety, depression, and feelings of helplessness and isolation (Rubenstein, 1997). They may become fearful of participating in normal everyday activities. This resulting lack of exercise and functional decline, in turn, causes them to grow weaker, which only increases their risk of falling again in the future (Vellas et al, 1997).

WHAT PUTS PATIENTS AT RISK FOR FALLS?

Nursing home falls can be caused by many factors. It's the nursing home's responsibility to identify and address risk factors that could contribute to a patient's fall or accident. That responsibility includes evaluating the patient's:

- environment
- risks factors
- need for supervision
- need for assistive devices

Let's look at patient risk factors in detail…

Environmental Risk Factors

Sixteen to 27% of patient falls are caused by clearly foreseeable environmental hazards, such as wet floors, poor lighting, improper bed height and poorly maintained or fitted wheelchairs (Rubenstein, 1997; Rubenstein, 1988; Ray et al, 2000).

Environmental risk factors may include:

- Excessive bed height
- Wet or slippery floor
- Ill-fitting or inappropriately soled footwear
- Use of full length side rails
- Inadequate assistive devices

- Unfamiliar environment
- Inadequate lighting
- Uneven flooring
- Inappropriate seating or positioning while sitting
- Poorly fitting or incorrect eyewear
- Lack of grab bars in bathrooms
- Malfunctioning emergency call systems or call lights
- Loose carpets or throw rugs

Medications That May Increase Fall Risk

Some medications can increase the risk of falls and fall-related injuries. Of special concern are sedatives and anti-anxiety drugs that affect the central nervous system (Mustard et al, 1997; Ray et al, 2000). The risk of falling has also been found to be significantly elevated during the three-day period following a change in these types of medications (Sorock et al, 2009).

Drugs that may increase the risk of falls include:

- Antiarrhyhmics
- Anticholinergics
- Antidepressants
- Anti-epileptics
- Anti-hypertensives
- Anti-Parkinsonian agents
- Antipsychotic medications
- Benzodiazepines
- Diuretics
- Narcotic analgesics
- Vasodilators

Common Risk Factors

Other foreseeable risk factors include muscle weakness and walking or gait problems, which are responsible for around 24% of falls in nursing homes (Rubenstein, 1997). Other causes of falls include difficulty in moving from one place to another (e,g., from bed to chair), poor foot care, poorly fitting shoes, and improper use of walking aids (Ray et al, 1997; Tinetti, 1997),

A more complete list of common risk factors includes:

- Age 80 years plus
- Arthritis
- Balance deficit
- Cognitive impairment
- Depression
- Gait deficit
- History of falls
- Impaired ability to perform activities of daily living (bathing, grooming, etc.)
- Muscle weakness
- Use of assistive device (cane, wheelchair, etc.)
- Visual deficit
- Cardiac arrhythmias
- Delirium
- Dizziness/lightheadedness
- Fear of falling
- Fluid and electrolyte imbalance
- Multiple medications
- Orthostatic hypotension
- Parkinson's disease
- Peripheral neuropathy
- Problems with mobility/gait
- Sensory impairments

- Stroke
- Transient ischemic attacks
- Urinary or fecal urgency that leads to frequent visits to the toilet

HIDING FALLS, BLAMING PATIENTS, AND MAKING EXCUSES

As you're beginning to see, the culture of cover-up is pervasive throughout the nursing home industry. In wrongful death cases, the neglected patients are obviously not alive to tell their own stories about what happened to them. Even patients who survive neglect or abuse are often unable to offer their version of the facts due to physical or mental disabilities. Often, the only evidence as to what led to a patient fall or accident is what the nursing home staff chooses to write in the medical record.

Nursing home corporations that strategically understaff their facilities, inadequately train the staff they do have, and cut corners on equipment and other resources are in no position to argue that falls are simply bound to happen. As with pressure sores, if nursing homes haven't taken every precaution they should have to prevent falls in the first place, they can't credibly argue that the negative outcome was simply "inevitable," rather than the inevitable result of not having taken precautions they knew to take.

To conceal the underlying truth, nursing homes may use any number of excuses to explain patient falls and accidents. Here are some of the most common ones...

The patient didn't "fall..."

As was illustrated by the tragic case of Evelyn, staff in some nursing homes intentionally try to conceal patient falls. In Evelyn's case, the nursing staff documented that Evelyn's "knees buckled" and that the nurse aide "lowered" Evelyn to the bed-side commode. The 911 call, however, made clear that Evelyn *fell*. Had the 911 tape never been obtained, this truth would never have been revealed. When patients fall, but nursing staff chooses instead to chart a seemingly innocuous version of events such as, "patient was gently lowered to the floor," the false charting has the effect of covering the trail of negligence, making it much more difficult for state investigators and families to get to the truth and obtain accountability.

The patient suffered a "spontaneous fracture..."

While nursing homes cover up falls and accidents by choosing not to document that a fall occurred, they must still explain the injuries. In Evelyn's case, the nursing home attempted to hide behind the notion that Evelyn suffered a "spontaneous fracture" (of both legs) due to osteoporosis. In other cases, nursing homes have argued that broken ribs can occur when patients with brittle bones simply sneeze.

X-rays, however, can often reveal whether a fracture was caused by an abrupt external force, such as twisting or otherwise. The effect of not acknowledging a fall is especially problematic because if a physician isn't notified of the fall — even if the patient "seems" okay — crucial testing may not be ordered to ensure that the patient didn't suffer a broken bone, or internal injury or bleeding. The nursing home staff may hope that if they can cast enough doubt upon the cause of the injury, they can avoid being cited by state investigators, or held accountable by the patient's family. But, in truth, this is just another example of how nursing homes seek to avoid responsibility by blaming the patient (or in this case, the patient's condition) for the result of their own neglect.

"We can't restrain patients to prevent falls..."

Nursing homes often dismiss responsibility for a fall by telling the family: "The law says we cannot use restraints to prevent falls, so falls are going to happen." This statement is both untrue and misleading because it misses the point. When restraints are deemed necessary in order to prevent a patient from suffering a fall, they can be used if the nursing home obtains a physician's order for them.

The reality is, however, there are many measures less intrusive than restraints that will suffice to protect patients in the vast majority of situations. But, you see, these measures require a sufficient number of properly trained staff in order to conduct an accurate fall risk assessment, determine which measures will effectively address the patient's specific risk factors, develop a written plan of care to direct all nursing staff as to what needs to be done to protect the patient, and to actually follow the care plan and provide the supervision, assistive devices, and other interventions needed.

The problem is not that restraints can't be used. The problem is that nursing homes far too often won't pay for enough trained staff to adequately protect the patient using the myriad of other protective measures available to them.

The patient was "non-compliant and got up without calling for help..."

Patients who do not appreciate their own safety limitations must be identified during the fall risk assessment process. Measures must be implemented to account for the fact that these patients may forget that they need help getting out of bed or going to the bathroom.

Supervision and frequent anticipation of patients' needs are key. If patients have not been toileted for hours, it is clearly foreseeable that they may urgently attempt to get to a restroom on their own without assistance. Plus, there's a variety of alarm devices on the market today — impressive adaptations of technology — that can alert nursing staff when a patient is attempting to get up in an unsafe manner. But these devices alone cannot prevent falls. There must *also* be sufficient and motivated staff to respond to the alarm in a timely fashion in order for this intervention to be effective. When there aren't enough staff to respond to the alarms, falls happen. And worse, the understaffed, overworked nurses often turn off the alarms because they know they can't get to them all.

The patient has "a right to fall..."

Some nursing homes like to justify allowing their patients to fall by telling family members that patients have a right to be free from restraints — "they have a right to fall." There *is* no "right to fall." There is, however, a right to receive protection from a foreseeable fall.

Initially, the vast majority of patients don't need restraints to be protected. For those few who may need restraints, the decision to use or not use restraints is one that must be made by the patient (or more commonly, the patient's family if the patient is unable to make clear decisions), the nursing staff, and the patient's physician. While no one wants every patient at risk of falling to be restrained, there are limited instances in which patients whose particular circumstances justify the use of devices that may restrict their ability to move in some fashion in order to keep them from serious harm.

The use of restraints is a complex decision, but it is certainly true that most patients can be properly protected without the need for restraints.

For that majority of patients for whom restraints are not needed, they must not be forced to exercise a fictitious "right to fall," as the nursing home industry likes to phrase it. All patients have a right to be protected from foreseeable falls. With proper assessment, evaluation, planning, supervision, and care, this can and should be done. No patient should ever be forced to suffer injury or death from this so-called "right to fall" imposed upon them by a nursing home industry that would rather propose false choices than hire enough staff and ensure that they're trained to provide adequate care to their patients, which, it should be pointed out, is required by state and federal law. With this "right to fall" argument, nursing homes are essentially blaming the patient (or a phony "patient right") for the harm caused by their care failures.

ANTICIPATING AND PREVENTING FALLS AND ACCIDENTS

The key to preventing falls is assessing fall risk, anticipating what may lead to a patient fall, and implementing a care plan that thoroughly addresses those risks. Often, after a fall occurs, nursing homes tell families something to the effect of: "Sorry about your mother's fall, but unfortunately, falls are to be expected."

This is only partly true. The reality is that yes, falls are to be expected, but *only when proper precautions are not implemented to prevent them and to protect patients when they do occur.*

The fact that falls can be anticipated and prevented is even reflected in the federal nursing home regulations.

So what can nursing homes do to prevent falls and accidents? A lot. While there may be no single magic bullet that works in every situation, there are many solutions that can be thoughtfully considered and collectively implemented to address almost any patient's circumstances.

For starters, every nursing home should conduct a "fall risk assessment"

> **Federal Regulation 42 C.F. R. §483.25(h) Accidents:**
>
> The facility must ensure that —
>
> 1. The resident environment remains as free of accident hazards as is possible; and,
>
> 2. Each resident receives adequate supervision and assistance devices to prevent accidents.

upon admission, and reevaluate when any significant change in patient condition occurs. Most nursing homes utilize a fall risk assessment tool to identify risk factors and measure risk levels that make a patient more susceptible to falling, which will then guide the development of an appropriate care plan.

There are several fall risk assessment tools — all intended to score a patient's risk — but each tool varies slightly. One of the most commonly used tools is the *Morse Fall Scale*. This tool scores the patient on several factors, including: History of falling, Secondary Diagnosis, Use of Ambulatory Aid, Intravenous Therapy, Gait, and Mental Status.

(This tool, along with the *Hendrich Fall Risk Assessment*, can be found at www.abusesandexcuses.org)

Morse Fall Risk Assessment		
Risk Factor	**Scale**	**Score**
History of Falls	Yes	25
	No	0
Secondary Diagnosis	Yes	15
	No	0
Ambulatory Aid	Furniture	30
	Crutches / Cane / Walker	15
	None / Bed Rest / Wheel Chair / Nurse	0
IV / Heparin Lock	Yes	20
	No	0

	Impaired	20
Gait / Transferring	Weak	10
	Normal / Bed Rest / Immobile	0
Mental Status	Forgets Limitations	15
	Oriented to Own Ability	0

* Based on most common scores used in VA

To obtain the Morse Fall Score add the score from each category…

Morse Fall Score*	
High Risk	45 and higher
Moderate Risk	25 - 44
Low Risk	0 - 24

THE INDIVIDUALIZED PLAN OF CARE

Once a patient's unique risk factors and needs have been assessed, the nursing home care team must develop strategies to address them and implement an individualized "Plan of Care." The interventions chosen to address the patient's fall risk are an integral part of the patient's plan of care. Often, the most effective fall prevention interventions address multiple factors or may use a multidisciplinary team (Neyens et al, 2009).

The care plan should assess risk factors that have been identified as putting the patient at risk of falling with the intention of greatly reducing, if not eliminating those risks entirely. Because every patient is different, the interventions detailed in the care plan should differ with each patient.

For example, patients who suffer from gait and balance disturbances should be managed by implementing restorative and rehabilitative care to improve strength, balance, ability to walk, and transfer. The underlying causes of these gait and balance disturbances should be assessed and treated as necessary.

Another example, patients with orthostatic hypotension should rise to a sitting position after lying down, and then slowly stand up. The patient's medication use should be examined closely. Medication that causes dizziness or postural hypotension should be evaluated to determine if drug administration times or doses need to be adjusted. A consulting pharmacist can help review medications to assess potential risks and benefits, and to minimize use.

It should be determined whether the patient can benefit from exercise programs that improve balance, strength, walking ability, and overall physical functioning.

For patients who are confused or unaware of their own safety limitations, it may be necessary to increase supervision, which can be accomplished, for example, by moving the patient closer to the nurse's station, ensuring that the patient is within the nursing staff's line of sight, or even having a family member or hired sitter present during certain key times (e.g., during walking or transfer).

Staff must ensure that call buttons are within reach of patients in bed and they must answer call lights in a reasonably prompt manner. So often, we hear that patients in need of help press the call light, only to be left waiting for staff to respond for an hour or more.

Staff must consider using bed or wheelchair alarms for patients who may tend to try to climb out of bed or out of the wheelchair on their own. Of course, alarms alone cannot prevent falls or accidents. The facility must also have a sufficient number of properly trained staff present to respond to the alarms in a timely manner. Too often, the nursing home staff fails to ensure that the alarms are properly engaged and working. When staff discover that a patient is capable of disarming the alarm on their own, other means of protection may need to be implemented, such as increased supervision and monitoring.

TIP: Obtain a copy of the patient's individualized fall risk care plan from the nursing home, which will reveal the interventions that the nursing home staff believe should be implemented to protect against injury from falls and accidents. That way, you can decide for yourself whether the facility staff has chosen the appropriate interventions and help ensure that they actually implement the interventions set forth in the care plan.

For patients who are at risk of falling out of bed, the nursing staff must consider making environmental changes, such as the use of a "low bed" and floor mats, which can reduce the impact of falls. Providing patients with hip pads may also prevent a hip fracture if a fall occurs (Kannus et al, 2000).

The use of night lights, canes, walkers, and bedside tables may help patients with peripheral neuropathies and visual impairments get out of bed and move safely move about their rooms. Facilities can also use visual reminders and signs as memory triggers to remind patients to get up slowly and carefully. This is especially true for stroke victims.

Nursing staff must ensure that they anticipate patient needs, such as toileting and hydration, so that at-risk patients don't have to attempt to get up on their own. Often, short-staffed nursing homes leave patients unattended for far too long, forcing patients to attempt to get up for toileting on their own, with no staff assistance.

Facilities must ensure that they have an adequate number of nursing staff available to safely transfer patients. Far too often, patients who require two-person transfer assistance are transferred by a single staff member because the facility is understaffed. This poses a significant and unnecessary risk to the patient, and all too often, results in a clearly foreseeable harm.

These are just a few examples of how intervention strategies can be tailored to a patient's individual needs. The key, though, is that the nursing home staff must first take time to properly evaluate the patient's fall risk factors, develop individualized interventions to address those risks, monitor the effectiveness of those interventions, and continue to reevaluate and implement new interventions as needed. These functions can and should be undertaken by every nursing home staff, but they can only be safely executed when nursing homes have a sufficient number of staff members who are properly educated about fall risk factors and prevention strategies.

THE HIGH COST OF FALLS

The financial burden of nursing home falls is significant, both in the aggregate, but also for the individual. Fall injuries are, in fact, in the top 20 most expensive medical conditions (Carroll et al, 2005).

In 2013, direct medical cost of falls for people over age 65 in the U.S. was $34 billion (Stevens et al, 2006), compared to $19 billion in 2000 (Centers for Disease Control and Prevention, 2008). Since the U.S. population is aging and the cost to treat is ever-increasing, the number of falls and the cost to treat the resulting injuries are likely to continue rising unless nursing homes get better at preventing falls.

As for the individual cost, a study of adults 72 and older found that the typical direct medical cost of treating a fall injury was $19,440 (Centers for Disease Control and Prevention, 2008). For hip fractures, the average cost was more than $35,000 (Findorff et al., 2007) and can reach as high as $86,000 (Findorff et al., 2007).

The costs of treating fall injuries increases with age (Stevens et al, 2006). In fact, studies show that nursing homes patients are more prone to serious complications after a fall (Becker & Rapp, 2010).

These direct medical costs cited include fees for hospital and nursing home care, doctors and other professional services, rehabilitation, community-based services, use of medical equipment, prescription drugs, and insurance processing. But direct costs do not account for the suffering that the patient must endure, or the long-term effects such as disability, dependence on others, and the reduced quality of life that inevitably accompanies a fall injury.

It's worth mentioning that preventing falls helps reduce risk for other costly and painful conditions such as pressure sores, since many patients who ultimately go on to develop pressure sores may have been rendered immobile due to injuries such as falls.

THE BOTTOM LINE

Falls are not only the cause of serious injury and disability among nursing home patients, but much heartache and suffering, too. Since most nursing home patients are likely to have multiple risk factors for falls, it is only by thoroughly assessing the unique strengths, risks and needs of each individual patient that falls can be prevented.

TIPS

1. Ask for copies of fall risk assessments that should be done upon admission, periodically, and with significant changes in the patient's condition. Make sure the fall risk factors are properly scored. Many times they aren't and the patient's risk is not properly identified.

2. Obtain a copy of the fall risk care plan to see what interventions (e.g., bed or chair alarms, non-slip socks, floor mats, lowered bed, etc.) are supposed to be implemented. If these interventions have not been implemented, alert the shift supervisor and/or director of nursing.

3. Make sure that the nursing staff ensures that the call light is within the resident's reach. If it's not, alert the supervisor and/or the director of nursing.

4. Make sure the nursing staff is keeping the patient's room free of clutter and obstacles that could cause the patient to trip or stumble.

5. Monitor whether staff is responding to the call light in a timely manner in order to prevent the patient from trying to get up without needed assistance.

6. Make sure the nursing staff is following the care plan and using the proper number of staff to assist the patient with transfers.

7. Make sure nursing is regularly toileting patients who need assistance with getting up and using the toilet. This helps prevent patients from getting up on their own to toilet without needed assistance.

6

MEDICATION "ERRORS"

From error to error, one discovers the entire truth.

— **Sigmund Freud**

*R*obert *was born in 1940. He grew up in America's heartland, and as a young adult, felt compelled to join the Marines. He met his wife at the Marine Corp Ball at Glenview Naval Air Station in Illinois in the early 1960's. They married not long after and had three children. After serving his country for 11 years, including in Vietnam, Robert became one of the pioneering students who attended computer science school in Quantico, Virginia. He went on to enjoy a fulfilling career working for some of America's top technology companies. After retiring, he had more time to enjoy his passions, Hoosier basketball, Colts football, and gardening.*

One day in 2015, he suffered a fall at home and broke his arm. He was admitted to a nursing home for rehabilitation so that he could return home to live independently. The nursing home's marketing pitch was convincing and his family felt comfortable that this nursing home was the place for him to recover. The nursing staff noted Robert's great interest in life and his enthusiastic attitude. He was ready to do what he needed to do to go home and get on with his life.

Because Robert had atrial fibrillation, he had been taking blood thinners (anticoagulants) for some time. The medication was effective, but he required routine blood tests of his INR levels to ensure that his blood was clotting properly. If his INR level was greater than 1.8 — meaning his blood was too "thin," or taking too long to clot — nursing was to notify his physician, who would adjust his medication.

One day, Robert fell while the nursing home staff watched. He was standing in a doorway and started to fall forward but twisted around and landed on his back, with his head bouncing off the floor. He lay unconscious for a few seconds, with the back of head bleeding. An enormous hematoma formed on the back of his head. Later the nursing staff noted Robert's head was still bleeding. His doctor ordered lab testing of his INR level. This INR level was 10.5 — dangerously high, so far above the 1.8 "warning" level that it would be extremely difficult for his blood to clot in order to stop the brain bleed. Robert was rushed to the emergency room.

A head CT revealed that Robert's brain was still bleeding, forming a subdural hematoma, exactly the type of danger that results from allowing the blood to become too thin. Surgeons were able to open Robert's skull and drain some of the pooled blood, but they couldn't stop the bleeding.

Robert would never return home. He died as a result of the brain bleed.

How could this happen? How could Robert's INR (International Normalized Ratio) levels have increased so severely without anyone realizing it? Here's what Robert's family later learned…

Around the same time that Robert was admitted to the nursing home, the facility had been investigated and cited for failing to comply with multiple state and federal regulations. Investigators had found that doctors weren't being notified of significant changes in patient conditions which, in turn, would require changes in treatment. And physician orders were not being carried out by the nursing staff.

Also unbeknownst to Robert's family, the facility was investigated again while Robert was a patient and cited with multiple care violations that are indicative of gross systemic failures in the hiring, training, oversight and management of facility personnel. The investigation report contained evidence of neglect, gross medication errors, and apparent attempts to misrepresent facts to investigators. Incredibly, the investigation revealed that the facility had *a medication error rate of 53%!* In other words, there were errors associated with more than *half* of the medication administrations during this one investigatory sample alone.

But there was no legal requirement that the nursing home notify the patients' families or prospective patients of these extraordinary care failures. Had Robert and his family known, they certainly wouldn't have admitted him to this nursing home.

As for what caused Robert's death, the nursing staff at some point, for some unknown reason, continued to give Robert blood thinner medication without checking his INR levels. Day after day, nursing continued to administer his blood thinners without notifying his doctor that no testing was being performed. Not only did his critically thin blood likely lead to his collapsing to the floor, once his head slammed against the floor, the profuse bleeding caused by the impact — and further exacerbated by the excessive blood thinner medication administered to him — was in all likelihood unstoppable.

A medication error ultimately led to the needless death of a man who was admitted to the nursing home simply to recover from a broken arm.

Almost every nursing home patient takes at least one medication. Medication use, unfortunately, has simply become a fact of living in our modern world.

As you might expect, prescription drug use is much higher within the aging population: 89.8% of people over 65 use at least one prescription drug in a 30-day period (National Center for Health Statistics, 2015). But medication rates are much higher for nursing home residents. On average, elderly people *not* living in nursing homes are prescribed three to four medications; whereas elderly people residing in nursing homes are prescribed seven to eight medications (Avorn & Gurwitz, 1995).

While medications may offer great therapeutic benefit, errors in administering them can be dangerous — even life-threatening. With so many patients taking so many medications, perhaps it's not surprising that there are an alarming number of medication errors, especially in the nursing home setting where, as you're beginning to see, vigilance is, unfortunately, too often lacking.

HOW COMMON IS THE "ERROR" PROBLEM?

Medication errors are pervasive in nursing home facilities. But they're also preventable. These preventable errors are responsible for a significant number of deaths and injury to the nursing home population.

> **MYTH:** Medication errors are relatively rare.
>
> **REALITY:** In nursing homes, 1 out of 5 medication doses are administered in error.

We use the term "error" in this book because most of the medical literature uses that phraseology. However, one should not conclude that the use of the term *error* suggests that these care failures are either insignificant, excusable incidents, or even necessarily the product of unknowing mistake. As you're about to learn, life-threatening "errors" can result from profoundly careless actions. Worse, many of these so-called medication errors are the result of intentional (and sometimes even criminal) acts by nursing staff.

So, how common is this problem?

Some studies estimate that approximately 800,000 medication errors occur each year in U.S. nursing home facilities (Gurwitz et al., 2005). But this estimate may vastly understate the true extent of the problem. One researcher suggests that for every medication error that harms a patient, there are perhaps 100, mostly undetected, errors that do not (Bates, 1996).

One obstacle to pinpointing the extent of medication errors is that many estimates rely upon the self-reported data from the nurses who committed the errors. Because it's unlikely that all nurses report all of their errors — whether because they don't notice the errors or because they fear reprimand — some studies gather medication error data by having independent researchers observe medication administrations.

In one of the most extensive observational studies, researchers monitored medication administrations in 36 randomly selected health care facilities in the U.S., including nursing homes. Of the 3,216 doses observed, 605 doses contained at least one error. That's an error rate of nearly 20%, or one of every 5 doses (Barker, 2002)!

> **A study of rural nursing homes found that 67% of the residents had suffered an adverse drug event (Cooper, 1996). Even worse, 50% of these adverse drug events were deemed preventable.**

Other studies have found that between 19 and 42 percent of hospital admissions of elderly individuals are attributable to adverse drug reactions (Lindley et al, 1992; Mannesse et al, 1997).

Federal regulations require nursing homes to guard against medication error. However, at least one study shows that the average medication error rate in U.S. nursing homes exceeds 12% (Barker, 1992.) Errors included: administering a non-prescribed drug, administering the wrong doses, and administering medication through the wrong administration route (Barker, 1992).

> **Federal Regulation 42 C.F. R. §483.25(m) Medication Errors:**
>
> The facility must ensure that —
>
> • It is free of medication error rates of 5 percent or greater; and,
>
> • Residents are free of any significant medication errors.

A 2014 report by the Office of the Inspector General of the Department of Health and Human Services about adverse events in skilled nursing facilities found that *one in three* patients who stay in a nursing home will suffer harm or injury *within the first 35 days* as a result of the care they receive. The report also found that most of these incidents are "clearly or likely preventable," and attributed much of the preventable harm to "substandard treatment, inadequate resident monitoring, and failure or delay of necessary care" (Levinson, Office of Inspector General, 2014).

In that report, 37% of the adverse events were related to medication issues and 43% of the events which caused temporary harm to nursing home patents were related to medication issues. The harm included hypoglycemic episodes (e.g., low or significant drop in blood glucose), a fall or other trauma with injury associated with medication, medication-induced delirium, or other change in mental status, thrush and other non-surgical infections related to medication, and allergic reactions to medication.

What percentage of those medication events were preventable? Sixty-six percent, according to physician reviewers. The report further found an estimated 7,203 hospitalizations for medication events, which, on average, cost an estimated $8,372. The estimated total spending related to hospitalizations for medication events was an estimated $57,729,935. And this cost was just for the month of August 2011.

This cost is subsidized largely by taxpayer-funded sources of revenue for nursing homes, such as Medicare and Medicaid. And these dollar figures, of course, cover only the actual medical costs. They don't begin to cover the human suffering inflicted by these many preventable medication mistakes.

HOW MEDICATION ERRORS HAPPEN

In a nursing home, the ordering physician and the nursing staff participate in and are responsible for the medication process. It's called a "process," because it involves a series of actions or steps taken in order to achieve the particular end of ensuring the patient receives the proper medication in the proper dose to provide the desired therapeutic effect. Errors anywhere in this process can be catastrophic.

The Medication Process

The medication process includes five stages (Institute of Medicine, 2007):

- **ordering/prescribing:** the decision to order medication and the selection of medications;
- **transcribing and verifying:** receiving the order from the physician, verifying that it is an appropriate medication and dose, and accurately transcribing the medication into the medical records;

- **dispensing and delivering:** ensuring that the exact medication and dose are dispensed and prepared for administration to the patient;
- **administering:** administering the medication to the patient, whether orally, through a g-tube or an IV, etc.;
- **monitoring and reporting:** involves monitoring the patient to determine if the medication was effective/ineffective, or caused any side-effects.

You can see why diligence is required at every stage of the process. The medication process can be compromised at any of the steps along the path of administration, and any error at any point along the way has the potential to harm the patient.

Every nurse is responsible for the correct administration of medications. This responsibility is often referred to as the "5 Rights," and includes:

- *Right* patient
- *Right* drug
- *Right* dose
- *Right* route
- *Right* time

In other words: *It's the responsibility of nursing staff to ensure that the correct drug, in the correct dose, is given to the correct patient, at the correct time, in the correct manner.*

But the nursing staff's responsibility doesn't end there.

It's also the nursing staff's responsibility to monitor the effect of drugs they administer to determine whether the drug had the intended effect, little or no effect, and/or resulted in any adverse reactions.

To get a better idea of how medication errors happen, let's look at what can go awry at each stage of the medication process.

Prescribing and Ordering Errors

This is the stage that can provoke a series of errors that ultimately results in a patient receiving the wrong medication, wrong dose, or wrong route or delivery. Another error common to this stage is ordering medications to which the patient has known allergies.

Many drugs carry FDA "black box warnings" that were designed to alert healthcare providers of well-known, serious risks involving some medications. These warnings are intended to be the strongest labeling warning for drugs or drug products that can cause serious adverse reactions or potential safety hazards, especially if these reactions or hazards could result in death or serious injury (Murphy & Roberts, 2006).

Yet, one study funded by the Agency for Healthcare Research and Quality found that 40% of patients were taking a medication with a black box warning and that many of those patients did not receive the recommended laboratory monitoring (Wagner et al, 2006).

While physicians are typically responsible for ordering most medications, they are not the only healthcare provider who bears some responsibility for ensuring that medications are not prescribed in error. It is a fundamental nursing responsibility to be familiar enough with the general effects of medications that they would be able to spot obvious errors and alert physicians. Nurses cannot simply administer medications ordered by a physician with a blind eye towards the potential effect upon the patient. Nurses have an affirmative duty to look out for, identify, and report possible medication prescription errors in a timely fashion.

Transcribing, verifying and dispensing

In the nursing home setting, it's not uncommon for nurses to receive orders from physicians by telephone. These nurses must ensure that the order is properly received and transcribed into the medical record, specifying the drug, dose, and method of administration. They must then document the time of administration into a medication administration record each time the medication is given. Too often — far too often — nursing staff incorrectly document the physician's telephone order, or, subsequently, when the order is transcribed onto the medication administration record. This sets up a scenario in which a medication error will be repeated again and again — perhaps *never* discovered unless the patient suffers an adverse reaction and someone discovers the connection to the original transcription.

Even when the order has been properly given and transcribed, errors can be made in preparing and delivering the medication for administration. Pharmacy dispensing errors have been found to account for between 4 to 42 percent of medication errors (Walsh et al, 2005), the most common of which are: wrong medication taken from a shelf, wrong dose, and wrong preparation (Raju et al, 1989).

Nurses may also be responsible for both the dispensing and preparation of medications, such as crushing pills or drawing a measured dose for injections. Whether nursing is responsible for dispensing the medication in preparation for administration, or the medication is received from a pharmacy, the nurse is responsible for double-checking to ensure that the proper medication and dose are dispensed for administration.

Medication administration

In nursing homes, medications are typically administered by a nurse or "certified medication aide," who is a certified nursing assistant (CNA) who has completed additional classroom training to become certified to dispense medications to patients while working under the supervision of a registered nurse. Certified medication aides usually have four months of training, which includes 140 hours of supervised clinical practice.

Medication administration errors can result when the nursing staff fails to strictly adhere to physician orders when administering medication. Common examples of this type of error include omitting a dose, administering the wrong strength of the medication, administering the wrong medication, administering the medication improperly (e.g., by mouth when the medication was supposed to be administered by G-tube).

Early research on medication administration errors reported an error rate of around 60 percent, primarily due to medication being administered at the wrong time, wrong rate, or wrong dose (Raju et al, 1989). In later studies, approximately *one out of every three* adverse drug events were attributable to the administration of medications by nurses to patients (Bates et al, 1995; Pepper, 1995).

In a study that looked at the cause of deaths due to medication errors reported to the FDA over a five-year period, the error most often involved drugs that were injected (Phillips, 2001). Overdose was the most common error found, with the wrong drug being administered as the second most common error.

Monitoring and Reporting

Nursing home staff must monitor the patient after administering medication to ensure that the patient's response to the medication is consistent with what's expected. If not, the reason for the inconsistency must be assessed. An inconsistent response may indicate that a properly ordered and administered drug is not going to be effective to treat the patient's condition. This may signal that the diagnosis that prompted the order is wrong.

But the inconsistent response may also be a warning sign that the drug was administered in error — that is, wrong drug, wrong dose, wrong time, etc. Nursing staff must understand that their responsibilities don't end with the administration of the drug.

In Robert's case, nursing staff failed to ensure that necessary lab testing was performed as ordered. Because Robert was on blood thinners, he needed to have his PT/INR checked routinely but nursing failed to do that. This error led to his death.

MOST COMMON MEDICATION ERRORS

A: When I was released, they had me sign a form about the medication that you're on, and they give you your medication to come home with. And one of the medications I was prescribed to, one of them was Lortab, and they're the pain medications. The whole time I was there, I never took any, but when she gave the prescription to bring home, there were nine tablets missing from the sheet of medication. And I asked her, "Where'd it go?" I said, "I haven't taken any pain medication while I was here." And the nurse's comment to me was, "Well, I never gave you any. I never did anything with it." So on the paperwork, they have it in writing, because I wrote it in my own signature with my own writing, that I never took any of these pain meds, and nine are missing.

Q: *Did she have any answer for that, at all?*

A: *No answer whatsoever. And then once I got home, I was going through my medications, to take the medications, and I noticed that I had a whole sheet of like, 40 to 50 pills that belonged to another patient there.*

— Deposition of nursing home patient

Several common medication errors are identified in the medical literature:

- Choosing the wrong medication to prescribe
- Giving the patient the wrong drug
- Giving the wrong dose
- Ordering a medication for a patient who has a known or suspected allergy to it
- Missing a dose
- Administering the medication at the wrong time
- Administering the medication with the wrong frequency
- Administering the medication using the wrong technique
- Failing to recognize an adverse drug-to-drug interaction
- Administering a medication using the wrong route
- Administering an extra dose
- Failing to give a test (e.g., blood glucose or INR blood test)
- Failing to take proper action after testing
- Equipment failure (e.g., IV malfunction)
- Inadequate monitoring after administration
- Medication preparation error

Medication errors most commonly attributed to physicians are: wrong dose, wrong choice of drug, and adverse reactions as a result of a known allergy.

As for nursing administration errors, the most common errors include: wrong dose, wrong technique, and wrong drug.

In an attempt to get a better handle on the prevalence and impact of medication errors in nursing homes, the North Carolina General Assembly passed a bill in 2003 which mandated development of an advisory committee and an annual report of medication errors. Through this initiative, data was collected regarding nursing home medication errors for a period of nine years. Results of those reports are instructive. In 2012, there were more than 61,000 medication errors in North Carolina nursing homes alone (Williams et al, 2012).

The study found that the most common medication error was the omission of a dose of medication, which accounted for 36.2% of the errors. Obviously, failing to administer medication that has been ordered is troubling as the patient is not receiving the therapeutic benefit of the medication to address the medical condition which prompted the physician to order the drug in the first place. Missing doses of antibiotics, for example, increases the risk that the infection will proliferate. Missing doses of pain medication mean patients suffer needlessly. Missing doses of blood thinner medication can result in dangerous, life-threatening clotting.

Unfortunately, as we'll discuss in detail in the next section, patients often miss doses because nursing home staff is diverting (in other words: *stealing*) their medication.

Administering overdoses was another significant error identified by the North Carolina study. An overdose is an excessive and dangerous dose of a drug. Overdose can result from a physician or nurse practitioner prescribing an excessive dose, although nurses do have a duty to review dosage before administering. Overdose can also result when the nursing staff fails to comply with a physician's order and administers a larger dose than what was prescribed. Too much narcotic pain medication, for example, can substantially slow or even halt the ability to breathe, and even lead to death.

Too much blood thinner medication can result in the dangerous inability to clot, which leads to excessive bleeding and even death, as in Robert's case.

The North Carolina study also noted the frequency of other nursing errors, including administering the wrong strength and administering medications for which a physician order had expired, among others.

FACTORS THAT CONTRIBUTE TO MEDICATION ERRORS

The 2012 North Carolina study also investigated the causes of medication errors. The most frequent causes were:

- Staff did not follow policies
- Transcription error
- Distractions on nursing floor
- Poor communication
- Pharmacy dispensing
- Medication unavailable

The study found that licensed practical nurses (LPNs) were the most common caregivers involved in 69.4% of the medication error incidents. Registered nurses (RNs) were involved 22.6% of the time. Medication aides were involved in 4.1 percent of the errors.

Interestingly, the study also found that the rate of medication errors was highest on the first shift, followed by the second shift.

- Medication Errors By Shift
- 7:00 a.m. to 3:00 p.m. — 38,372 errors (62.2%)
- 3:00 p.m. to 11:00 p.m. — 20,318 (32.9%)
- 11:00 p.m. to 7:00 a.m. — 3,040 (4.9%)

These findings may suggest that family members should be vigilant even during first shift when facilities typically have more nursing staff on duty, including the administrator and director of nursing who work regular office hours. The fact that management is on-site and more nursing staff is on hand doesn't mean that preventable medication errors can't happen.

Understaffing Increases Medication Error

As with so many aspects of nursing home care, the consequences of understaffing can take a devastating toll. Nurses in various settings have frequently cited understaffing and excessive workloads to explain why medication errors occur (Stratton et al, 2004; Beyea et al, 2003a; Beyea et al, 2003b; Tang et al, 2007; Hicks et l, 2004).

An inadequate number of nursing staff, coupled with heavy workloads, can result in lengthy workdays that compromise the staff's ability to perform effectively and increase the odds of medication error. In fact, one study found that self-reported errors by nurses showed that the likelihood of medication error *tripled* after the nurse worked more than 12.5 hours per day providing direct patient care. (Rogers et al, 2004).

In another study involving the review of incident reports, researchers linked the importance of sufficient and adequately trained nursing staff, finding that major contributing factors to medication errors were inexperienced staff, followed by insufficient staffing, and agency/temporary staffing (Wolf et al, 2006).

A CULTURE OF COVER-UP

As you've seen in previous chapters, there's a pervasive effort in many nursing homes to hide errors from the patient, the patient's family, and state investigators. Medication errors are no exception.

> *"I was asked by Caroline [the corporate nurse supervisor] and also by Annette [the director of nursing] to omit or err out certain things in -- I can't remember whose chart, but -- specifically. You know, but they would be like, 'Just draw a line through there and write 'Error. Wrong chart.'"*

> *"I said, 'No, that's what happened. That's what I did. That's what I saw. That's what I've written down.' You know, and twice I noticed that they erred out my entry, and that's -- you, basically, can't do that. I don't know why they would do it."*

> *— Deposition of nursing home nurse*

> **MYTH:** If a medication error occurs, you'll be informed.
>
> **REALITY:** 75-90% of medication errors go unreported.

Research shows that even when nursing staff voluntarily report medication administration errors, only 10 to 25 percent of errors are actually reported (Pepper, 1995). What this means, of course, is that 75 - 90 percent of medication errors go undetected and unreported.

What motivates this failure to report? A nursing facility culture in which the nursing staff disagree about the definition of "reportable errors," fear of the response by management/administrators and peers to a reported error, and the effort required to document and report an error.

None of these are sufficient excuses for failing to report medication errors. What is clear, however, is that the errors that *are* reported certainly do not represent the true prevalence of medication errors.

And even when patients file formal complaints about medication errors, their complaints are often ignored or dismissed, as this patient deposition illustrates…

> *A: One of the problems I had was — I'm on dialysis and I'm a diabetic. And when I would go for my dialysis treatment, they had to hold my meds, because I couldn't take my blood pressure pills or my thyroid medicine or my diabetes medicine because of dialysis. I had to wait because they would flush it out of my system. Several times, they wouldn't give me my medicine when I would come in from my dialysis treatment. On two occasions, they gave me the wrong medication. They gave me someone else's medication. I wrote up complaints that never got any response for them. I did formal complaints. They never responded.*
>
> *Q: Was that a complaint you sent to the management of the facility?*
>
> *A: I did it through the social service person that works there at*

the facility. She wrote up a complaint. She signed it, told me they would investigating, they'd come and see me, and they never did.

Q: Never even gave you any feedback at all about it?

A: None whatsoever. None whatsoever.

— Deposition of nursing home patient

MOST COMMON DRUGS INVOLVED IN ERRORS

The North Carolina study found that the following medications were most commonly subject to medication errors:

- Warfarin
- Insulin
- Oxycodone
- Hydrocodone
- Lorazepam
- Fentanyl
- Furosemide
- Alprazolam
- Metoprolol
- Omeprazole
- Clonazepam
- Aspirin
- Potassium chloride
- Levothyroxine
- Polyethylene glycol
- Zolpidem
- Docusate
- Morphine

- Gabapentin
- Mirtazapine
- Quetiapine
- Acetaminophen
- Lisinopril
- Simvastatin
- Multivitamin
- Calcium-Vitamin D
- Enoxaparin
- Tramadol

SPECIAL "HIGH-ALERT" MEDICATIONS

The Institute of Safe Medication Practices (ISMP), which is a nonprofit organization devoted entirely to medication error prevention and safe medication use, has designated certain "High-Alert medications" as drugs that bear an increased risk of causing significant patient harm when used in error. Regardless of the fact that these medications may be more prone to error, the consequences of an error are clearly more devastating.

It's impossible to cover, within the scope of this book, every single significant medication-related error that occurs in the nursing home setting, but let's discuss two High-Alert medication categories that merit special attention.

Blood Thinners (Anticoagulants)

Blood thinners or anticoagulants may be a necessary medication for many patients, but it's crucial that nursing staff is diligent when administering these medications and vigilant in assessing the medication's effects on the patient. Errors with blood thinner administration can result in tragic outcomes and calibrating the medication can be a delicate balance: too much and the patient can bleed uncontrollably; too little, and the patient can develop life-threatening clots.

Coumadin (or its generic, Warfarin) dosage can be tricky to manage even for otherwise healthy patients who don't live in nursing homes. A study by Quest Diagnostics laboratories found that the lab results of patients taking Coumadin or Warfarin showed that the drug had the desired effect only 54% of the time (Dlott et al, 2014). So, given the challenges of managing anticoagulants and the amount of coordination required between doctors, nurses, pharmacists and labs, nursing homes are the perfect setting for a perfect storm of medication errors.

- A July 2015 *Washington Post* article warned that administering blood thinners without taking proper precautions was causing deaths and injuries in nursing homes, citing several studies that suggested the true prevalence of such serious incidents:

- A July 12, 2015 ProPublica analysis of government inspection reports found that, from 2011 to 2014, at least 165 nursing home patients were hospitalized or died as a result of errors involving Coumadin or its generic, Warfarin (Ornstein, 2015).

- An American Journal of Medicine study revealed that nursing home residents suffer 34,000 fatal, life-threatening or serious events related to Warfarin (or Coumadin) each year (Gurwitz et al, 2007).

- The 2012 North Carolina nursing home study found more medication errors in nursing homes involving Coumadin than any other drug (Williams et al, 2012).

- A 2011 New England Journal of Medicine report found that Warfarin accounted for 33.3% of emergency hospitalizations among the elderly from 2007 to 2009, more than twice as many as the next-highest drug, insulin (13.9%) (Budnitz et al, 2011).

On the heels of the 2015 *Washington Post* article, the U.S. Department of Health and Human Services issued a memorandum on July 17, 2015 to state nursing home survey agency directors warning that the dangers associated with errors related to blood thinning medication "merits close attention by top management and staff throughout the facility." The memo, which unveiled an Adverse Event Trigger Tool to assist government investigators, expressed concern about "the prevalence of adverse events involving such medications."

The government investigates incidents that trigger complaints or surface in routine inspections and may issue *immediate jeopardy* citations, fining nursing homes and threatening to withhold federal funding if quick action isn't taken. More commonly, though, ProPublica's 2015 analysis shows that nursing homes are *not* fined and are simply asked to correct the problems and put policies in place to keep them from happening again.

It's true that vigilance can be tricky to enforce. But because errors involving blood thinner medications pose such dangerous risks to patients, families should closely confer with and observe the nursing staff (to the extent possible) to help ensure that the physician's orders are being carried out properly and that the patient is not suffering any adverse reactions.

Other "High-Alert" Medications

Following is a list of the Institute of Safe Medication Practices (ISMP) High Alert medications for nursing home patients:

Classes/Categories of Medications

- anticoagulants, parenteral and oral (including Warfarin and newer drugs)
- chemotherapeutic agents, parenteral and oral (excluding hormonal agents)
- hypoglycemics, oral (including combination products with another drug)
- insulins, all formulations and strengths (e.g., U-100, U-200, U-300, U-500)
- parenteral nutrition preparations
- opioids — parenteral, transdermal, and oral (including liquid concentrates, immediate- and sustained-release formulations, and combination products with another drug)

Specific Medications

- digoxin, parenteral and oral
- epinephrine, parenteral
- iron dextran, parenteral
- methotrexate, oral, non-oncology use (All forms of chemotherapy are considered high-alert medications. Oral methotrexate for non-oncology purposes has been singled out for special emphasis to call attention to the need for distinct strategies to prevent wrong frequency errors that occur with this drug when used for non-oncology purposes that can result in death)
- concentrated morphine solution, oral (All forms of opioids are considered high-alert medications. Concentrated morphine solution has been singled out for special emphasis to bring attention to the need for distinct strategies to prevent wrong frequency errors that occur with this drug that can result in death.)

Families of patients who are administered one or more of these medications should make every effort to help ensure that the nursing home staff is administering these drugs diligently.

Stolen Medications ("Medication Diversion")

Another significant and growing problem involves nursing home employees stealing pain medications from the patients they're being paid to care for. The industry likes to call this practice of medication theft "drug diversion."

But to be clear, theft of pain medication is yet-another form of nursing home neglect and abuse. And it's a very real problem in nursing homes, as is illustrated by this interview excerpt from a former Indiana State nursing home investigator…

> *"I think it's on the rise. Vicodin. The very impaired nurses, especially if they're going to give it to somebody who's not quite with it, they go, 'I just gave you that. Don't you remember?' Or they'll take a fentanyl patch, and they'll take a syringe and take*

the medicine out of the fentanyl patch because the hole will be so small. Then they'll use it and put the fentanyl patch on the patient, and they'll say, 'Here's your patch. It's on you right here. What's the problem?' But the Vicodin is the big thing."

"They're so vulnerable. And they'll say, 'Look. Look right there.' Or the other thing you'll see is if you — I don't know if you get these records, but it's called a controlled drug sheet. It's supposed be part of the clinical record. But when you see a lot of things crossed out, or you'll see one nurse is giving it all the time, you can generally figure out there's a problem going on. I had a nursing home on the west side where they were taking the drugs and actually selling it out in the parking lot to people. And it was all mentally-handicapped residents, so they didn't know.

Vicodin kind of looks like a Tylenol to them. They didn't know."

— Interview with a former Indiana State nursing home investigator

---

MYTH: Nursing homes wouldn't hire convicted criminals to care for patients.

REALITY: More than 90% of U.S. nursing homes employ at least 1 convicted criminal. Nearly half employ 5 or more convicted criminals.

Drug theft is, unfortunately, all too common across the country, particularly as more and more nursing home employees become addicted to narcotic medications. A 2012 study conducted by the Mayo Clinic reported that drug diversion was "a considerable and ongoing problem." In 2015, it was reported that a former nurse at an Indiana nursing home had been charged with 11 criminal counts after an investigation revealed the theft of prescription pain medications from residents at his facility. According to reports, the former employee indicated in an affidavit that he would sign out the medication on the resident's narcotic sheet, then keep the medication for himself. The employee said he knew that the theft was "very wrong" and illegal, but he couldn't stop because his addiction was so strong.

How can this happen so frequently? Because the nursing home setting supplies a perfect storm of factors that make it possible:

- Pain medications are prevalent in nursing homes because a significant percentage of nursing home patients require medication for pain control;

- More than 90% of U.S. nursing home facilities employ one or more people who have been convicted of at least one crime; nearly half employ five or more people with at least one conviction (Levinson, Office of Inspector General, 2011).

- Nursing homes typically don't have the same stringent medication controls that hospitals have;

- There's very little supervision during medication administration to ensure the patient actually receives the medications ordered;

- Due to dementia or other medical conditions, nursing home patients often cannot communicate that they've been denied pain medication;

- Record falsification within a nursing home is not difficult, so verification is very difficult.

The drug theft problem is likely to only grow worse as: (1) the nation's drug addiction problem grows worse, and; (2) a greater percentage of the population, including baby boomers, require nursing home care.

Drug addiction is often considered to be a "victimless crime." But drug theft in a nursing home is particularly dangerous to the patient. The patient is denied the medication he or she needs to control what may be excruciating, unrelenting pain that can cause both physical and psychiatric harm. And ultimately, the patient is put at risk of being harmed by mistakes made by the impaired healthcare provider who stole and used the medication.

WHAT YOU CAN DO

While it can be very difficult for families to confirm that medications are being properly administered, there are some things you can do to help protect your loved one from medication error.

TIPS

- Confirm that nursing home staff is aware of any medication allergies, reactions or problems. Don't assume that they'll discover it from other medical records.

- Obtain a list of all medications ordered, along with the method of administration and the times/days administered.

- Research to determine if there are any Black Box warnings for the medications being administered. (https://blackboxrx.com/) Make sure that any Black Box warnings that may affect the patient are brought to the attention of the nursing home staff and/or the physician.

- Attend care conferences and confirm whether there have been any changes to the patient's medications, method of administration, and administration times.

- Be present during medication administration. While it may not be possible to always be present, plan visits around medication administration times whenever possible to observe whether the medications are being administered as they should be.

- Be actively involved in "medication reconciliation," i.e., comparing current medication orders to all medications you've been taking to avoid medication errors such as omissions, duplications, dosing errors or drug interactions. Reconciliation should be done at *every transition of care* when new meds are ordered, or existing orders rewritten. Transitions in care include any changes in facilities, after-hospital stays, etc.

- Look for evidence of torn or damaged pain patches that may have been removed and/or replaced. Some drug-seeking caretakers steal medications directly off the patients' bodies.

- Look for signs that the patient is experiencing unusual pain. This may be an indicator that they are not receiving the medications that have been ordered for them.

- Look for obviously impaired caretakers. Drug-seeking caretakers will often attempt to continue working, even under the influence of drugs.

- Report any suspicion of drug theft to the facility administrator and director of nursing. If you don't receive a satisfactory response, report the concern to your state's Department of Health.

- Research the facility using Medicare's Nursing Home Compare website portal for information about staffing levels, quality of care measures, and government investigations. (https://www.medicare.gov/nursinghomecompare/search.html)

- Get to know the people caring for the patient. Don't ever be afraid to confront them if you feel something isn't right.

- Don't be afraid to ask questions. Be an advocate for the patient. You're not "bothering" the staff by asking questions intended to ensure the patient's safety. If the staff suggests that you're bothering them, that may be a good indicator that you should consider another facility.

ADDITIONAL RESOURCES

- Updated Information on High-Alert Medications: http://www.ismp.org/tools/highalertmedicationLists.asp

7

PHYSICAL, SEXUAL AND PSYCHOLOGICAL ABUSE

Abuse is the weapon of the vulgar.

— **Samuel Griswold Goodrich**

If a society is to be judged by how it treats its weakest members, then there is perhaps no greater test of our priorities today than that of our willingness to allow the profit-driven nursing home industry to continue to neglect and abuse the sick, vulnerable, elderly patients for whom they're responsible. This industry has choices as to how it executes this responsibility. Far too often, those within the industry wrongly choose profits over patients.

It's not that there are no laws in place to protect nursing home patients. There are…

LAWS MEANT TO PROTECT PATIENTS FROM ABUSE

The vast majority of nursing homes reap substantial funding from Medicare and Medicaid in exchange for the *promise* of providing quality care to their patients. In fact, a 2015 Centers for Medicare and Medicaid Services report found that, in 2014, of the 15,634 nursing homes across the U.S., 92.2% (14,407) were dually certified to receive both Medicare and Medicaid payments. In other words, federal government taxpayer funding pays for most nursing home care. And the truth is that these nursing home corporations rely upon this steady source of income — government payments — to generate profit. Many, in fact, generate very substantial profits from it.

In an effort to help ensure that nursing home patients' individual care needs are met in return for these government payments, both state and federal regulations require that nursing facilities provide adequate staffing, training, and quality assurance oversight. But most importantly, these regulations specifically *prohibit any form of patient abuse or neglect.* Yet, tragically, some form of abuse is inflicted upon patients by employees each and every day in U.S. nursing homes.

> **One elderly person is victimized every 2.7 minutes (Teaster et al, 2004).**

In 1986, institution-wide neglect and abuse of patients was highlighted in a landmark report on nursing home care authored by the Institute of Medicine (Institute of Medicine, 1986). With industry researchers estimating that 43% of older Americans will enter a nursing home sometime during their lives (Kemper & Murtaugh, 1991), concern about the prospect of future nursing home abuse increased. Federal legislators finally took up the cause and passed the Nursing Home Reform Act on December 22, 1987 as part of the Omnibus Budget Reconciliation Act (OBRA, 1987)(42 USC § 1819).

> **A 2001 U.S. House Investigative Report found that over 30% of U.S. nursing homes (1 in 3) were cited for an abuse violation over a 2-year period.**

Prior to the passage of this landmark legislation, nursing home patients were only protected from abuse by their general state laws against assault. When the U.S. Congress passed the Nursing Home Reform Act in 1987, nursing home patients received important new protections against mistreatment. For the first time, they were entitled to protection from specific forms of mistreatment, neglect and physical abuse in nursing home facilities.

What constitutes abuse and neglect under the law?

Medicare defines these acts as follows:

Abuse: "The willful infliction of injury, unreasonable confinement, intimidation, or punishment with resulting physical harm, pain or mental anguish." (42 CFR § 488.301.)

> **Neglect:** "Failure to provide goods and services necessary to avoid physical harm, mental anguish, or mental illness." (42 CFR § 488.301)

Common Examples of Abuse and Neglect

> "I've seen a blind resident slapped across the face… I've seen a nurse push a wheelchair resident down a flight of stairs… I was a CNA for over 25 years… what a sad cruel world."
>
> — Sally (former nursing home nurse aide)

While the above definitions may seem pretty straightforward on the surface, classifying specific acts as abuse or neglect is not always so simple.

Federal Regulation 42 C.F. R. §483.13 Abuse and Neglect:

- *Restraints.* The resident has the right to be free from any physical or chemical restraints imposed for purposes of discipline or convenience and not required to treat the resident's medical symptoms.

- *Abuse.* The resident has the right to be free from verbal, sexual, physical, and mental abuse, corporal punishment, and involuntary seclusion.

- *Staff treatment of residents.* The facility must develop and implement written policies and procedures that prohibit mistreatment, neglect, and abuse of residents and misappropriation of resident property.

Acts of abuse can be classified into several general subtypes, including include physical abuse, sexual abuse, mental/psychological abuse.

When does neglect become abuse? Neglect is sometimes difficult to clearly define because the perpetrator is *failing to act* rather than overtly abusing a patient. But generally speaking, acts that are neglectful become abuse when the perpetrator *knowingly* inflicts harm or deprives the patient of the care they need. The legal principle, *mens rea* (the intention or knowledge of wrongdoing), must be established — the perpetrator must be acting with knowledge or intent. Examples include knowing that a patient must be turned and repositioned every two hours to prevent pressure sores, but willfully failing to make sure that happens. That's abuse — it's a knowing infliction of injury or harm. Simply forgetting about patients, and thereby allowing them to fall and injure themselves is neglect. Choosing not to answer call lights because it's a bother, thus forcing patients to soil themselves or try to get to the bathroom on their own without the needed assistance, is a form of abuse.

As a practical matter, abuse and neglect can take so many forms that it's virtually impossible to produce one all-inclusive list. Most of us, as humans, instinctively sense when someone is being mistreated. In other words, "we know it when we see it." If your gut tells you that something is not right, it very well may not be.

The following are examples of abuse and neglect commonly found in nursing homes that you can be on the lookout for:

- Nursing home employees punching, hitting, slapping, kicking, pulling hair, or any other physical act of aggression towards the patient
- Threatening to cause physical harm to a patient
- Emotional or verbal abuse of the resident, such as humiliation of a patient (e.g., shaming incidents when the patient has soiled his/her clothing)
- Refusing to allow the patient to contact a relative, friend or other person when they want to
- Leaving a patient in a soiled garment or bed for an unreasonable period of time; failure to take residents to the toilet (leaving them in soiled garments or beds)
- Punishing patients, such as being rough with patients when changing their soiled garments, as punishment for soiling themselves
- Failing to ensure the patient has fresh water accessible
- Failing to ensure patients receive meals and snacks on time

- Failing to provide adequate supervision to prevent patients who are at fall risk from sustaining falls that will cause injury; failure to take reasonable precautions to prevent falls or take adequate precautions to prevent injury to the resident; using dilapidated or broken equipment to transfer patients, causing falls and injuries

- Failing to protect a patient from another patient who is a known risk to other patients

- Allowing patients to wander away from the facility putting them in harm's way

- Serving cold meals to patients when they should be warm or hot

- Unplugging patients' telephones so they cannot call others

- Moving the patient's call button out of reach so that they cannot call nursing staff; failure to answer call lights in a timely fashion

- Forcing patients to rise earlier than they want to simply for the convenience of the nursing staff

- Lining up patients in the hall or at the nursing station with no activity to occupy them simply because it's convenient for the nursing staff

- Failing to use a sufficient number of staff to transfer a patient, causing injury

- Failing to turn and reposition a patient with sufficient frequency to avoid skin breakdown

- Failing to reposition a wheelchair patient at least once per hour, causing undue pressure to their skin

- Failing to give patients medication as prescribed, including over-medication or under-medication, or e.g., over-medication which may cause preventable falls likely to cause bodily injury

- Failing to conduct laboratory tests to ensure proper dosages for patients who take blood thinners or other medications which require regular, ongoing testing

- Attempting to administer food or medications to patients who are not to receive anything orally

- Feeding patients food or medications without ensuring they are properly crushed or pureed if ordered by a doctor

- Using restraints on patients without proper physician orders and proper precautions to ensure that it is done appropriately and safely
- Sexual abuse: inappropriately touching or otherwise sexually assaulting, molesting or raping a patient
- Theft of the resident's money, jewelry or other personal property
- Stealing or "diverting" the patients' medications
- Failing to properly change Foley catheters, putting patients at risk for infection
- Failing to administer proper care to patients who have a tracheostomy
- Refusing to allow the patient to see a doctor when requested
- Ignoring significant changes in the patient's condition that require calling a physician or transfer to the hospital
- Failing to give the patient required passive range-of-motion exercises to prevent stiffness and contractures
- Taking inappropriate photographs of patients and/or posting them on social media or another public domain, violating the patient's right to privacy and dignity
- Failure to assist personal hygiene tasks when needed
- Failure to turn residents in their beds (leading to pressure sores)
- Use of unwarranted chemical or physical restraints
- Retaliation against a patient who files a complaint or grievance
- Failure to provide any appropriate medical care

As this list demonstrates, an act doesn't have to involve overt physical or sexual aggressiveness to be considered *abuse*. The following witness statements illustrate knowing acts of abuse that can ultimately be just as harmful to patients as overt acts of physical abuse.

> *"He needed a bath. I asked, 'When is he going to get a bath?' They said, "Well, he refused it." ... In fact, I asked him why he hadn't had a bath. He said, 'Well, she [the CNA] told me she would be right back, but she never came.' I said, 'Well, I want him to have a bath today.' And he never got it. A couple of days later, he*

finally got a bath. Well, like you or me, you need a bath… you feel horrible laying in that bed all the time."

— *Witness interview: Wife of nursing home patient*

"One night they [nursing staff] came in and said, 'What are you doing sitting up?' I said, 'Well, I'm not tired.' And I was reading a book. She said, 'You've got to go to sleep,' this aid or nurse — I'm not sure which one she was. They kept pestering me, so finally, I laid down. Well, they were gone about five minutes and I sat back up and they came back again. They said, 'Okay, now you've got to lay down.' So they put my wheelchair way on the other side [of the room] so I couldn't go anywhere. Then one was talking to me and the other one, I didn't see her, but she went under the bed and unplugged my telephone so I couldn't call out.

"The night people would be outside talking to their boyfriends. I know because I'd hear the horns go beep, then it would be a sign that they should come outside [and meet up with their boyfriends in the parking lot]. They thought we were dumb and didn't know what the hell was going on."

— *Witness interview: Patrick, nursing home patient with physical limitations but otherwise lucid and intelligent*

Sexual Abuse

Sexual abuse deserves special discussion. It is one of the most heinous abuses committed against nursing home patients, many of whom are too sick, debilitated or fearful of retaliation to refuse unwanted sexual advances or fight back. It is also the least detected, least reported and least acknowledged form of elder abuse. Yet, we know that thousands of elder Americans suffer from sexual abuse every year (Hawkes, 2006).

What constitutes sexual abuse? Some definitions of elderly sexual abuse by industry professionals are broader, such as:

"Any form of sexual conduct or exposure without consent
and when the victim is incapable of giving consent" (Lingler,
2000).

This definition includes such acts as inappropriate sexual comments,
sexualized interest in another person's body, which may result in emotional
harm but not physical harm (Lingler, 2000). Not all sexual abuse involves
physical assault of the victim. Other types of sexual abuse include unwanted
discussion of sexual conduct and sexual jokes (Burgess, 2000).

One study found that oral-genital contact, penetration, and vaginal
rape occurred in approximately 5% of the cases reported. For example, in a
California case, a male employee exposed his penis to a 90-year-old female
patient and asked her to put it in her mouth (Burgess, 2000). While the
victim suffered no physical harm from this abuse, she suffered tremendous
emotional harm from this offensive, unwelcome proposition.

> **MYTH:** Nursing homes promptly report allegations of abuse
> and neglect.
>
> **REALITY:** Nearly 4 in 10 allegations of abuse or neglect are not
> properly reported.

In this study, nearly half of the cases involved multiple types of abuse.
Multiple types of abuse were most likely to occur with older victims and
those requiring assistance with ambulation. Surprisingly, roughly half of the
incidents were witnessed by at least one other person, usually either another
patient or a staff member (Burgess, 2000).

Another study found that most victims of sexual abuse in nursing homes
were female; most perpetrators were male; the majority of victims had at
least some cognitive impairment; and more than half had impaired mobility
(Teaster & Roberto, 2005).

How common is sexual abuse? Historically, it's been difficult to determine
just how much of all nursing home abuse reported is sexual abuse. One study
derived from Medicaid Fraud Reports found that 8.8% of 488 abuse cases
in nursing homes were sexual in nature (Payne & Cikovic, 1995). Another

study compiled from 1998 National Ombudsman Reporting System data found over 1700 complaints of sexual abuse over a two-year period (Teaster & Roberto, 2004).

But because there are perhaps countless specific forms that sexual abuse may take, many of which may not have been consistently defined, reported data is often skewed, which makes it more difficult for policymakers to understand the sexual abuse problem and devote resources to its prevention. Further complicating matters, elder sexual abuse definitions vary by jurisdiction, not to mention that many victims of sexual abuse are either too humiliated or traumatized to report the abuse, or unable to do so due to cognitive impairments.

Physical signs and symptoms of sexual assault include vaginal and rectal bleeding, vaginal and rectal discharge, genital and rectal scarring, sexually transmitted diseases, and urinary irritations. Other signs of physical abuse which may be related to sexual assault include bruises, abrasions, lacerations, fractures, general body soreness, fatigue, and rope burns, which could occur if the victim was restrained (Capezuti & Swedlow, 2000).

But since not all forms of sexual abuse leave physical markers, often making signs of sexual abuse more difficult to detect than signs of physical abuse, many cases of sexual abuse go undetected and unreported, both by families and caregivers. And too often, nursing facility management certainly isn't eager to report abuse because they fear negative publicity, state sanctions and potential loss of federal funding.

But one fact seems clear: The nursing home setting is a significant risk factor for sexual abuse, the extent of which was demonstrated in a study of elder sexual abuse in Virginia from 1996 through 2001 which researched sexual abuse in both institutional and residential settings. Nearly three-quarters of all sexual abuse occurred in nursing homes (Teaster & Roberto, 2005).

In other words, in an environment where residents are supposed to be safe, they're actually in more danger than the average person on the streets of a typical U.S. city.

Emotional/Psychological Abuse

"One day I was in the dining room, sitting at the table with the ladies. And the girls were bringing the trays out, and just throwing the plates in front of people. And the lady said, 'I don't like this. I don't eat this. I'd like to have — " She was an elderly lady. And the girl told her: 'You are going to eat what I put in front of you…" and just walked off.'"

— Witness interview: Georgia, former nursing home patient

Verbal abuse by nursing home staff such as, threatening, berating or humiliating a patient, can take a heavy psychological toll. Physical abuse — certainly sexual abuse — takes an emotional toll, as well. For example, a 92-year-old victim was sexually abused on around 100 occasions by a male employee in a Missouri nursing home. Ultimately, the condition of the patient, who suffers from Alzheimer's disease, was described as "retracted." She curled up in a fetal position, unable to give or refuse consent.

Emotional signs and symptoms of abuse include: denial, humiliation, flashbacks, intense fear, guilt, anxiety, depression, feelings of hopelessness and helplessness, phobias, and rage. These conditions are often indicative of *post-traumatic stress disorder*, or in the case of sexual abuse — *rape trauma syndrome*. In fact, abuse victims suffering from Alzheimer's disease or other forms of dementia often display post-assault emotional distress, including disorganized or agitated behaviors, sleep disturbance, and extreme avoidance of certain staff members (Capezuti & Swedlow, 2000).

Because victims of nursing home abuse are often cognitively impaired, they're unable to describe the abuse event, their fears, or their feelings of helplessness. They may be unable to express their needs, which makes it more difficult for physicians (including mental health professionals) to treat them effectively, to provide them with the care they so desperately need.

Thus, in addition to the physical injuries that victims may suffer as a result of abuse, the emotional fallout alone may ensure that these victims are relegated to, as author Henry David Thoreau once wrote, "leading lives of quiet desperation," devoid of dignity and peace.

STAFF'S DUTY TO REPORT

All nursing home facilities that receive Medicare and/or Medicaid payment must be certified as meeting federal nursing home facility quality and safety requirements, which specifically include *reporting allegations of abuse or neglect.*

These regulations require that nursing homes develop and implement written policies that prohibit abuse and neglect (42 CFR § 483.13(c)). These policies must address seven components:

- screening employees
- training employees
- prevention of abuse and neglect
- identification of abuse and neglect
- investigation of abuse and neglect
- protection from abuse and neglect
- reporting and responding to allegations of abuse and neglect

Nursing facility staff are required by law to report any allegations of abuse or neglect immediately to the facility administrator or designee, the state survey and certification agency (state survey agency), and other officials in accordance with state law (42 CFR § 483.13(c)(2)). An allegation of abuse or neglect is to be reported *immediately*, with an investigation to follow in order to substantiate the allegation. Medicare clarifies the term *immediately* to mean "as soon as possible, but not to exceed 24 hours after the discovery of the incident," in the absence of a shorter state timeframe requirement (CMF, 2004).

Unfortunately, too often, nursing home staff choose not to comply with this regulation.

In addition to reporting the abuse event immediately, nursing home staff are required to report *the results of the investigation* to the nursing facility administrator or designee, state survey agency, and to other officials in accordance with state law *within 5 working days of the incident* (42 CFR § 483.13(c)(4)). State laws may require that nursing facilities also report investigative results to other state officials beyond those specified in the federal requirements. No state law can override the obligation of a Medicare and/or Medicaid certified nursing facility to fulfill the reporting requirements.

But the obligations of the nursing home staff don't end there.

The Elder Justice Act of 2009 requires owners, operators, employees, managers, agents, and contractors of nursing home facilities in nursing facilities to report *any reasonable suspicion of crimes* committed against a resident of that facility to the appropriate entities (law enforcement agencies) (Section 6703(b)(3) of the Elder Justice Act of 2009).

This same law also prohibits nursing facilities from retaliating against individuals who lawfully report a reasonable suspicion of a crime (SSA § 1150B(b)(3)). Nursing facilities are required to clearly post a notice for employees informing them of their right to file a complaint if the facility retaliates against them for reporting a crime. Examples of retaliation or punishment include: firing/discharge, demotion, threatening to fire, threatening demotion, harassment, denial of a promotion or any other employment-related benefit, or any discrimination against an employee in terms and conditions of employment.

So if there are federal laws in place that: (1) require nursing facility staff to report abuse and neglect and; (2) prohibit management from retaliating against employees who do... why does abuse go unreported?

CULTURE OF COVER-UP

To avoid accountability, nursing homes often deliberately conceal patient abuse and neglect from the patient's family and investigators.

They may do it by failing to report abuse incidents to investigators and family, once the incidents are discovered.

They may do it — whether knowingly or unknowingly — by hiring convicted criminals and/or employees with a history of abuse who they could have reasonably foreseen might abuse patients, and then conceal this fact from families and investigators.

They may do it by casting doubt upon the victim-patient's credibility, especially when the abuse is committed against a patient who has cognitive deficits (e.g., dementia).

And if all else fails, they can do it by, essentially, blaming the patient — turning the act of abuse into a he-said-she-said situation; for example, claiming that a patient refused to comply with treatment, or that a fall that caused serious injury was the patient's fault because the patient didn't follow doctor's orders.

All these tactics, of course, are designed to allow the nursing home to escape accountability, to make the case unprosecutable, liability unassignable, damages unrecoverable.

Abuse, Too Often, Goes Unreported

Despite the fact that there are federal laws which clearly require nursing facilities to report incidents of abuse and neglect, abuse still too often goes unreported.

> **MYTH:** All nursing homes have policies in place for reporting abuse and neglect.
>
> **REALITY:** Nearly 1 in 4 nursing homes do not have proper policies for reporting abuse and neglect.

A 2014 study conducted by the Department of Health and Human Services Office of Inspector General found that nearly one-fourth of all nursing home facilities had no policies in place to address either the reporting of abuse and neglect or the reporting of investigation results. The study also found that in 2012, nearly 40% of nursing home facilities had no documentation showing that they had notified the owners, operators, employees, and other relevant parties annually of their obligation to report any reasonable suspicion of a crime, or that they had posted a notice specifying the employee's right to file a complaint for retaliation by facility administrators.

The study found that only 63% of the allegations of abuse or neglect were immediately reported to the nursing facility administrator or designee and the state survey agency, as required. Moreover, only 63% of the investigation results of allegations of abuse or neglect were reported to the appropriate individuals within five working days as required by federal law.

This failure to report occurs even when abuse results in death. In one case, an Indiana nursing home employee was charged with violently pulling a patient from her walker, breaking the patient's vertebra and causing death. Meanwhile, according to news reports, the employee maintained that she never hurt the patient, claiming that the patient's heart stopped beating while she was on the toilet. The employee was fired by the facility, but authorities were never notified of the patient's death until the subject was inadvertently brought up at a Christmas party, where a detective heard about the incident.

> **MYTH:** The majority of nursing homes ensure that patient abuse and neglect does not occur.
>
> **REALITY:** In 2012, 85% of nursing homes reported *at least* one allegation of neglect or abuse.

It's clear that nursing homes are failing to properly report incidents of abuse and neglect, and thus, are no doubt underreporting the true incidence of abuse and neglect. Even so, the 2014 OIG study confirmed that 85% of nursing homes had reported at least one incident of neglect or abuse in 2012 (a total of 149,313 allegations) (Levinson, OIG, August 2014).

Incidents were categorized as follows:

- Abuse (50.7%)
- Injuries of unknown source (18.6%)
- Misappropriations of resident property (14.9%)
- Neglect (11.8%)
- Mistreatment (3.9%)

This OIG study also found that, given the increasing elderly population in the United States and the growing number of people over age 65 receiving care in nursing facilities, the neglect-abuse problem will only grow worse.

But here's an even more troubling reality…

Some researchers estimate that only about 20% of nursing home abuse is ever reported. If that's true, the vast majority of abuse incidents aren't even accounted for in the nursing home abuse statistics you've just read. Federal regulators have, in fact, admitted that the statistics conceal how serious the abuse problem is inside America's nursing homes. State inspections are often unreliable, and most problems in nursing homes go unreported, especially with respect to cases of physical abuse (CBS News, 2002).

So, the reality, now and for the future, is likely far worse than we know.

NURSING HOMES HIRE CRIMINALS

Why in the world would nursing homes hire criminals? In some cases, they don't realize they're hiring criminals because their background check process is inadequate. But in others, nursing homes simply choose to hire criminals, individuals whose past actions have demonstrated that they should never be entrusted with the care of vulnerable, sick patients. It's no secret that nursing homes are almost always understaffed and hiring criminals, after all, is less expensive, as convicted criminals generally can't demand top dollar in the workforce.

Ultimately, hiring criminals allows facilities to reduce labor costs and, therefore, maximize profitability.

> A CBS News analysis of the federal government's nursing home inspection database found that more than 1,000 nursing homes were cited in 2015 for hiring staff with a history of abuse.

Yet, in reality, family members who have entrusted nursing homes with the care of their loved ones may unknowingly be placing them into the care of employees who should never be caregivers. It's hard to imagine that any family would knowingly allow an unknown convicted criminal into their home, much less allow them to administer medication to a loved one, or permit them to assist a loved one with bathing or other personal hygiene activities. But unbeknownst to patients and their families, the nursing home industry allows this to occur every single day, in practically every nursing home in the country.

With nursing home neglect and abuse occurring with alarming frequency all across the country, the nursing home companies to which families entrust their loved ones should be rigorously and continuously examining those whom they entrust to take care of vulnerable patients.

But the evidence suggests that they aren't…

> *One time she was hit in her back. This one aide just yanked her from the bed because she couldn't get up and down on her own. She yanked her so badly and then sat her out in the hallway — this is at 5:00 in the morning — and there she sat. Well she had bed sores throughout all this and they made her sit in that hallway on the bed sores.*
>
> *They'd bring her tray in and she couldn't even sit up on the side of the bed, by herself, without help. They'd bring her a tray and then leave it. I'd walk in and there would be that tray sitting there, and she couldn't get to it.*
>
> — *Witness interview: Sister of nursing home patient*

The federal government has attempted to hold the nursing home industry accountable by penalizing federally-funded nursing homes that hire convicted criminals. But levying monetary penalties isn't enough. We must also make sure that our state legislators are aware of our concerns. If there were greater public awareness of the fact that over 90% of nursing homes are staffed with one or more convicted criminals, there would surely be support for legislation to ensure adequate background checks and to prohibit the hiring of criminals.

It's time for society to hold accountable a nursing home industry that reaps tremendous profits from its promise to protect and care for society's weakest individuals, but too often chooses to entrust the care of its vulnerable and dependent patients to convicted criminals.

Difficulties in Prosecuting Elder Abuse Cases

Those who target our most vulnerable Americans for the most heinous crimes may, ironically, be rewarded with lighter penalties *because* the patients are so vulnerable.

For example, because the best evidence to prosecute sexual abuse is the testimony of the victim, especially without other witnesses, the quality of that testimony is crucial. Victims with dementia or other cognitive deficits may not be able to describe the abuse or neglect in detail, even though this lack of ability is a function of the disease rather than the veracity of the report. Crisis resulting from the assault may lead to further confusion about details. In some cases, it may be several weeks before a traumatized victim can provide an adequate account of the assault, which runs counter to the typical presumption that a victim's recollection of an event is best (and truest) immediately following the event.

Nursing home patients often have dementia or other mental or physical limitations which can prevent them from enduring the rigors associated with testifying against predators who abuse and neglect them. This is true not only in criminal cases, but also in civil cases where families sue derelict nursing homes that allow their patients to be cared for by criminals or otherwise permit neglectful or abusive treatment. Many patients can't testify at all due to their cognitive or physical status. Moreover, because criminal and civil cases can take a long time to prosecute, often the patient's health declines so much before the case ever reaches trial that the patient either dies or is unable to testify.

Consider, for example, a recent case involving an Indiana nursing home aide charged with sex crimes against multiple patient victims. According to court records and multiple news reports, the 20-year old male nurse aide was charged with three counts of sexual battery and three counts of attempted sexual battery as a result of multiple complaints that he had engaged in sexual misconduct with patients at a nursing home in Greenfield, Indiana.

The incidents at the center of the charges are more than disturbing. According to reports and court records, two patients at the nursing facility sobbed as they told police in separate reports that the male nurse aide had exposed his genitals and asked them to touch him. A woman reported that he was "doing things, with his hands, to her that he shouldn't have been doing" — "bad things… sexual things." The court records and reports further state that he rubbed himself on one woman's face — even as she told him "no." According to court records, another patient with dementia and mental illness reported to police that the male aide was his boyfriend and that he and the aide had "touched each other."

But here's the legal problem…

Because his victims would have had a hard time articulating what happened to them in court, the male nurse aide was given a plea deal that allowed him to avoid any jail time. His plea deal didn't even require him to register as a sex offender. Instead, the perpetrator pled guilty to felony battery against a disabled person and was sentenced to one year of home detention followed by 545 days on "sex offender probation." The other six felony charges were dismissed.

How often do the perpetrators of nursing home abuse pay for their crimes? A study found that over half of all nursing home sexual abuse cases, for example, resulted in a criminal *conviction*. But only one-quarter of those offenders were actually sentenced to *prison* (Payne & Cikovic, 1995).

So perhaps the answer is: too often, the perpetrators don't pay *enough*. And that list of "perpetrators" surely includes the industry that employs them in the first place.

THE BOTTOM LINE

The first step in preventing abuse and helping victims is uncovering and recognizing incidents of abuse. Second, victims of abuse must be properly treated and nursing home facilities must take measures to protect the victims from future abuse. Third, incidents of abuse must be reported immediately and investigated thoroughly. Finally, the perpetrators of abuse, and the nursing home corporations that enable them, must be held accountable.

Nursing homes must improve their detection and prevention programs.

State and federal governments must establish effective regulations to prevent sexual abuse and enforce those regulations.

Patients and families must arm themselves with knowledge in order to spot the warning signs of abuse.

With a concerted effort from all stakeholders, hopefully, America's future elderly population will be free to enjoy the twilight years without the threat of abuse, no matter what form it may take.

As United Nations Secretary-General Ban Ki-moon once so eloquently stated:

> "The distressing crime of elder abuse often occurs in quiet, private settings, making a vocal, public response that much more important. Let us strengthen our resolve to end this problem as part of our broader efforts to create a life of dignity for all."

WHAT YOU CAN DO

So, what can you do if your loved one resides in a nursing home and you're concerned about whether the staff can be trusted to provide proper care? The following tips are a good place to start.

TIPS

- Ask the nursing home administrator to detail the specific procedure they use to conduct employee background checks. Suggested questions include:
  - What databases do they access for employee background checks? If they only use state databases, they may not know if an employee was convicted of a crime in another state.
  - How often do they run background checks? If they only check prior to hiring, they may have employees rendering care to patients who have been convicted of crimes since they were hired.
- Are they currently employing any employee with a criminal conviction? The facility may run background checks on direct caregivers (e.g., nurses and nurse aides), but do they also run background checks on the janitorial staff, food service workers, any independent contractors who work in the building, etc.?

- Be on the lookout for evidence of abuse or neglect and demand immediate investigation. Follow up to ensure that remedial action was taken, and file a formal complaint with state authorities, if necessary. The following indicators, for example, warrant investigation:
  - bedsores (also known as "pressure sores", "pressure ulcers", and "decubitus ulcers")
  - pervasive urine and/or feces odor
  - lack of attention to resident's personal hygiene
  - falls resulting from lack of adequate precautions or assistance
  - skin tears
  - bruises, contusions, or lesions
  - bone fractures
  - significant weight loss
  - significant dehydration
  - unexpected disorientation, depression or feelings of isolation
- Consider installing hidden video cameras if your state laws allow it.
- Check on your loved one frequently and at different times of the day so the staff cannot anticipate when you will or won't be around.
- Learn the names of the caregivers who provide hands-on care to your loved one and research them on social media to look for anything that may be cause for concern.
- Ensure that water is always within the patient's reach.
- Ensure that the call button is always within the patient's reach.

ADDITIONAL RESOURCES

Updated information comparing nursing home quality measures and state ratings: https://www.medicare.gov/nursinghomecompare/search.html

8

THE LIST GOES ON:
EXAMPLES OF OTHER HARMS

Dehydration, Malnutrition, Restraint Injuries, Elopement & Social Media Abuse

We need, first of all, for there to be accountability,
for there to be somebody who is responsible for enforcing
standards and holding people's feet to the fire.

— Jennifer Granholm

Nursing home abuse and neglect can affect different patients in different ways. Because patients' medical conditions and treatment needs vary, the types of harms that can be inflicted upon them from neglect and abuse are practically infinite, thus it's impossible to cover them all in this book. But bear in mind, even if this book doesn't happen to mention a specific type of harm, that certainly doesn't mean it wasn't *harm* and that this harm did not result from wrongful conduct.

In this chapter, we'll focus on some additional examples of common harms caused by nursing home neglect and abuse: dehydration and malnutrition, restraint injuries, elopement, and social media abuse and exploitation.

DEHYDRATION AND MALNUTRITION

Eighty-one-year-old Theresa, a loving wife, mother, and grandmother, suffered debility following a hospitalization and had difficulties walking and performing some of her daily living activities. With the assistance of her husband, she was able to cope and live at home. But one day, Theresa fell, though she broke no bones, she suffered a number of injuries and needed advanced care and monitoring, which her husband, in light of his own increasing debility, was unable to provide. Theresa was taking medication for cognitive deficits such as confusion and required professional nursing care and therapy services. So she was admitted to a local nursing home.

But unbeknownst to Theresa and her family, this nursing home facility had recently been cited by state surveyors for various care deficiencies, including the failure to properly care for patients who were at risk for dehydration. When Theresa was admitted to the nursing home, she was known to be at risk for fluid balance fluctuation (caused by dehydration).

In the weeks to come, the nursing home staff failed to assess whether Theresa was receiving proper hydration. She was supposed to receive at least 30 cc's/kg of fluid intake each day, which for her was approximately 2,000 cc's per day. Instead, the nursing home's own intake records showed that Theresa was receiving significantly less than half that amount on many days, and sometimes received less than 100 cc's in a given day. Theresa's physician was never made aware of this significant fluid insufficiency, nor was she notified of Theresa's decline. In fact, there was no indication that the nursing home staff even assessed Theresa's hydration intake during that critical time period, despite the fact that they noted that Theresa was "lethargic" and "moaning out."

Ultimately, Theresa was transported by ambulance to the local hospital, where the emergency staff noted Theresa's lips were "very dry and cracked" and that she was unresponsive to any stimuli. The emergency room staff also documented that Theresa's mucous membranes were very dry and pale and a "large amount [of] dried food and sputum [were] suctioned from [her] mouth." She had become so dehydrated that she was literally unable to form the saliva necessary to swallow her food. Blood tests confirmed her condition; she was diagnosed with severe dehydration, acute renal failure, urosepsis, and possible aspiration pneumonia, which was likely due to receiving inadequate fluid intake. Her condition deteriorated and she died several days later.

My law firm filed suit on behalf of Theresa's family and discovered critical information that, had Theresa and her family known it at the time, would have led them to have her admitted to another nursing home.

When the facility was cited by state investigators prior to Theresa's admission, investigators found that on 27 of 30 days in the month reviewed, a patient received at least 600 cc's of fluid less than the patient needed. The investigator noted: "Documentation was lacking to reflect the 24-hour totals and ongoing assessments of intake and status communication to the physician prior to dehydration and complications warranting hospitalization." To address the citation, the nursing home administrator submitted a plan of correction which included the promise that the facility would offer special training to its employees on hydration issues. But according to a facility employee, this training never happened. This employee testified during her deposition that she was never made aware by facility administrators that state investigators had concerns about patient hydration, nor did she recall any special hydration training during this period.

This broken promise likely caused Theresa's premature death.

In 1974, Dr. C.E. Butterworth suggested in *Nutrition Today* that malnutrition was "the skeleton in the hospital closet" (Butterworth, 1974). But in the 1970s, studies had yet to document that an even more ominous skeleton was lurking in nursing home closets as well: Dehydration.

The importance of proper hydration to human health cannot be over-emphasized. Water accounts for about two-thirds of the average adult's total body weight. As humans age, this percentage decreases to about 50% for elderly males; 45% for elderly females (Davis et al., 1998). Dehydration and fluid/electrolyte imbalances can lead to serious health consequences, including death.

Nutrition provides the energy and building blocks required for all bodily processes and fuels the body's ability to maintain and repair its structures. Inadequate nutrition impairs these processes and can prevent the body from carrying out vital functions necessary to maintain itself.

Malnutrition and dehydration in elderly populations are associated with poor clinical outcomes and increase the risk of mortality. Patients with severe malnutrition are at higher risk for a variety of complications and a number of chronic medical conditions, such as cardiac and pulmonary diseases, cancer, impaired immunity, infections and many others (Thomas et al., 2000).

Preventing dehydration and malnutrition in nursing home patients is a matter of taking simple but effective measures aimed at ensuring adequate levels of fluid and nutrition intake. Ultimately, the key to proper hydration and nutrition in the nursing home setting is, as in so many contexts, an adequate number of properly trained and supervised staff, a reality that has been confirmed by the American Medical Directors' Association. "Adequate, competent staff working under skilled supervision are essential to maintaining an appropriate hydration program. Designated members of the care staff should be expressly assigned responsibility for assisting with patient intake of fluids" (American Medical Directors Association, 2001).

Because of the importance of proper hydration and nutrition, federal regulations require nursing homes to take specific steps to ensure the safety and well-being of patients, including:

- The facility must ensure that a patient who is unable to carry out activities of daily living receives the necessary services to maintain good nutrition. 42 C.F.R. §483.24 (a)(2)
- The facility must ensure that the patient maintains acceptable parameters of nutritional status, such as usual body weight or desirable body weight range and electrolyte balance, unless the patient's clinical condition demonstrates that this is not possible or patient preferences indicate otherwise. 42 C.F.R. §483.25 (g)(1)
- The facility must ensure that the patient is offered sufficient fluid intake to maintain proper hydration and health. 42 C.F.R. §483.25 (g)(2)
- The facility must ensure that the patient is offered a therapeutic diet

when there is a nutritional problem and the health care provider orders a therapeutic diet. 42 C.F.R. §483.25 (g)(3)

- The facility must ensure that a patient who has been able to eat enough alone or with assistance is not fed by enteral methods unless the patient's clinical condition demonstrates that enteral feeding was clinically indicated and consented to by the patient. 42 C.F.R. §483.25 (g)(4)

- The facility must ensure that a patient who is fed by enteral means receives the appropriate treatment and services to restore, if possible, oral eating skills and to prevent complications of enteral feeding, including but not limited to aspiration pneumonia, diarrhea, vomiting, dehydration, metabolic abnormalities, and nasal-pharyngeal ulcers. 42 C.F.R. §483.25 (g)(5)

- The facility must provide each patient with a nourishing, palatable, well-balanced diet that meets his or her daily nutritional and special dietary needs, taking into consideration the preferences of each patient. 42 C.F.R. §483.60

- The facility must employ sufficient staff with the appropriate competencies and skills sets to carry out the functions of the food and nutrition service, taking into consideration patient assessments, individual plans of care and the number, acuity and diagnoses of the facility's patient population (42 C.F.R. §483.60 (a)).

- The facility must ensure that menus meet the nutritional needs of patients in accordance with established national guidelines, be prepared in advance; be followed; Reflect, based on a facility's reasonable efforts, the religious, cultural, and ethnic needs of the patient population, as well as input received from patients and patient group; Be updated periodically; and be reviewed by the facility's dietitian or other clinically qualified nutrition professional for nutritional adequacy. 42 C.F.R. §483.60 (c)

- The facility must ensure that each patient receives and the facility provides food prepared by methods that conserve nutritive value, flavor, and appearance. 42 C.F.R. §483.60 (d)(1)

- The facility must ensure that food and drink that is palatable, attractive, and at a safe and appetizing temperature. 42 C.F.R. §483.60 (d)(2)

- The facility must ensure that food is prepared in a form designed to meet individual needs and accommodates patient allergies, intolerances, and preferences. 42 C.F.R. §483.60 (d)(3)(4)

- The facility must ensure appealing food options of similar nutritive value to patients who choose not to eat food that is initially served or who request a different meal choice. 42 C.F.R. §483.60 (d)(5) and

- The facility must ensure that patients are provided drinks, including water and other liquids consistent with patient needs and preferences and sufficient to maintain hydration. 42 C.F.R. §483.60 (d)(6)

- The facility must provide — and must ensure that each patient receive — at least three meals daily, at regular times comparable to normal mealtimes in the community or in accordance with patient needs, preferences, requests, and plan of care. 42 C.F.R. §483.60 (f)(1)

- The facility must ensure that there are no more than 14 hours between a substantial evening meal and breakfast the following day, except when a nourishing snack is served at bedtime, up to 16 hours may elapse between a substantial evening meal and breakfast the following day if a patient group agrees to this meal span. 42 C.F.R. §483.60 (f)(2)

- The facility must ensure that suitable, nourishing alternative meals and snacks are provided to patients who want to eat at non-traditional times or outside of scheduled meal service times, consistent with the patient plan of care. 42 C.F.R. §483.60 (f)(3)

- The facility must provide special eating equipment and utensils for patients who need them and appropriate assistance to ensure that the patient can use the assistive devices when consuming meals and snacks. 42 C.F.R. §483.60 (g)

Despite these clear and specific regulatory mandates, nursing homes too often fail to protect patients' nutritional and hydrational status. A 2000 Atlanta Ombudsman report revealed that when patients were asked the question, *If you could do one thing to change this nursing home, what would it be?*, "Nutrition Concerns" was the second most frequent of the top three concerns. (The top response was "More Help;" the third, "Better Quality Staff.")(Atlanta Long-Term Care Ombudsman Program, 2000).

> **Studies have shown that as many as 85% of nursing home patients are malnourished.**

One study found that up to 85% (a range of 23 – 85%) of nursing home patients are malnourished (Thomas et al., 2000; Silver et al., 1988; Shaver et al, 1980; Burger et al., 2000). For example, a prevalence of 54% malnutrition was found in one Baltimore long-term care facility (Thomas et al., 1991).

Lawmakers have long been aware of the problem. In 2003, noted Department of Health Policy and Management Director at Southwest Rural Health Research Center Professor Catherine Hawes, Ph.D. offered the following testimony before the U.S. Senate Committee on Finance, which highlights the impact of understaffing on dehydration and malnutrition (Hawes, 1997):

> "A discussion of 'staffing' and "ratios' sounds technical. However, CNAs are eloquent about what it means to work short-staffed. What gets ignored first, out of necessity, according to CNAs, is range of motion exercises — which leads to contractures. Next, staff report, they are unable to provide sufficient help with eating and drinking. Undernutrition, malnutrition, and dehydration inevitably follow such neglect, with the concomitant sequelae of skin breakdown, pressure ulcers, poor healing of wounds, and premature mortality — not to mention the daily misery of being hungry and thirsty."

It is astonishing that any nursing home patient in this country should ever have to endure the daily misery of being hungry and thirsty. Proper nutrition and hydration represent the most fundamental level of care — the very least — that nursing homes promise to, should be able to, and are being paid to provide for all patients.

HOW DOES DEHYDRATION AND MALNUTRITION HAPPEN?

A variety of factors can play a role in malnutrition and weight loss; however, it is undeniably true that nursing homes too often fail to ensure that patients are receiving the care they should be receiving, and often, the reason is that the facility has an insufficient number of trained and supervised staff available. Patients who struggle to physically move food from the plate to their mouths because of paralysis, contractures, tremors and other disabilities require staff assistance with eating. If the staff doesn't provide this assistance because they're too busy performing other tasks, patients won't receive the daily nutrition and hydration they need. Similarly, when the nursing staff is too shorthanded to ensure that patients have drinking water available and within reach — as well as assistance with drinking if needed — patients won't receive adequate hydration.

This harm is preventable. And understaffing is no excuse.

Other preventable factors can play a role, as well. Patients who have missing or ill-fitted dentures or untreated teeth or gum problems often have difficulty meeting their nutritional needs. Even when patients are capable of eating and drinking, other factors within the nursing home staff's control may negatively impact the patients' nutrition, such as serving meals that are visibly unappealing, are of poor quality, or served at the wrong temperature. Likewise, an unappealing eating environment can impact a patient's nutritional intake. For example, too often, incontinent patients are not changed in a timely manner, which needlessly results in foul odors within the facility that diminish patients' appetites. Other common problems include allowing inadequate time for patients to chew and swallow their food, and failing to assist patients with eating (Basler, 2004).

Sometimes patients don't receive sufficient hydration because the nursing home staff intentionally and inexcusably withholds fluids in order to avoid having to take the patient to the bathroom or providing incontinence care.

Signs of weight loss

It's important for patients and families to take notice of significant weight loss. The first step is to ensure the patient is being properly weighed on a routine basis. The nursing home is supposed to conduct regular weight checks, but this doesn't always happen. In some cases, nursing homes document that they checked a patient's weight when they didn't.

The chart below suggests parameters that put weight loss into context and may help you determine whether a patient's weight loss represents a significant change that requires further evaluation and intervention (Centers for Medicare & Medicaid Services, 2017).

Parameters for Evaluating Significance of Unplanned and Undesired Weight Loss

Formula for Determining Percentage of Weight Loss:

% of body weight loss = (usual weight - actual weight) / (usual weight) x 100

Interval	Significant Loss	Severe Loss
1 month	5%	Greater than 5%
3 months	7.5%	Greater than 7.5%
6 months	10%	Greater than 10%

The fluid requirement for older persons without cardiac or renal disease is approximately 30 mL/kg body weight/day. (2.2 lbs = 1 kg)

(American Medical Directors Association, 2009)

Symptoms of dehydration

It's important to be on the lookout for signs and symptoms of possible dehydration or electrolyte imbalances. Many symptoms of dehydration can be non-specific, and are also associated with other medical conditions. However, the more symptoms present, the more critical it becomes for a physician consider the possibility of dehydration as an underlying issue that may need to be treated.

Symptoms of dehydration include:

- Lethargy
- Confusion
- Decline in function that may be abrupt
- Dry mucous membranes
- Sunken eyes
- Hypotension
- Recent rapid weight loss
- Dry eyes and/or mouth
- Change in mental status
- Fever
- Vomiting
- Small amount of concentrated urine
- Urinary tract infections
- Elevated pulse
- Dizziness
- Falling
- Change in ability to carry out activities of daily living
- Increased combativeness and confusion
- Constipation and/or fecal impaction

Dehydration and malnutrition are all-too-common, yet preventable, harms. Be watchful and questions the nursing home staff to ensure they're being vigilant in their responsibilities to ensure adequate hydration and nutrition.

RESTRAINT INJURIES

> *Patricia was a 56-year-old woman suffering from Huntington's disease who was unable to care for herself at home. When a nursing home chain's management made a "corporate consolidation" decision to close the nursing home facility in which Patricia resided, she was transferred to a nearby sister facility with a troubled history*

— the facility had recently been cited for multiple, systemic care problems indicative of inadequate staffing, inadequate training and lack of other resources. Unfortunately, Patricia and her family were not aware of these ominous citations.

Patricia required specialized care and equipment to remain sitting upright, including a special wheelchair, a harness restraint and a special wheelchair cushion. Unfortunately, her new caregivers never received the proper training necessary to care for Patricia and to use this special equipment. According to a physical therapist from the facility, the staff received no training with respect to the equipment needs of the patients transferred into the facility, including Patricia's.

One day, the cushion that Patricia normally sat on in her wheelchair "came up missing," according to this physical therapist. Without the cushion, Patricia's bottom would slide towards the back of the chair and into the gap created between the seat and the chair back. The physical therapist reported the cushion missing two or three times, but no steps were taken to replace the cushion. A qualified medication aide who cared for Patricia at the new facility revealed that she would arrive at work and find that Patricia's harness had been put on upside down or backwards. This aide also confirmed that Patricia had a tendency to slide around in her chair without the cushion, and that in the two-week period that the cushion was missing, Patricia's bottom slid out of the back of the chair on multiple occasions and she began choking on the harness. The aide was able to rescue Patricia before any injury occurred.

But, one morning, Patricia was improperly restrained into her wheelchair by the facility staff, still without her seat cushion, and in a manner that allowed her to slide backwards into a position that could cause her to become strangled by the harness. Patricia was then left alone in her room, with no supervision. She slid backwards into this dangerous position that caused her to become strangled by the harness, where she remained alone, helpless, with no one to rescue her until finally, she died from asphyxiation.

The autopsy confirmed that Patricia's cause of death was: "positional and ligature asphyxiation… slid out of wheelchair, improperly placed safety straps." The nurse aide who placed Patricia in her wheelchair on the day Patricia died confirmed to a state investigator that she had not been properly trained and that she "thought the Velcro strap was one piece…" adding that she "didn't know she had to check to see if the Velcro on the strap was secured in position." Tragically, the same nurse aide reported similar problems with the chair when Patricia was at the prior sister facility and was "puzzled over that… if [it was] broken, why [wasn't it] fixed?"

A state investigation concluded: "The lack of training, and the failure to place the contour cushion, resulted in the death of [Patricia] by asphyxiation."

Patricia's case is disturbing for many reasons, the first of which is that her death was foreseeable and entirely preventable. And while state investigators didn't cite the facility for using an improper restraint, there are questions as to whether the wheelchair and restraint system they used were proper equipment for Patricia. The use of the wheelchair with the vest restraint was likely not the safest, least restrictive option for protecting Patricia. Indeed, one of the nurse aides commented that the wheelchair "sucked" and described it as a "bootleg wheelchair."

Federal regulations require that when restraints are indicated to treat the patient's medical condition, the facility must use the *least restrictive alternative* for the least amount of time and document ongoing re-evaluation of the need for restraints.

There are other special padded chairs designed for patients like Patricia, which likely would have been much safer, more effective options. But given that her wheelchair, wheelchair cushion, and vest restraint were deemed proper for her at the time, it was incumbent upon the nursing home to train the nursing staff to properly use her equipment. When restraint devices are used, there's a risk that if used improperly, the patient may suffer significant harm, including death. For Patricia, the facility's failure to train the staff to ensure that her equipment was properly used was a fatal mistake. The failure to ensure that the proper seat cushion was installed to prevent her bottom from sliding out the back of her chair caused Patricia to suffer a horrific, needless death.

Federal Regulation 42 C.F. R. §483.12 Freedom from Abuse, Neglect, and Exploitation:

The patient has the right to be free from abuse, neglect, misappropriation of patient property, and exploitation as defined in this subpart. This includes but is not limited to freedom from corporal punishment, involuntary seclusion and any physical or chemical restraint not required to treat the patient's symptoms.

483.1(2)(a) The facility must— (2) Ensure that the patient is free from physical or chemical restraints imposed for purposes of discipline or convenience and that are not required to treat the patient's medical symptoms. When the use of restraints is indicated, the facility must use the least restrictive alternative for the least amount of time and document ongoing re-evaluation of the need for restraints.

What Constitutes a "Restraint?"

"Restraints" encompass a broad range of interventions that limit a patient's free will to move, including (Department of Health and Human Services, CMS, 2006):

- **Chemical Restraints:** any drug that is used for discipline or convenience and not required to treat medical symptoms.

- **Physical Restraints:** any manual method or physical or mechanical device, material, or equipment attached or adjacent to the patient's body that the individual cannot remove easily which restricts freedom of movement or normal access to one's body (e.g., leg restraints, arm restraints, hand mitts, soft ties or vests, lap cushions, and lap trays that the patient cannot remove easily).

Facility practices that meet the definition of a restraint also include the following:

- Using side rails that prevent a patient from voluntarily getting out of bed;

- Tucking in or using Velcro to hold a sheet, fabric, or clothing tightly so that a patient's movement is restricted;

- Using devices in conjunction with a chair, such as trays, tables, bars or belts, that the patient cannot remove easily, that prevent the patient from rising;

- Placing a patient in a chair that prevents a patient from rising; and,

- Placing a chair or bed so close to a wall that the wall prevents the patient from rising out of the chair or voluntarily getting out of bed.

For many years, nursing homes routinely used physical and chemical restraints to restrict patients' ability to move freely. Too often, nursing homes were using restraints for improper purposes, including for their own convenience, which actually constitutes abuse. Public outrage over this practice contributed to the passage of the Nursing Home Quality Reform Act (Omnibus Budget Reconciliation Act [OBRA], 1987),[2] which resulted in regulations intended to ensure that patients have a right to be free of physical and chemical restraints not *required* to treat the patient's symptoms.. After the implementation of OBRA, restraint use declined.

In 1996, the Health Care Financing Administration (HCFA) launched the Restraint Reduction Initiative in an attempt to reign in the use of restraints in nursing homes (HFCA, 1996). A 1999 HFCA survey revealed that the national restraint rate was around 13.5%, down from approximately 20% in 1996. However, another study found that the rate was still as high as 26% in the states sampled (Neufield et al., 1999). This study also found that a substantial decrease in restraint use *did not lead to an increase in serious injuries.* Although minor injuries and falls increased, restraint-free care was found to be safe when: a comprehensive assessment was performed; nursing home staff was properly educated; and restraint alternatives were used.

---

2   (OBRA 1987. Pub L. No. 100-203)

The Dangers of Using Restraints

The use of restraints has been associated with a variety of negative outcomes for the patient. These included, for example (Department of Health and Human Services, CMS, 2006):

- Muscle atrophy
- Cardiovascular stress
- Incontinence
- Functional decline
- Social isolation
- Depression
- Loss of self esteem
- Anxiety
- Agitation
- Anger
- Broken bones, sprains, or other serious injuries as patients try to escape the restraints
- Strangulation
- Decreased peripheral circulation
- Pressure sores
- Infections
- Death

When Are Restraints Allowed?

MYTH: The only effective intervention to prevent falls are restraints.

REALITY: There are many less restrictive and less dangerous interventions that are often effective in preventing serious injuries from falls.

Use of restraints requires a physician order. CMS guidelines dictate that restraints may not be used simply for the convenience of staff. However, if the patient needs emergency care, restraints may be used for brief periods to permit medical treatment to proceed unless the facility has a notice indicating that the patient has previously made a valid refusal of the treatment in question.

However, if a patient's unanticipated violent or aggressive behavior places him/her or others in imminent danger, the patient does not have the right to refuse the use of restraints. In such situations, the use of restraints is a measure of last resort to protect the safety of the patient or others, and must not extend beyond the immediate episode. The facility may not use restraints in violation of the regulation solely based on a legal surrogate or representative's request or approval (Department of Health and Human Services, CMS, 2006).

Side rails.

The use of side rails as a restraint can cause confusion in some circumstances. Can side rails prevent patients from accidentally rolling out of bed? Yes, but their impact depends upon the patient and the situation. Side rails are considered a restraint when they serve to prevent or impede a patient from voluntarily getting out of bed. The use of side rails as restraints is prohibited unless they're necessary to treat a patient's medical symptoms or assist with physical functioning.

But as the CMS Manual (Pub. 100-07) details, the danger of side rails lies in the fact that patients who attempt to exit a bed through, between, over or around side rails are at increased risk of injury or death. They may become stuck, entrapped or wedged between the rails, the bed, and/or the wall. Serious injury may also be more likely if the patient falls out of a bed with raised side rails than in a fall from a bed with side rails that are lowered since, if patients attempt to climb over the rails, they end up falling from a greater height. A secondary problem with side rails is that they also potentially increase the likelihood that patients will spend more time in bed, becoming less able to get out of bed on their own (Department of Health and Human Services, CMS, 2006).

As a practical matter, the same bed rails may have the effect of improperly restraining one patient but not another, depending upon the individual patient's condition and circumstances. For example, partial rails may assist one patient to enter and exit the bed independently while acting as a restraint or impediment for another.

Restraint Assessment

The CMS Manual outlines instances where, after assessment and care planning, a least-restrictive restraint may be deemed appropriate for an individual patient to attain or maintain his or her highest practicable physical and psychosocial well-being. But this doesn't diminish or negate the nursing home facility's responsibility to assess restraint use on an ongoing basis and alter the care plan as needed.

Before using a restraining device for mobility or transfer, assessment should include a review of the patient's:

- Bed mobility (e.g., would the use of a device assist the patient in turning from side to side? Is the patient totally immobile and unable to change position without assistance?); and,

- Ability to transfer between positions, to and from bed or chair, to stand and toilet (e.g., does the raised side rail add risk to the patient's ability to transfer?). The facility must design its interventions not only to minimize or eliminate the medical symptom, but also to identify and address any underlying problems causing the medical symptom. (Department of Health and Human Services, CMS, 2006)

Interventions that a facility might incorporate in care planning include:

- Providing restorative care to enhance abilities to stand, transfer, and walk safely;

- Providing a device such as a trapeze to increase a patient's mobility in bed;

- Placing the bed lower to the floor and surrounding the bed with a soft mat;

- Equipping the patient with a device that monitors his/her attempts to arise;

- Providing frequent monitoring by staff with periodic assisted toileting for patients who attempt to arise to use the bathroom;

- Furnishing visual and verbal reminders to use the call bell for patients who are able to comprehend this information and are able to use the call bell device; and/or,

- Providing exercise and therapeutic interventions, based on individual assessment and care planning, that may assist the patient in achieving proper body position, balance and alignment, without the potential negative effects associated with restraint use.

Physical and chemical restraints should be an option of last resort. If restraints are used, question the facility about what safety risks the restraints pose and whether there are any other safer alternatives.

ELOPEMENT

Leonard was 74 years old, a proud military veteran and father of two. He was physically able and enjoyed long walks, but had been diagnosed with Alzheimer's. His cognitive functioning ultimately diminished to the point where he had to be admitted to an assisted living facility. His physicians specifically instructed the facility: "The patient should not leave the facility without supervision, he is not safe to go on walks on his own..." The facility was equipped with locked doors that required access codes to prevent patients, like Leonard, who needed supervision, from leaving on their own. The facility promised it could, and would, keep Leonard safe.

But at around 9:00 pm one hot, humid summer evening, facility staff noticed that Leonard was missing from the facility. He had been allowed to walk right out of the supposedly locked unit, even though the staff had received explicit instructions from Leonard's physician not to allow him to leave the building alone. Rather than notify Leonard's family and law enforcement right away, the facility delayed notifications for some reason, wasting valuable time that allowed Leonard to venture farther away as the darkness of night deepened.

After belated notification, local law enforcement, Leonard's family, and the community organized and conducted search after search, combing the small community in a desperate search to find Leonard. But as the days, weeks, and finally, months went by, hope faded, and the prospect of finding Leonard alive grew dimmer.

When Leonard's whereabouts were revealed months later, the horrific events that transpired after he went missing became clear. After leaving the facility, Leonard wandered into a massive cornfield just down the road from the facility. In the darkness of night, row after row of the thick, abrasive corn rows would have all looked the same. It is unknown exactly how many hours and days Leonard suffered, hopelessly disoriented and lost in a wilderness of tall cornstalks during the peak of that sweltering summer. It's hard to fathom the confusion, agony, hunger, dehydration, and desperation Leonard must have experienced — exposed to the elements and wildlife as he was, perhaps finally realizing that he would never be found.

Just short of three months after his disappearance, Leonard's body was found just a quarter mile down the road from the nursing home by a farmer harvesting corn. His body was horribly mutilated, dismembered, and in an advanced state of decomposition. His remains had been spread across the field by a combine.

After the police notified the family that they had recovered what was left of Leonard's body, the family proceeded to a distant part of the cornfield to reflect on their father's life and have a quiet moment together to remember him. To their horror, they stumbled upon what was later confirmed to be the mangled torso remains of their father.

State investigators cited the facility for a variety of deficiencies. But these citations amounted to a slap on the wrist considering the unspeakable harm that the facility's neglect caused and the gruesome horrors that Leonard and his family were forced to endure.

What is elopement?

Wandering is a common behavior among nursing home patients, especially older adults with dementia and other cognitive deficits. The statistics vary somewhat…

One 2006 study reported that one in five people with dementia wander (Wick & Zanni, 2006); another reported that 31% of nursing home patients with dementia wander at least once (Lai & Arthur, 2003). Another reported that 65% of all nursing home patients wander, as compared to 36% of community dwellers (Smith & Schultz, 2009).

But, as Leonard's case painfully demonstrates, when wandering *around* becomes wandering *away*, older adults — especially those with dementia — are at high risk of injury and even death.

What causes nursing home patients to wander? There are several different classifications of wandering, each with their own motivating factors (Lester et al., 2012)…

- *Environmentally-cued wandering:* Patients respond to signals received from their environment; for example, seeing a hallway cues the patient to walk, whereas a chair cues the patient to sit.

- *Tactile wandering:* Patients use their hands to explore the environment as they travel.

- *Reminiscent wandering* or *fantasy wandering:* Patients attempt to reach a familiar place from the past.

- *Recreational wandering* is linked to a need for exercise and activity.

- *Agitated, purposeful wandering* occurs among confused, frightened patients who cannot be reasoned with and who may become combative (Hall et al, 1995).

The medical community distinguishes between the terms "wandering" and "elopement." *Wandering* describes a person with dementia walking away from, or into an area, without permission (Taber & Thomas, 1997). *Elopement*, on the other hand, describes a person with dementia walking away from or into an area without permission *who is seeking an exit*. Elopement, in which the confused person leaves an area and does not return, is the most dangerous kind of wandering. People who elope are typically distinguished from those who merely wander by the former's purposeful, overt, and often repeated attempts to leave the premises (Lester et al., 2012).

Some researchers have found that patients are least likely to elope between 12 am and 7 am, and that the majority of those who elope are repeat offenders, with approximately 72% of successful elopers attempting to do so again (Wick & Zanni, 2006). A review of elopement claims against nursing homes found that 80% involved patients described as "chronic" wanderers; of note, 45% of these incidents occurred within 48 hours of admission (Rodriguez, 1993).

Interventions for elopement

The dangers posed by an elopement are significant and foreseeable. For example, a patient who leaves a safe area could be at risk of heat or cold exposure, dehydration and other medical complications, drowning, or experiencing an accident, such as being struck by a vehicle.

One study explored the circumstances, environmental risks, and injuries sustained in elopements from long-term care facilities by elderly patients with dementia, finding three primary culprits behind elopements (Aud, 2004):

- a lack of effective precautions to prevent elopement when patients had indicated an intent to elope, had repeatedly attempted to elope, or had a history of elopement;

- a lack of awareness by the staff of patient location; and

- ineffective use of alarm devices intended to alert staff to elopement attempts.

Because of these clear and obvious dangers, facilities should firmly establish policies that address the mechanisms and procedures for monitoring and managing patients at risk for elopement. The at-risk patient's plan of care should include interventions for potential elopement, as well. And the facility's disaster and emergency preparedness plan should include a plan to locate missing patients (Boltz, 2003).

Interventions and procedures can include the following, among others:

- Ensure that each patient's risk of elopement is assessed upon admission, periodically, and upon significant changes in condition that may affect the risk;

- When a patient is discovered missing, a search should begin *immediately* and law enforcement should be contacted immediately to assist in the search. The longer the search is delayed, the greater the chance that the patient will suffer harm;

- Ensure that the patient's physician is notified of any elopement attempts, and review and modify the care plan to ensure it adequately protects the patient;

- Ensure that measures are in place to notify all on-site personnel of which patients are at risk for elopement so they can help keep a watchful eye. Patients who exhibit sundowning behavior (increased confusion and behavioral issues as the day progresses into the evening) may warrant closer monitoring during these timeframes;

- Conduct routine and timely checks each shift to make sure each patient is accounted for;

- Ensure that doors that would allow a patient at risk for elopement are monitored by staff at all times, or may be accessed only with special codes that are not available to these at-risk patients;

- Maintain recent photographs of the patients to help those monitoring doors identify the patients, as well as to help locate patients who do manage to elope;

- Ensure that the patients have adequate activities available to them to help keep at-risk patients occupied;

- Utilize electronic bodily monitoring systems (bracelets, anklets or necklaces designed to trigger or sound the alarm) that can alert staff when patients at risk for elopement leave the secured area;

- Ensure that electronic bodily monitoring systems are given periodic and timely maintenance to ensure they are working properly;

- Use video monitoring (in addition to the other interventions) to help ensure that patients don't leave the premises;

- Consider placing patients at risk for elopement on lower floors so that if they try to escape through the window they will not fall far;

- If one unit is on a busy street and another unit is not, the patient may be best placed in the unit on the less busy street;

- Windows on a dementia unit should be secured so that they cannot be opened wide enough for the patient to exit;

- Linen shoots and trash shoots should be secured so that patients who are at risk of elopement will not attempt to use the shoot to exit the facility.

Nursing home excuses

Nursing homes sometimes attempt to justify allowing (or at least, failing to prevent) a patient's elopement by claiming that the patient has a "right" to not wear a tracking or alarm device. They maintain that doing so would have violated the patient's dignity or privacy rights. This is nonsense!

Once a patient is identified as an elopement risk, the nursing home staff is fully aware of the risk of not implementing the appropriate precautions. They have a duty — a professional responsibility — to comply with applicable standards of nursing care, which require the facility to implement precautions to keep the patient safe. If the staff won't utilize alarm systems, citing patient rights, they must take other measures to ensure that the patient does not elope.

In a situation where family members believe that the patient need not wear electronic tracking devices that the facility deems necessary, educating the family will typically resolve the issue. But even if it doesn't, the nursing facility still has a duty to the patient, first and foremost, to ensure that preventive measures are taken to keep him or her safe.

SOCIAL MEDIA ABUSE / LOSS OF DIGNITY

It has become appallingly obvious that our technology has exceeded our humanity.

— Albert Einstein

Over the past few years, the digital age has provided a vehicle for one of the most appalling abuses of nursing home patients. Nursing home employees across the country are posting dehumanizing, humiliating photos and videos of their elderly patients on social media networks such as Snapchat, Instagram, Facebook and others, an egregious violation of these patients' privacy, dignity and the law.

In 2015, ProPublica, an independent, nonprofit investigative public interest news website compiled and published dozens of examples of social media abuse (e.g., naked photos and videos of defenseless patients) that had been substantiated and had resulted in criminal charges or reported in law enforcement or state investigation reports (Ornstein, 2015).

Following are a few examples…

Fremont, Michigan — September 2013. A nursing assistant snapped a photo of a female patient with Alzheimer's disease on the toilet with her private parts exposed, drew a picture of a penis with the caption "limp dick" over the photo, and shared it on Snapchat. She was fired and pled no contest to a felony charge of using a computer to commit a crime. It's worth noting that the facility had written up the employee twice previously for using her cell phone and social media at work.

St. Charles, Illinois — March 2014. One nursing home assistant recorded another using a nylon strap to lightly slap the face of a 97-year-old patient with dementia. In the video, which was posted on Snapchat, the patient could be heard crying out, "Don't! Don't!" as the employees laughed. They were fired, pled guilty to a misdemeanor count of battery and were sentenced to probation and community service.

Gridley, California — April 2014. Five nursing assistants were fired and prosecuted for shooting and sharing photos and videos of patients on Snapchat. In one, a nursing assistant was "twerking" (dancing in a sexually provocative way) over a patient's head. In another, a patient wearing only underwear was carried by a male nursing assistant over his shoulder. Some involved patients were inappropriately exposed or appeared to be deceased. One nursing assistant said pictures and videos were sent on many occasions. The facility failed to report the abuse in a timely manner because, the administrator told inspectors, "there was no concrete evidence that it had occurred." Two of the former employees entered pleas of guilty or no contest to felony elder or dependent adult abuse; the others of failing to report the abuse, a misdemeanor.

Hubbard, Iowa — March 2016. A nursing assistant was fired after sharing a photo on Snapchat of an elderly, incapacitated patient with his pants down and feces on his legs, shirt and left hand. The patient had extreme cognitive impairments due to dementia. The staff member captioned the photo "shit galore" and sent it to several other employees, one of whom reported it to the home's administration. The Hardin County Deputy Sheriff said his office recommended that the nursing home contact state regulators, but did not file any criminal charges. The Iowa Department of Inspections and Appeals fined the facility a mere $1,000 for the incident but did not pursue criminal charges because the patient's genitals were not exposed.

Green Bay, Wisconsin — November 2012. Two nursing home employees shot photos and videos of nude and partially nude elderly patients and shared them on Snapchat. One picture showed a patient vomiting; another video showed a patient being assisted with an obstructed bowel. Both employees were fired and pled no contest to misdemeanor counts of disorderly conduct and invasion of privacy through use of a surveillance device.

Los Angeles, California — November 2015. Police were notified after a video was posted to Instagram showing one employee "bending his rear-end over the patient's head and [expelling] gas over the patient's face." The incident was reported to the nursing home's administration by an employee. The patient told inspectors that "facility employees passed gas in his face as often as every month." These two employees no longer work at the facility.

Bear in mind that these examples cover only a short timeframe and constitute only some of the very small number of perpetrators who actually got caught. No doubt, countless others haven't yet been caught. Consider how many others have shot and shared cruel, dehumanizing photos or videos of patients but were never caught because they didn't use social media, or because they weren't exposed by someone who cared enough to hold them accountable. Finally, consider those who abused patients and were able to avoid detection because they weren't foolish enough to photograph their own criminal acts, and you begin to realize that this problem is much more prevalent than we know.

In a 2016 follow-up, ProPublica published nine more horror stories. The report also pointed out that no long-term care facility has been penalized by the U.S. Department of Health and Human Services for violating the federal patient privacy laws (Ornstein & Huseman, 2016a).

The ProPublica reports prompted some lawmakers to take action. U.S. Senator Tom Carper wrote a letter to the Office for Civil Rights of the U.S. Department of Health and Human Services in March 2016 to ask regulators what, if anything, they were doing to stop nursing home workers from exploiting patients on social media (Ornstein & Huseman, 2016b). "This type of abuse is unacceptable," Carper said, "and falls short of our moral obligation to the 'least of these' in our society."

Sen. Charles Grassley wrote a letter to the executives at Facebook, Instagram and Snapchat, questioning what measures were in place to prevent nursing home employees from posting exploitative content about patients on their platforms. These social media executives responded that their companies had policies in place to remove abusive content from their platforms and that all users had the capability to report inappropriate content (Brahm, 2016).

But these small stopgap measures don't stop predators from posting exploitive content in the first place, which, meanwhile, will have already been viewed by who knows how many people.

How have we, as a nation, reached the point where what we see depicted in our nation's nursing homes resembles the systematic and illegal abuse of detainees that occurred at Abu Ghraib? Our nation was collectively appalled at what our own soldiers did to those prisoners of war. We all saw the lurid photographic evidence of guards committing depraved acts. We wondered why "the system" and those responsible ever allowed such a thing to happen.

To be charged with caring for a vulnerable nursing home patient who needs help, and instead of helping them, taunting them and forcing them to assume humiliating and degrading poses for the twisted pleasure of their caretakers is almost beyond comprehension. It is arguably worse than the atrocities perpetrated at Abu Ghraib. In a nursing home, after all, we aren't even dealing with guards securing prisoners who might be criminals or foreign combatants. We're dealing with *patients* — the known-innocent parents and grandparents of our communities whose only crime was growing old and defenseless and having to rely upon their custodians, who are being paid to provide the care they need, in their time of need.

Such dehumanization is unacceptable in any culture. And as outraged as we were about the treatment of prisoners at Abu Ghraib — and rightly so — shouldn't we be even more outraged about a nursing home "system" that allows these shameful abuses of innocent patients, again and again? If these same abuses were being perpetrated on teenaged hospital patients or children, would they be met with greater outrage and urgency?

Yet, currently, as you can see from the outcomes in the ProPublica examples, there seems to be no sufficient deterrent to stop social media abuse and exploitation of nursing home patients.

By way of contrast, consider the 2008 case of cable sportscaster Erin Andrews. Insurance executive Michael David Barrett secretly videotaped Andrews in a Nashville Marriott hotel room and published a nude video of her on the Internet, which, of course, "went viral." Barrett had arranged to be put in a room next to Andrews' after an employee confirmed to him that she was staying there on a certain date. He rigged a peep hole to shoot video of Andrews while she was changing clothes. The case generated major media attention and public outrage, and of course, it should have, although the media sensation was due, at least in part, to her celebrity. But this time, the result was that a jury found the hotel partners liable for 49% of a $55-million award, with Barrett liable for 51% of the damages. In a separate criminal action, Barrett plead guilty and was sentenced to 27 months in prison. The accountability obtained in the civil and criminal cases were hailed as deterrents for similar such future misconduct.

It begs the question: Why hasn't any nursing home corporation or employee ever been held similarly accountable for allowing the same types of atrocities and invasions of privacy against innocent, vulnerable victims, especially when those atrocities are being committed by the nursing home corporations' own employees? The abuse perpetrated on them by the very individuals who were entrusted with their care is at least equally egregious, if not worse.

Why is this Abuse Happening?

To answer this question, one must consider the modern cultural environment, a microcosm of which exists in today's U.S. nursing homes. The following factors, and others, have colluded to ignite an explosion of patient abuse using social media as the modus operandi for robbing the vulnerable of their dignity and right to privacy.

- **The people.** To save money, nursing homes hire often poorly screened, low-wage workers (many with criminal histories) to care for vulnerable patients who won't or can't fight back. These caregivers have ready access to their defenseless victims in the most private and intimate of settings.

- **The technology.** The rampant proliferation of cell phones with photography and video capability — so many people literally carry this technology around with them everywhere they go. Add to that the explosive growth of social media, which allows easy and instantaneous distribution of those photos and videos to a mass audience. Some devices of modern technology encourage those who distribute lurid content on the Internet to believe (usually mistakenly) that they can cover their tracks, or that they're operating under a cloak of anonymity that will protect them.

- **The corporate interests.** Nursing home corporations that prioritize profit over people are hardly motivated to report employee misconduct that would surely generate negative publicity and trigger investigation.

- **Law enforcement failures.** Our overburdened law enforcement system struggles to keep pace with these untraditional, non-violent crimes.

- **The global culture of acquiescence.** And finally, we live in an increasingly coarse and desensitized culture that accepts — if not promotes — the mass distribution of increasingly shocking and disturbing content.

Certainly, a culture of acquiescence is pervasive throughout the nursing home industry, as well. One of the most disturbing aspects of social media abuse is the cavalier attitude toward this crime that seems to permeate many nursing homes. Consider the case of Taylor Waller, a former nursing assistant in Indiana, who pled guilty to one count of voyeurism for sharing a photo of a patient's back side and buttocks on Snapchat. After entering a plea agreement, she served only three days in jail and is currently on probation. The nursing home received no citations and paid no penalties.

In an interview, Waller tried to justify her conduct by claiming she didn't take the picture for malicious reasons and the patient didn't even know it happened. "They just blew everything out of proportion," she claimed. "It was just a picture of her butt. How many people take a picture of people's butts?... I worked in health care for five years. Everybody takes pictures of the patients all the time. I'm not the only one" (Ornstein, 2015).

This employee's attitude echoes the perspectives of too many in the nursing home industry. As with the excuses offered by the Abu Ghraib guards involved in systemic torture and abuse ... "Everyone does it." As if that makes it okay.

Waller also had the audacity to argue that people searching for nursing homes for relatives have bigger issues to worry about than privacy violations involving social media. "There is so much abuse that goes on," she said. "Nursing homes are so short staffed. Every facility I worked in, every time I went in, patients would be soaked from head to toe in pee and they sat in it for hours. They were treated like animals. I understand taking pictures is bad, but there are so many worse things that need to be taken care of, too."

While it's certainly true that we should be concerned about the many other dehumanizing acts of neglect and abuse that nursing home caregivers perpetrate upon patients, social media exploitation matters, too. A culture of acquiescence is effectively a culture of implied consent.

Federal Regulations Prohibit Social Media Abuse

Make no mistake, federal law guarantees patients certain inalienable rights designed to protect their dignity and prevent exploitation, including:

- the right to be treated with respect and dignity in recognition of individuality and preferences
- the right to privacy in one's room and during bathing, medical treatment, and personal care
- the right to be free from verbal, physical, sexual, and mental abuse; corporal punishment; neglect; and involuntary seclusion

Prompted by media reports and lawmaker focus, the Centers for Medicare & Medicaid Services (CMS) recently instructed State Survey Agency Directors to survey "nursing home policies and procedures related to prohibiting nursing home staff from taking or using photographs or recordings in any manner that would demean or humiliate a patient(s)," including posting on social media. CMS also specifically referenced requirements related to training of staff and the facility's response to allegations of abuse. CMS makes clear that violations can occur even if the images are not ultimately posted or shared, and that the mere taking of a photograph can constitute abuse if it, or the way in which it is used, "demeans or humiliates a patient(s), regardless of whether the patient provided consent and regardless of the patient's cognitive status."

Current federal regulations for nursing homes are as follows, with language pertinent to exploitation and abuse highlighted:

42 C.F.R. §483.10 Resident Rights:

- *Residents rights.* The resident has a right to a dignified existence, self-determination, and communication with and access to persons and services inside and outside the facility, including those specified in this section.

  o A facility must treat each resident with respect and dignity and care for each resident in a manner and in an environment that promotes maintenance or enhancement of his or her quality of life, recognizing each resident's individuality. The facility must protect and promote the rights of the resident.

42 C.F. R. §483.12 Freedom from abuse, neglect, and exploitation.

The resident has the right to be free from abuse, neglect, misappropriation of resident property, and exploitation as defined in this subpart.

Even though the venue of sharing incidents of patient abuse through social media is new, abuse of patients by caregivers certainly isn't. But in November 2016, CMS acknowledged social media exploitation by revising the original definition of *abuse* to include the phrase "including abuse facilitated or enabled through the use of technology:"

Abuse. Abuse is the willful infliction of injury, unreasonable confinement, intimidation, or punishment with resulting physical harm, pain or mental anguish. Abuse also includes the deprivation by an individual, including a caretaker, of goods or services that are necessary to attain or maintain physical, mental, and psychosocial well-being. Instances of abuse of all residents, irrespective of any mental or physical condition, cause physical harm, pain or mental anguish. It includes verbal abuse, sexual abuse, physical abuse, and mental abuse including abuse facilitated or enabled through the use of technology. Willful, as used in this definition of abuse, means the individual must have acted deliberately, not that the individual must have intended to inflict injury or harm. (42 C.F.R. §483.5).

FUTURE CONSIDERATIONS

Unfortunately, it would be a mistake to assume that the new federal regulations have sufficiently deterred the horrific exploitation of nursing home patients from occurring all across this country.

Clearly, nursing home management *must* pay closer attention to their employees' use of social media. Facilities must develop dedicated social media policies, train — or retrain — staff on those policies and encourage staff to report violations. They must enforce those rules, not just pay lip service to them. If there's no punishment for social media abuse because no one is watching, staff have no incentive to follow the rules. At the very least, employees caught exploiting patients on social media should be terminated immediately and reported to law enforcement.

Some lawmakers have advocated for banning cell phones or other devices that allow nursing home staff to photograph patients in areas where patients are receiving care. But, of course, the ideal solution is to hire workers who would never commit these crimes in the first place.

It's a sad commentary about the nursing home industry, and perhaps society in general, that we've reached a point where there's even a need to develop policies and procedures to ensure that patients' privacy and dignity are protected from abuse and exploitation by staff. But this need is very real. And it is inevitable that as technology evolves, so will the means and mechanisms by which nursing home patients can be targeted and exploited by staff.

While it is absolutely necessary to conduct training and develop and enforce rigorous policies to address these evolving technologies, clearly, that's not enough. Too many individuals who lack the necessary empathy, accountability, and basic human decency to be entrusted with caring for our nation's elders are nonetheless being hired to do so because it makes economic sense for nursing home corporations. So, our society must find a way to hold accountable nursing homes that fail to protect patients from these atrocities through adequate screening, training, and monitoring of their employees.

Pursuing the perpetrators of abuse committed through the vehicle of technology may require more innovative approaches. Or as Boston Mayor, Thomas Menino, once said: "We must be vigilant in our actions towards criminals, and innovative in our approach towards solving crime."

WHAT YOU CAN DO

Hopefully, the information provided in this, as well as the previous chapters in *The Harm* section, will help you spot the early warning signs of nursing home neglect or abuse. But bear in mind that the examples of harm that we've discussed so far (e.g., pressure sores, fall injuries, etc.) are just that — examples — rather than an all-inclusive list of harms that can result from neglect or abuse. If you suspect that you or your loved one has been harmed in any way by nursing home neglect or abuse, you can and should take action. The investigatory tools and strategies provided in the next section, *Empowerment*, will show you how to pursue remedies and accountability.

PART III: EMPOWERMENT

Never doubt that a small group of thoughtful, committed citizens can change the world; indeed, it's the only thing that ever has.

— Margaret Mead (1901 - 1978)

9

YOU HAVE A RIGHT TO MEDICAL RECORDS

> Knowledge is power.
>
> — **Francis Bacon**

Accurate and *complete* — those are the watchwords when it comes to a patient's medical records. Having access to those medical records is your inalienable right. And yes, it's true: knowledge and information equals *power*.

Accurately and completely documenting the medical record is a solemn responsibility of the healthcare provider. It's also their legal duty, as you'll soon see. Documentation isn't some optional exercise, done primarily for the benefit of the healthcare provider. All healthcare providers, including nursing home facilities, are being *paid* to maintain accurate and complete records *for the benefit of the patient* as an intrinsic part of the care they promise to provide.

If you've had trouble accessing medical records, what you're about to read will be empowering. By the time you finish this chapter, you'll understand the nursing home's legal obligations with respect to medical records, you'll know the federal laws granting patients the right to access and receive copies of their medical records, and you'll have access to forms and instructions that will enable you to obtain the records.

THE RIGHT TO ACCESS ACCURATE, COMPLETE MEDICAL RECORDS

Medical records contain vitally important information that is intensely personal in nature. The duty to document a patient's medical history, health conditions, treatment administered and response to treatments represents a fundamental component of the care that healthcare providers — including nursing homes — are paid to perform. When medical records appear to reflect substandard or negligent care, nursing home staff often dismiss the documentation and claim "we spend our time providing *care* to patients, not *documenting* the medical chart."

This excuse is based upon a false premise — that carefully documenting the patient chart is somehow a separate issue from "providing care." Accurately and completely documenting the medical record is not only inextricably tied to the care staff are rendering, it's *part of* the care that they're providing. It is a critical component of *how* a patient receives care, and how healthcare providers render care.

There are several reasons why accurate and complete documentation is necessary. First of all, it's required by federal law. As you can see in the box below, federal nursing home regulations make it clear that nursing staff is, in fact, required to keep accurate and complete records.

Federal Regulation 42 C.F.R. § 483.75 (l)(1)

- *Clinical records.*

    ◦ The facility must maintain clinical records on each resident in accordance with accepted professional standards and practices that are -

    ◦ Complete;

    ◦ Accurately documented;

    ◦ Readily accessible; and

    ◦ Systematically organized.

Second, it's necessary to ensure *continuity of care* and to evaluate whether a patient is improving or not. After all, if staff haven't documented what's been done for the patient (or not done), it's impossible for other healthcare providers involved in the patient's current or future care (e.g., doctors or hospitals) to know what interventions and treatment measures have been administered. Thus, it's impossible for them to assess whether these treatments and interventions are working or not and make determinations as to what additional treatments may be necessary. It could actually be *dangerous* to the patient if other caregivers are unaware of which treatments have been previously administered to the patient. For example, as we discussed earlier, tragedy can occur if the nursing staff loses track of whether a patient receives his/her morning medications, resulting in either an overdose or necessary medications not being given. Documentation of the medication administration is every bit as important as the administration of the medication itself.

Third, nursing home staff are largely self-accountable; that is, *only they* have the ability to document the care provided and any other relevant medical events, not the patient. They work under circumstances in which their patients of course, are typically sick and disabled, thus often in no condition to report their own status. And even if they were, they aren't allowed to document their own medical records. Therefore, it's incumbent upon healthcare providers to properly, accurately, and completely account for their actions and document the record. The only entity responsible for accounting for the fact that staff did its job are the staff members themselves. They're legally and ethically obliged to document in the medical record that they did what they were supposed to do.

CULTURE OF COVER-UP

You'd think that it should go without saying that patients should have access to viewing and obtaining copies of their own medical records. After all, the healthcare provider has actually been compensated by, or on behalf of (e.g., through Medicare or Medicaid), the patient to accurately and completely prepare the medical record.

Yet, healthcare providers — and nursing homes, in particular — have a long history of attempting to prevent patients from obtaining access to their own records. Nursing homes add insult to injury when they harm a patient in some way, then refuse to provide medical records to the patient or his/her legal representatives. So often, we hear that patients or their families have requested to view or obtain copies of medical records, only to be thwarted by the facility staff who offer one excuse or another.

Nursing home medical records provide critical evidence as to the nature and quality of care provided to the patient. Nursing home staff often attempt to conceal medical records in order to hide evidence of neglect and abuse by staff, which, in turn, helps them avoid potential accountability. After all, accountability that may result from others learning of staff's care failures may well be reflected in those records.

By avoiding accountability in the form of citations by state investigators, possible fines or liability payments, and public scrutiny arising from substandard care, nursing homes can increase profits. But this not only harms patients and those paying for the substandard care, it allows "bad" nursing homes to unfairly compete with "good" nursing homes. Some like to claim that holding nursing homes accountable somehow harms the industry as a whole. It doesn't. Rather, it levels the playing field for the nursing homes that are actually trying to provide quality patient care. They're forced to compete with greedy nursing home corporations that are willing to cut every corner to put profit over patients. If we don't hold the bad nursing homes that try to cheat the system accountable, what incentive is there for the others to provide the best care possible?

The truth is that medical records are often the best (or *only*) tangible evidence of neglect or abuse. Without some tangible evidence, it's often difficult to establish misconduct under the law. And nursing homes know this. So they often use the following tactics to obstruct medical record requests:

- They may pretend that the nursing home records are "the property of the facility" and implicitly or explicitly communicate that the patient (or the patient's legal representative) is not entitled to access them.

- They may attempt to charge an exorbitant fee for copies of the patient's own record, making it cost-prohibitive for the patient to obtain them.

- When the nursing home does provide access to the records, not all of the records are made available, or records that are made available are altered or falsified in some manner.

Record Falsification

Perhaps the most egregious tactic for avoiding accountability within the nursing home industry is record falsification. Nursing home staff may falsify the patient's medical records by either changing the patient's record retroactively (after the fact), or failing to document incidents that would reveal neglect or abuse altogether.

Not only does record falsification breach the very essence of "accuracy" and "completeness," it violates a critical aspect of patient trust. Our firm has found some form of record falsification in a substantial percentage of our cases, but it almost certainly occurs more frequently than we've been able to prove. Typically, through meticulous analysis of the records, we discover discrepancies in the record that reveal false documentation. For example, nursing homes commonly document that they gave the patient water, bathed them, and turned and repositioned them in bed on days in which the medical record shows that the patient was not even present in the nursing home because they had been hospitalized. If the nursing home staff is documenting that they rendered care on days the patient is not even in the building, can we really trust the documentation of care on the days when the patient *is* there?

As another example, often we receive copies of nursing home records that were sent to the hospital by the nursing home when the patient was hospitalized. We find the copy of the records we receive from the hospital (which was documented in real time) doesn't match the copy we receive from the nursing home when we later request the records and they've become aware that they're being investigated. The records we later receive from the nursing home will often reflect significant edits that would have the effect of covering up neglect or abuse if we had not been able to obtain the copy that the nursing home sent with the patient to the hospital. When we interview former employees during litigation, they often reveal that they were routinely pressured to document care that they didn't provide or omit incidents that point to neglect or abuse. In other words, record falsification was considered to be "part of the job."

But fortunately, because so many nursing homes and other healthcare providers have unfairly and unethically denied patients access to critical information in their own medical records, federal laws have been enacted to guarantee patients (and their legal representatives) access to medical records.

The bottom line is that the patient has an absolute right to access and obtain a copy of their medical record or have it sent to a person of their choosing, without being charged some exorbitant fee that exceeds the actual cost of providing the records.

HOW TO REQUEST RECORDS UNDER FEDERAL LAW

There are two federal laws governing patient medical record requests that specifically ensure that nursing home patients (and their legal representatives) can obtain access to their medical records. We'll refer to requests for medical records under these two federal laws as:

1. the *OBRA Request*
2. the *HITECH Request*

The OBRA Request is the quickest method of obtaining access to, and copies of, one's medical records. OBRA guarantees that records must be produced within 24 hours (record viewing only) or 2 days (record copies), depending on exactly what's requested.

A HITECH Request may take up to 30 days typically, but it does guarantee that the healthcare provider cannot extort outrageous fees and profit from the production of medical records, which would otherwise discourage or preclude patients from getting access to this information the healthcare provider has already been paid to document.

Let's look at each of these two forms of record request in depth…

THE OBRA RECORDS REQUEST

As you learned in previous chapters, federal legislators passed the Nursing Home Reform Act on December 22, 1987 as part of the Omnibus Budget Reconciliation Act in order to address concerns about the nursing home industry. (OBRA, 1987) (42 USC § 1819). In addition to protecting patients from abuse and neglect, regulations promulgated in furtherance of that legislation specifically require nursing homes that receive Medicare/ Medicaid funding to provide prompt access to, and copies of, records pertaining to a patient.

> **Federal Regulation (OBRA) 42 C.F.R. § 483.10 (b)(2)** provides:
>
> "The resident or his or her legal representative has the right – (i) upon an oral or written request, to access all records pertaining to himself or herself including current clinical records within 24 hours (excluding weekends and holidays); and (ii) after receipt of his or her records for inspection, to purchase at a cost not to exceed the community standard photocopies of the records or any portions of them upon request and 2 working days' advance notice to the facility."

There's a lot packed into that one sentence of the regulation set forth in the box above, so let's unpack it. There are several important aspects to this regulation…

The request can be made by either the resident (patient) "or his or her legal representative."

An OBRA record request may be made by the patient himself/herself, if the patient has the capacity to do so. If the patient has authorized others to act on his/her behalf with power of attorney ("POA"), then the POA can as the patient's "legal representative," request access to the records. Similarly, if a guardianship has been legally instituted for the patient, the guardian, as a legal representative of the patient, has the right to request records under OBRA.

In the event that the patient is deceased and an estate has been opened, the executor or administrator of the estate would be entitled, as the patient's representative, to request access to the records by way of an OBRA record request. Under the laws of some states, others may also be considered to be legally authorized as the patient's legal representative. In Indiana, for instance, state law provides that, in the event a patient is deceased, but no estate has been formally opened, the spouse of the deceased patient may obtain the medical records. (Indiana Code 16-39-1-3(c)) Under that same law, if there is no spouse, a child, or parent, guardian, or custodian of a minor child may request and obtain the records of the deceased patient, even without an estate being opened.

But, despite the clear mandate of this law, we've found that it's not uncommon for Indiana healthcare providers to wrongfully represent to families that they will not honor a medical record request without an estate being opened. It's only when they're confronted with the state law that requires access that those healthcare providers eventually relent.

Keep in mind that each state has its own laws with respect to who may act as a patient's legal representative, and these laws vary from state to state. Therefore, one should consider consulting a qualified elder law or medical malpractice attorney to assist with determining whether there is a person who is authorized to act as the patient's representative, if the patient cannot make the request herself/himself, and there is no POA, guardian, or personal representative or administrator of the estate. It's also worth considering to take the proactive step of discussing with the patient, in advance, the benefits of designating a person with POA to obtain medical records, just in case circumstances later warrant obtaining the medical records while the patient is unable to make the request herself/himself.

The request can be made orally or in writing.

OBRA does not require that the request for access to medical records be in writing, but it's prudent to make the request in some manner that can serve to evidence as to when and of whom the request was made. Perhaps the easiest way to do this is to make the request in writing, and have the administrator, records custodian, or other authorized staff member sign a copy of the request, acknowledging receipt. Be sure to have the facility staff member include the date and time of the request beside the signature. You can also fax or email the request, thus generating a "paper trail" of when the request was made.

The patient is entitled to "access," and does not have to request or pay for copies if desired.

OBRA does not require the patient to purchase photocopies in order to obtain access to view their records. If the patient or representative only wants to view the records, the facility must comply with such a request within 24 hours. After viewing the records, the patient can then decide if he/she wants a copy of some or all of the records.

The patient is entitled to see *"all records pertaining to [the patient],"* **including (but not limited to) the current clinical record.**

OBRA requires the nursing home to allow the patient to see "all records pertaining to the patient." This is not limited to only certain parts of the medical records. It includes all "clinical records," but that's not all…

The patient or representative has the right to view all other records pertaining to the patient, such as billing records, patient trust account documentation, admission agreement and other paperwork. While the nursing home staff may argue that they can only make certain records available, the clear language of the regulation makes it difficult for them to argue that clear that the intent of the law is anything other than to make *all records pertaining to the patient* accessible.

Access to view the records must be provided *"within 24 hours"* **of the oral or written request.**

If you're only requesting access to view the records, the nursing home must make the records available for viewing within 24 hours of receipt of the request. This time frame excludes weekends and holidays. If you're concerned that the nursing home may alter or falsify the records between the time the request for access is made and the time the facility makes the records available, consider making the request on a day other than Friday, or the day before a holiday. This will limit the amount of time the nursing home may have to review and "doctor" the records before showing them to the patient or representative.

Photocopies, if requested, must be produced within 2 working days.

If the patient or representative requests photocopies, the nursing home must provide them within 2 "working days." Obviously, nursing homes are responsible for caring for patients 7 days a week and presumably don't "close" on weekends. Thus it is not exactly clear what is meant in the regulation by the phrase "working days." Nursing homes will likely argue that the 2 days does not include weekends. One could also argue that a "working day" refers to one shift a day, such as 9-5. In that case, two working days could mean less than 48 hours, depending upon when the request was made. In any event, what *is* clear is that the nursing home should produce the photocopies within two work days, at the most.

Nursing homes cannot charge more than "the community standard" for copies.

With respect to cost, the OBRA request regulation provides that the cost is "not to exceed the community standard" for making photocopies. If state statute has defined the "community standard" rate, then facilities may argue that rate applies. Otherwise, the community standard for purposes of this regulation is to be determined by comparing the cost of copies by organizations such as the public library, the post office, or a commercial copy center, which would be selected by a prudent buyer in addition to the cost of the clerical time needed to photocopy the records.

Additional fees for locating the records or typing forms and envelopes may not be assessed. (Interpretive Guidelines § 483.10(b)(2)) As will be explained later in this chapter, if you're willing to wait up to 30 days to receive the records, you may wish to use a HITECH request for obtaining copies, which is generally less expensive.

How To Make An OBRA Request

Oral OBRA Request

An oral request made by the patient or representative for access to, or copies of, records pertaining to the patient is sufficient to obligate the nursing home to comply with the request. The problem with an oral request is that, because there is no paper trail to prove the request was made, it's easier for the nursing home to ignore the request without fear of consequence.

If you make an oral request, it's best to have some means of proving that the request was made. One way to help prove that the request was made is to have one or more witnesses present when the request is made. When making an oral request, the patient or representative must specify whether they're requesting only access to view the records or photocopies of the records. If access to view the records is requested, be sure to specify that access is requested within 24 hours. If photocopies are desired, your request should make clear that the records are sought within 2 working days. If the request is being made by a legal representative of the patient, the representative should be prepared to furnish paperwork to the nursing home that substantiates their legal authority to act on behalf of the patient (POA, guardianship paperwork, etc.)

TIP

Nursing home staff have no right to know *why* the patient wants access to medical records, and OBRA does not require he patient to sign any release, waiver, etc. in order to be granted access.

Written OBRA Request

While an oral request is equally valid, it may be wise to make the request in writing, if possible. This will help clarify the request for the nursing home, and provide proof that the request was made, and when it was made. Being able to prove when the request was made will help hold the nursing home accountable in the event that the records are not properly made available.

Another option for documenting the time and date of the request is to send the request by fax, email, or certified mail so there is a paper trail evidencing exactly when the request was made.

This proof may be used as evidence in the event that it's necessary to file a complaint against the nursing home if, as is often the case, the facility refuses to honor the request in a timely manner — in clear violation of federal law.

You can use the form below to make an OBRA request for medical records. (Download a .doc or PDF version of this form at: www. AbusesAndExcuses.org.)

You'll need to complete the following:

- Patient's Name and Address

- Healthcare provider's Name and Address

- Choose whether you want to only view records, or obtain copies. If you want copies, choose whether you wish to receive copies of *all* records or only records for certain specified types and dates.

- Signature of Patient or Legal Representative

- Signature of facility administrator or records custodian

- Date and time of request

NOTICE OF RECORD REQUEST PURSUANT TO 42 C.F.R. § 483.10(b)(2)

Attn: Administrator / Records Custodian
[insert name of nursing home]

Patient name: [insert patient name]

I request:

(check all that apply)

_____ Access to all records pertaining to the above referenced patient, including but not limited to clinical records within 24 hours (excluding weekends and holidays.

_____ To purchase at a cost not to exceed the community standard, photocopies of all records pertaining to the above-referenced patient, including but not limited to clinical records, within 2 working days of this notice.

_____ To purchase at a cost not to exceed the community standard, photocopies of only the following identified records pertaining to the above-referenced patient, including but not limited to clinical records, within 2 working days of this notice _____ [specify the dates and types of records requested] _____.

> **Name of patient or legal representative:** _____
>
> **Signature of patient or legal representative:**
>
> _____
>
> **Received by facility:** _____
> (signature of administrator or records custodian)
> **Date** _____ **Time** _____ **a.m. / p.m.**

Special notes about OBRA requests

Even as nursing home employees acknowledge the patient's right to access or obtain copies of his/her own medical records, often they'll attempt to impose other barriers or limitations. Here are some issues to be aware of:

- OBRA does not give the nursing home any right to know "why the records are being requested." "*Why?*" is the first question nursing home staff will often ask when patients request access to their records. Because the patient or family often feel the nursing home has power over them (e.g., over the care of the patient), nursing homes often intimidate and coerce the reason from the person requesting access. But to be clear: *Nursing home staff have absolutely no right whatsoever to know why a patient wants access to his or her records. None, whatsoever.* And it is a disgrace when nursing home staff pretend or assume that they do.

- OBRA does not require the patient to sign any release, waiver, or other agreement as a precondition to accessing or obtaining photocopies of the records.

- OBRA does not prohibit the patient (or the patient's representative) from taking photos of his own records during the inspection.

Filing a Complaint For An OBRA Record Request Violation

If the nursing home refuses to comply with a proper OBRA Records Request, the nursing home is violating federal law. You have the right to then file a complaint with the nursing home regulatory agency in your state, which will allow the agency to send an investigator to the facility to look into the matter by reviewing records and interviewing witnesses. If the investigator confirms that the nursing home failed to comply with the federal regulation which entitles you to access and/or obtain copies of medical records, the agency can require the nursing home to prepare a written *Plan of Correction* which identifies the corrective measures the nursing home will take to remedy the violation and ensure that it will not happen again. In some cases, the agency can levy fines against the nursing home for violating patient rights.

Once the investigation is complete, you'll receive a report called a Form 2567, which will include the results of the investigation and any Plan of Correction that was required. As a practical matter, the nursing home will likely have to provide you with the access and/or records you are entitled to as part of the corrective measures they will have to take. (The process for filing a complaint with the proper state agency will be explained in Chapter 11.)

HITECH RECORD REQUESTS

The second method of obtaining access to a patient's nursing home medical records is to request access pursuant to the Health Information Technology for Economic and Clinical Health Act (HITECH Act).

On February 17, 2009, the HITECH Act was signed into law. HITECH ACT, 42 USC § 300jj-11. This act was part of the American Recovery and Reinvestment Act of 2009. This legislation was a landmark victory for patients, and its beneficial effects cannot be overstated.

Under the HITECH Act, a patient has the right to obtain their own personal health information from healthcare providers, *including but not limited to nursing homes* (45 CFR § 164.524(a)(1)). The Act arose from a push towards the use of, and sharing of, electronic medical records. The noble purposes behind the encouragement to use electronic medical records is based upon the rationales that doing so would reduce errors, allow for better coordination of patient care among providers, and permit patients to more easily access their own records and take greater control over their own healthcare decisions.

> **Federal Regulation (HITECH) 42 C.F.R. § 17935**
>
> - **Access to certain information in electronic format**
>
>   In applying section 164.524 of title 45, Code of Federal Regulations, in the case that a covered entity uses or maintains an electronic health record with respect to protected health information of an individual —
>
>   - the individual shall have a right to obtain from such covered entity a copy of such information in an electronic format and, if the individual chooses, to direct the covered entity to transmit such copy directly to an entity or person designated by the individual, provided that any such choice is clear, conspicuous, and specific; and
>
>   - notwithstanding paragraph (c)(4) of such section, any fee that the covered entity may impose for providing such individual with a copy of such information (or a summary or explanation of such information) if such copy (or summary or explanation) is in an electronic form shall not be greater than the entity's labor costs in responding to the request for the copy (or summary or explanation).

What patient rights does HITECH cover?

The scope of the records covered by this Act is very broad. Protected health information (PHI) includes *all* information that is: (1) Transmitted in electronic media; (2) Maintained in electronic media; or (3) *Transmitted or maintained in any other form or medium* (45 CFR § 160.103). This broad definition means that the patient is entitled to receive copies of *all* of their medical records, medical bills, insurance payment records and more.

If the patient is deceased, or another individual has been given authority (e.g., power of attorney, guardian, etc.) to act for the individual, then the

Act mandates that the representative shall be treated "as the individual" for purposes of requesting protected health information records (45 CFR § 164.502(g)(1), (2); 45 CFR § 164.502(g)(4)).

The HITECH Act specifically provides that the individual requesting personal health information can designate a third-party (such as their attorney) to receive the information (42 USC § 17935(e)(1)).

Once the request is made, the healthcare provider *must* act on the request *within 30 days* from the receipt of the request by either: (1) providing the requested information (45 CFR § 164.524(b)(2)(i)(A)) or, (2) providing the requesting individual with written denial of the information (45 CFR § 164.524(b)(2)(i)(B)).

If the healthcare provider is unable to either provide the requested information or a written denial within 30 days, the healthcare provider can extend the time by no more than 30 days, provided that: (1) Within the time limit (30 days), the healthcare provider provides the requesting individual with a written statement of the reasons for the delay and the date by which they will complete its action on the request; and (2) the healthcare provider may only have one extension of time (45 CFR § 164.524(b)(2)(ii)).

Importantly: *If the state law in the jurisdiction of the healthcare provider provides for a shorter deadline in producing medical records, then the state law deadline applies — not the HITECH deadline.* Some states do have shorter deadlines than the 30 days allowed for under HITECH.

Since it can take up to 30 days to receive the records under HITECH, the primary benefit of making a HITECH record request is that this law limits the fee that can be charged for the records to the actual cost of copying the records, rather than some inflated charge designed to be cost-prohibitive to the patient and/or a profit center for the nursing home. Often, when families persist in requesting medical records, nursing homes will agree to produce the medical records, but only if the patient or the family first pays an exorbitant fee for the medical records. In some cases, state law would allow the healthcare providers to charge a per-page fee that one could argue is excessive ($1.00 per page or more), in addition to so-called "retrieval fees," or "preparation fees," etc.

OBRA provides a powerful mechanism for obtaining quick access to one's records, either to view or obtain photocopies. Often, however, the nursing home chart can be fairly voluminous, thus costly. Fees can total hundreds, even thousands of dollars, under state laws that were applied up until a few years ago. State laws have allowed them to charge hundreds and thousands of dollars for records that can often be printed in minutes with the push of a button. Yes, even the production of medical records has turned into a profit center for greedy nursing homes.

Aside from generating profit, nursing homes too often use this exorbitant cost to coerce families into either abandoning their request or agreeing to receive only limited and select records, which very well may not contain records that reflect abuse or neglect that has occurred. Fortunately, federal legislation, which still remains largely unknown to most nursing home patients and their families, provides a powerful tool for combating these terrible nursing home profit-driven tactics.

> **MYTH:** Nursing homes are free to charge any fee they wish for copying patient medical records.
>
> **REALITY:** Federal law requires nursing homes to only charge a "reasonable fee" for medical records.

Copying charges must be "reasonable and cost-based"

Perhaps the most significant impact of the HITECH Act is that it dramatically reduces the ability of healthcare providers, including nursing homes, to extort unreasonable fees and costs in exchange for allowing patients to have a copy of their own medical records. The HITECH Act prevents nursing homes and other healthcare providers from enriching themselves at the expense of their patients by converting their records department into a high-volume profit center.

The HITECH Act does this by specifically limiting the charge for the medical records to a *reasonable and cost-based fee* (45 CFR § 164.524(c)(4)). Significantly, the HITECH limit on fees preempts state law, meaning that if any state law allows for a higher fee, the federal HITECH Act supersedes it; that is, in such cases, the state law is to be disregarded. (45 CFR § 160.203; 45 CFR § 160.202).

The Act distinguishes between records that the healthcare provider maintains in electronic format, and those maintained in paper form. According to HITECH, the fee charged for providing the patient with a copy of the electronic records cannot exceed the healthcare providers' labor cost in responding to the record request (42 USC § 17935(e)(2)).

The healthcare provider's labor cost for providing the electronic records can only include (45 CFR § 164.524(c)(4)(i-iv)):

- labor for copying, whether in paper or electronic form;
- supplies for creating the paper copy or electronic media;
- postage, if the individual has requested the information be mailed;
- if an individual has requested or agreed to an explanation or summary, the cost associated with preparing an explanation or summary of the personal health information.

According to the U.S. Department of Health and Human Services (DHHS), the fees may not include costs associated with verification; documentation; searching for and retrieving the personal health information; maintaining systems; recouping capital for data access, storage or infrastructure; or other costs not listed above, *even if such costs are authorized by state law.* Furthermore, administrative and other costs associated with outsourcing the function of responding to individual requests for healthcare records cannot be included in the basis for any fees charged to the individual requesting access. (http://www.hhs.gov, 2016)

You can choose the format

The personal health information requested under a HITECH request *must* be provided by the healthcare provider in the form requested by the individual, including in a *readable electronic format* if the healthcare provider uses electronic health records (45 CFR § 164.524(c)(2)(i), (ii); 42 USC § 17935(e)(1), (2)). Thus, the patient may request the medical records in a

PDF document, or even an unencrypted email if the individual is informed of the security risk of using such format (78 Fed. Reg. 5636, at p. 5634 (Jan. 25, 2013)).

Your Rights Are Enforced By The Federal Government

The HITECH Act authorized the government to prosecute healthcare providers who violate the Act. More specifically, the Office of Civil Rights (OCR) of the Department of Health and Human Services (DHHS) is authorized to investigate complaints and fine violators of the act (*See generally* 42 USC 1320d-5). The OCR can impose mandatory fines of up to $250,000.00 and up to $1.5 million for repeat or uncorrected violators, if the healthcare provider "willfully neglected" the Act.

How to Make a HITECH Record Request

You can use the form below to make a HITECH request for medical records. (Download a .doc or PDF version of this form at: www. AbusesAndExcuses.org.)

You'll need to complete the following:

- Patient's Name and Address
- Healthcare provider's Name and Address
- Patient's Birthdate
- Choose the format to receive the records (electronic or print)
- Select record recipient with address (Patient or third-party designee)
- Signature of Patient or Legal Representative

NOTE: Additional forms are provided at www.AbusesAndExcuses.org for HITECH requests made on behalf of a living patient's records by a POA or guardian, or on behalf of a deceased patient by the personal representative or administrator of the patient's estate.

Date: Month DD, YYYY

Attn: Patient Records Custodian
Shady Acres Nursing Home
123 Main Street
Anytown, State 12345

Re: Health Records Request

Dear Records Custodian:

I am a patient of Shady Acres Nursing Home. My birth date is October 1, 1950.

I request copies of <u>any and all of my medical records</u> including, <u>but not limited to</u>, wound care records, wound photos, incident and accident reports, nursing notes, medication administration records, medication orders, physician orders, records of activity of daily living, physician records, admission and discharge documentation, radiological films, billing records, claim records, and outside healthcare records.

I am requesting an **ELECTRONIC COPY** of all of such records on a CD-ROM in a readable PDF (.pdf) format.

Please send the records to:

_____ Me, at this address:

Address: _____

Email address: _____

Or:

_____My designated representative: Name:_____

Address:_____

Email Address:_____

SIGNED:_____

(Patient Signature)

Please Note: This request is made pursuant to Health Insurance Portability and Accountability Act the federal regulations for which provide, in pertinent part that:

45 C.F.R. § 164.524(b) - A covered entity must permit an individual to request access to obtain a copy of the protected health information (PHI) about that individual,

45 C.F.R. § 164.524(c)(2)(i) - The covered entity must provide the individual with access to the PHI in the form or format requested by the individual.

45 C.F.R. § 164.524(c)(2)(ii) - If the PHI subject to a request is maintained electronically by the covered entity and the individual requests an electronic copy, the covered entity must provide the information in electronic format.

45 C.F.R. § 164.524(c)(4)(i-iv) - A covered entity may not charge any fees for providing copies of PHI except a "reasonable, cost-based fee."

45 C.F.R. § 164.524(c)(4) - Federal Law permits a healthcare facility to impose a reasonable, cost-based fee if the individual requests a copy of the PHI (or agrees to receive a summary or explanation of the information). The fee may include only the cost of: (1) labor for copying the PHI requested by the individual, whether in paper or electronic form; (2) supplies for creating the paper copy or electronic media (e.g., CD or USB drive} if the individual requests that the electronic copy be provided on portable media; (3) postage, when the individual requests that the copy, or the summary or explanation, be mailed; and (4) preparation of an explanation or summary of the PHI, if agreed to by the individual.

The Nursing Home Cannot Create Additional Barriers

Healthcare providers may not impose unreasonable measures on individuals requesting access to their medical records that serve as barriers to, or unreasonably delay, access.

For example, a nursing home may not *require* an individual to physically come to the nursing home to request the record and provide proof of identity in person. This is *not* required by HITECH.

A nursing home may not require the patient to mail the request for records, as this may unreasonably delay the nursing home's receipt of the request and thus obstruct the patient's right to access medical records. All that's required under HITECH is that the patient (or representative) must provide a written request — i.e., a letter in compliance with regulations (e.g., the forms provided at www.AbusesAndExcuses.org);

Here are some other important points:

- If the healthcare provider claims that another HIPAA authorization is required, it's not true. HITECH specifically states that the letter from the patient or the patient's legal representative is all that's needed.
- Healthcare providers are not allowed to charge "retrieval fees," or similar fees.
- If they don't comply with the 30-day deadline — i.e., have not produced the records or an explanation as to why not — they're in violation of the HITECH Act.
- They're not allowed to charge higher fees because a third party is receiving the records, or claim that the third party requires a separate authorization.
- If the nursing home uses a third-party record company to perform their record copying functions, the HITECH Act applies to this third-party company as well.
- Nursing home are not allowed to produce only limited records, or limit the request to "X number of records per year," or use any similar tactic. Requesting all records means *all records*. And the records can be requested as many times as the patient chooses to request them.
- The healthcare provider cannot require the patient to sign any other releases or agreements as a condition of receiving the records with the HITECH letter.

How To Enforce Your Rights If The Nursing Home Does Not Comply

If the nursing home does not comply with *any* of the regulations governing your HITECH request, you can file a complaint with the Office of Civil Rights, U.S. Department of Health and Human Services. The complaint must be made within 180 days of when you knew that the act or omission complained of occurred. The Office of Civil Rights may extend the 180-day period if you can show "good cause."

The complaint must be in writing and submitted in one of three ways: (1) by mail, (2) by email, or (3) by using the Office of Civil Rights Complaint Portal.

Your complaint must include the following information:

- Your name (and the name of the patient if you are making the complaint on behalf of someone else);

- Your full address;

- Your telephone numbers (including area code);

- Your email address if applicable;

- The name, address and telephone number of the healthcare provider (nursing home) that failed to comply with your HITECH request; and,

- A brief description the acts or omissions, you believed violated the HITECH Act. (e.g., the nursing home refused to provide a copy of the records, charged too much for the records, tried to impose additional requirements as a precondition for providing the records such as requiring to know "why" the records were requested, etc.); and

- Your signature and date of complaint.

If you plan to mail, email, or fax the complaint, the first step is to put your complaint into writing. You do not have to use a specific form; however, the Office of Civil Rights has a form available if you choose to use it. It's available at:

http://www.hhs.gov/sites/default/files/ocr/privacy/hipaa/complaints/hipcomplaintform.pdf

You can also find the form at: www.AbusesAndExcuses.org.

Once the complaint is in written form, it can be sent by mail to this address:

Centralized Case Management Operations
U.S. Department of Health and Human Services
200 Independence Avenue, S.W.
Room 509F HHH Bldg.
Washington, D.C. 20201

Instead of mailing the complaint form, you can submit it by email to this address: OCRComplaint@hhs.gov

(Please note that communication by unencrypted email presents a risk that personally identifiable information contained in such an email, may be intercepted by unauthorized third parties.)

One other option is to submit your complaint using the Office of Civil Rights Complaint Portal located at: https://ocrportal.hhs.gov/ocr/smartscreen/main.jsf. Open the OCR Complaint Portal and select the type of complaint you'd like to file. Complete as much information as possible, including:

- Information about you, the complainant
- Details of the complaint
- Any additional information that might help OCR when reviewing your complaint

You will then need to electronically sign the complaint and complete the consent form. After completing the consent form you'll be able to print out a copy of your complaint to keep for your records.

Federal Law Prohibits Retaliation

Families often fear the possibility of retaliation following the filing of a complaint of any kind. Federal law recognizes this important — and valid — concern. Under federal law, a healthcare provider cannot legally retaliate against you for filing a complaint. You should notify the Office of Civil Rights immediately in the event of any retaliatory action.

What Happens After the Investigation?

At the close of the investigation, the Office of Civil Rights will issue a letter detailing the resolution of the investigation. If it's determined that the nursing home violated federal law, the nursing home must:

- Voluntarily comply with the HITECH Rules

- Take corrective action

- Agree to a settlement with the Office of Civil Rights

TIPS

- Don't hesitate to request copies of medical records. It is your right as a patient or patient representative.

- Make sure you have healthcare powers of attorney (POA) properly prepared for the designated patient representative in advance to avoid difficulty in obtaining records if the patient becomes incapacitated.

- Don't allow the nursing home to charge exorbitant fees that exceed what the HITECH Act allows. They can only charge for their actual cost of producing the records, not some bloated per page charge.

- Don't allow the nursing home to argue that state law allows for a per page charge, because the HITECH Act preempts state law.

- Don't allow the nursing home to force you to tell them why you are requesting the records. It is none of their business, and the law does not require you to tell them.

- Make your record request in writing, and either fax it, email it, or have someone at the facility sign for the request so that you can prove when the request was made.

- Keep a copy of your medical records request so that you can prove what was requested.

- You can request to look at your medical records, even if you don't want copies, by giving the nursing home 24 hours notice.

- NEVER sign a release or waiver of liability in order to view or obtain copies of your medical records.

If the nursing home does not take satisfactory action to resolve the matter, the Office of Civil Rights may decide to impose civil monetary penalties on the nursing home. If civil monetary penalties are imposed, the nursing home may request a hearing in which a Health and Human Services administrative law judge decides if the penalties are supported by the evidence in the case.

As a practical matter, the end result will typically be that the nursing home will be forced to provide the complainant with the requested access or copies of the medical records in accordance with federal law, with the possibility of additional remedies and penalties being imposed upon the nursing home.

ADDITIONAL RESOURCES

- For more information about filing a HITECH record request complaint: www.hhs.gov/ocr/privacy/hipaa/complaints/

- Office of Civil Rights Complaint Form: http://www.hhs.gov/sites/default/files/ocr/privacy/hipaa/complaints/hipcomplaintform.pdf

10
ENGAGING AN OMBUDSMAN

Our lives begin to end the day we become silent
about the things that matter.

— Martin Luther King

"Penny, an 82 year old female who is mentally competent and resides in a nursing home was in severe pain. For several hours, facility staff prevented her from using the 911 system to get emergency help. After Penny was placed in the hospital, the family contacted our office and requested assistance. We were able to ensure that the facility changed its policy to allow competent residents access to 911. In addition, we were able to work with the 911 system operators to ensure that they respond to residents in care facilities."

— San Luis Obispo County, California Ombudsman

When your complaints about a patient's care aren't being heeded, it can be hard to know what to do first to get results. Many patients and their families are under the impression that their only choice is to discuss complaints about patient treatment directly with the administrator or nursing staff. But, as you'll learn in the next few chapters, that's *not* your only choice. One option is to voice your concerns confidentially to an Ombudsman, who will work to help resolve your complaints in the manner you choose.

Ombudsman programs tend to be one of the best-kept secrets in the nursing home industry. They seem to be under-publicized and under-utilized, perhaps, in part, due to a lack of funding for educating the public about their existence. But there's another reason, too: nursing homes that *could* educate patients and their families about this important resource too often fail to. As you can imagine, nursing home administrators don't welcome Ombudsmen poking around in their facilities, investigating patient complaints, as is illustrated by the following excerpt from an interview with a former state nursing home investigator…

> **Q:** *Do you think nursing homes genuinely encourage people to talk to the Ombudsmen, or do they sort of hope that they don't, frankly?*
>
> **A:** *I think that they hope that they don't because they feel that the fewer people in the building, the better off. They don't want those extra oversights if they can help it.*
> — *Interview with a former Indiana nursing home investigator*

Engaging an Ombudsman can be an effective first step that, hopefully, may even prevent you from having to escalate to additional steps. Ombudsman programs were intended by the U.S. federal government to empower patients and their families and promote self-advocacy. Ombudsmen, many of whom are volunteers, are generally a dedicated group of individuals whose priority is to advocate for you.

This chapter will tell you everything you need to know about engaging and working with an Ombudsman in your area.

WHAT IS AN "OMBUDSMAN?"

The word *Ombudsman* (om-budz-man), which may sound a bit odd to the English-speaking ear, is of Swedish origin. It means, simply: *one who speaks on behalf of another*. Ombudsmen can be extremely useful advocates — they're on *your* side. The Long-Term Care Ombudsman Program (LTCOP) is comprised of individuals in every state whose main responsibility is to help patients in long-term care facilities maintain or improve their quality of life by helping ensure that their rights are not violated.

Long-Term Care Ombudsman (LTCO) act as advocates for nursing home patients, as well as residents of other long-term care facilities, including: board and care homes, assisted living facilities, and other adult care facilities. In addition to more than 1,000 paid Ombudsmen, more than 8,000 certified volunteers also serve the program throughout the United States.

What is the Cost of Engaging an Ombudsman?

Not a cent. It's free! The Long-Term Care Ombudsman Program is funded by government dollars, so nursing home patients and their families don't have to pay for Ombudsmen services.

History of the Ombudsman Program

By the end of the 1960s, there were well-publicized reports of rampant nursing home abuse, neglect, and substandard care. The nursing home industry had grown as an unregulated industry, and the result was that substandard care became a significant, widespread problem. Legislators sought a way to address this systemic problem.

In 1972, the State Long-Term Care Ombudsman Program was created through an amendment to the Older Americans Act with the mandate to focus on nursing home complaint resolutions. By 1978, all states were required to establish an Ombudsman program. In 1981, the program was name was changed to Long-Term Care Ombudsman Program to reflect an expansion of Ombudsman responsibilities. While the program has evolved over the years, its purpose has remained dedicated to providing a voice for the elderly and people with disabilities who reside in nursing home settings. This program is separate from, and maintains a different role than, the state surveyor agencies that inspect and enforce nursing home regulations.

Pursuant to the Older Americans Act, each state is required to maintain an Ombudsman program that addresses complaints and advocates for improvements in the long-term care system. Each state has an Office of the State Long-Term Care Ombudsman, headed by a full-time State Long-Term Care Ombudsman who directs the statewide program. Each state Ombudsman designates staff and volunteers to serve as representatives to directly serve the patients of the nursing homes.

In 1987, amendments to the Older American's Act significantly strengthened the Ombudsman program. Ombudsman were granted access to patient records (with patient consent) and states were prohibited from willfully interfering with official Ombudsman duties and/or retaliation against an Ombudsman, patient or other individual related to Ombudsman duties.

WHAT OMBUDSMEN DO

In accordance with the Older Americans Act, Ombudsmen investigate and attempt to resolve complaints that "relate to action, inaction or decisions that may adversely affect the health, safety, welfare, or rights of the patients." This includes investigating and resolving complaints about abuse, neglect, and exploitation.

Older Americans Act of 1965, § 712(a)(3)(A)

- **FUNCTIONS.**—The Ombudsman shall serve on a full- time basis, and shall, personally or through representatives of the Office —
  - identify, investigate, and resolve complaints that —
  - are made by, or on behalf of, residents; and
  - relate to action, inaction, or decisions, that may adversely affect the health, safety, welfare, or rights of the residents (including the welfare and rights of the residents with respect to the appointment and activities of guardians and representative payees), of —
    - providers, or representatives of providers, of long-term care services;
    - public agencies; or
    - health and social service agencies;

The roles and responsibilities of state Ombudsmen and their designated representatives are multifaceted. Their responsibilities include:

- Identifying, investigating and resolving complaints made by, or on behalf of, patients;

- Educating patients, families and facility staff about patients' rights, good care practices, and long-term services and support resources;

- Ensuring that patients have regular and timely access to Ombudsman services;

- Providing technical support for the development of patient and family councils;

- Advocating for changes to improve patients' quality of life and care;

- Providing information to the public regarding long-term care facilities and services, patients' rights, and legislative and policy issues;

- Representing patient interests before governmental agencies; and

- Seeking legal, administrative and other remedies to protect patients.

Thus, depending on what a patient's particular situation requires, an Ombudsman may play different roles, including, for example:

- **Advocate:** Acts on behalf of patients, patient families or the patient's legal representatives.

- **Facilitator:** Helps patients prepare and file complaints.

- **Investigator:** Gathers relevant information from many source and evaluates the evidence.

- **Educator:** Provides educational materials to facility staff, families, patients and the public, thus encouraging self-advocacy and problem-solving.

- **Collaborator & Problem-Solver:** Works with patients and staff toward mutually beneficial resolutions.

- **Mediator, Intermediary, Negotiator:** Promotes and mediates communication among all parties involved in the complaint/case; acts as a mediator and negotiator to help the parties reach resolution.

- **Broker:** Refers patients (or their representatives) to other individuals or agencies that provide solutions and tracks progress to ensure that the problem is solved.

One goal of the Ombudsmen program is to diminish patients' sense of isolation and help them achieve a sense of self-determination, especially when they don't have family or other representatives to advocate for them.

Nursing home facilities are required by law to offer a grievance procedure for patients, but many patients hesitate to voice concerns and complaints to staff members for a number of reasons, including the fear of retaliation, as the following excerpt from an interview with an investigator illustrates…

Q: A lot of families just sort of fear retribution of some kind if they make too big of a stink about problems. Do you think that's a legitimate problem in the industry?

A: I think if they complain and actually name people, it could be a problem. I think they could hurt them. Even if it wouldn't be physical, it would be like, "Yeah, just keep pushing that call light button, I'm not going to come," or, "No, you don't need your pain medicine now, and I'm the one who determines that." In the nursing homes, Jeff, you have a lot of LPNs. So they don't have the assessment skills that the RNs have. So the RNs are over the LPNs — most of the time, they're in management. They're not watching what's going on. But generally, and they don't have — if they go to the social service person, that person could have helped them as far as the Ombudsmen.

— Interview with an Indiana nursing home investigator

Ombudsmen, however, are not affiliated with, controlled by, beholden to, or working for the facility, thus, they're typically more objective and receptive to complaints. In fact, through regular contact over time, Ombudsmen often become trusted friends and confidants to patients. And trusted Ombudsmen can provide education and encouragement that may enable the patient to handle complaints herself/himself. The Ombudsman will also speak on the patient's behalf to facility administration or other parties regarding problems. The Ombudsman is responsible for providing prompt feedback to the patient regarding progress in resolving complaints.

Ombudsmen have resolved 73% of complaints to the satisfaction of the patient or other person who complained. (ACL, 2013)

Confidentiality

> **MYTH:** If you complain to an Ombudsman, the facility will find out who complained.
>
> **REALITY:** Ombudsmen must keep concerns confidential unless the patient consents to disclosure.

You can feel comfortable that complaints are received and held by Ombudsmen in the strictest of confidence. Federal law grants Ombudsmen access to patient information (with patient permission), but they're are required to keep that information confidential. Ombudsmen do not pursue investigation and resolution without the patient's permission, except when the problem affects a number of patients and can be discussed as an aggregate or overarching problem affecting many patients, without breaching any individual patient's confidentiality.

What Ombudsmen Are Not

Ombudsman programs *do not*:

- Conduct licensing or regulatory inspections or investigations (This function is performed by agencies that oversee nursing homes in each state);
- Conduct Adult Protective Services (APS) investigations; or
- Provide direct care for patients.

In seeking a resolution, Ombudsmen are always directed by the goals of the patient, to the extent possible (assuming that the patient is capable of participating). Thus, the Ombudsman program's role in investigating the abuse allegations is distinct from that of other entities, including adult protective services and state licensing and certification agencies. The goal of the Ombudsman program is to attempt to *resolve* complaints to the satisfaction of the patient. It's not their job to gather evidence to substantiate whether or not abuse occurred, or to determine if a law or regulation was violated for the purposes of enforcing a penalty.

However, when a patient advises the Ombudsman that he or she has a desire for regulatory, protective services and/or law enforcement action, the Ombudsman program will assist the patient in contacting the appropriate agency and/or disclose information for which the patient has provided consent (45 C.F.R. 1324.19(b)(3)(i)).

How Many People Use Ombudsmen?

Each year, the Long-Term Care Ombudsman Program (LTCOP) is actively involved in the process of investigating and resolving patient complaints against the nursing home industry. LTCOP data shows that, in 2013, Ombudsman services were provided by 1,233 full-time staff and 8,290 volunteers, who were trained and certified to investigate and resolve complaints (ACL, 2013).

Here are some statistical highlights of 2013 Ombudsmen activities…

- Worked to resolve 190,592 complaints initiated by patients, their families, and other concerned individuals. (In 2014, the LTCOP investigated 191,533 complaints in nursing homes and board and care facilities nationwide (LTCOP, 2016).)

- Of those 2013 complaints, 73% of the complaints were resolved to the patient's or complainant's satisfaction.

- Visited 70% of all nursing homes at least quarterly.

- Conducted 5,417 training sessions in facilities on topics such as resident rights.

- Provided 335,088 consultations to individuals.

- Provided 129,718 consultations to long-term facility managers and staff.

- Participated in 21,812 resident council meetings and 2,371 family council meetings.

While the statistics suggest that Ombudsman services are used extensively, imagine how much higher the numbers would be if more patients had knowledge of the existence of Ombudsman programs and a better understanding of how Ombudsmen can help them. These reported incidences, in other words, are likely only a drop in the bucket.

COMPLAINT INVESTIGATION

Ombudsmen regularly visit nursing home facilities to look for problems and provide easy patient access to their services, though the frequency of these visits varies from program to program (e.g. weekly, monthly, or quarterly). However, you can contact an Ombudsman program at any time to request help concerning a specific complaint.

Ombudsmen investigate individual complaints, as well as address concerns that impact several or all patients in a facility. For example, Ombudsmen can address general concerns they personally observe during a visit (e.g. odors, environmental issues). And complaints don't necessarily have to be only about the care provided by a nursing home facility. Some complaints are about outside agencies, services or individuals (e.g. Medicaid or Medicare benefits).

Don't be afraid to report "small" problems to an Ombudsman. No problem is too big or too small for an Ombudsman to investigate. In fact, Ombudsmen are often able to resolve small problems before they become big problems.

What Types of Concerns Do Ombudsmen Address?

Typically, Ombudsman address problems that revolve around these issues…

- Violation of residents' rights or dignity
- Physical, verbal or mental abuse, deprivation of services necessary to maintain residents' physical and mental health, or unreasonable confinement
- Poor quality of care, including inadequate personal hygiene and slow response to requests for assistance
- Improper transfer or discharge of a patient
- Inappropriate use of chemical or physical restraints
- Any resident concern about quality of care or quality of life

Ombudsman address such a wide variety of problems that it would be impossible to list them all here. But, in 2013, the five most frequent nursing facility complaints investigated by Ombudsmen were:

- Improper eviction or inadequate discharge/planning
- Unanswered requests for assistance
- Lack of respect for residents, poor staff attitudes
- Quality of life, specifically resident/roommate conflict
- Administration and organization of medications

The five most frequent complaints at board and care and similar facilities in 2013 were:

- Quality, quantity, variation and choice of food
- Administration and organization of medications
- Inadequate or no discharge/eviction notice or planning
- Lack of respect for residents, poor staff attitudes
- Building or equipment in disrepair or in hazardous condition

THE OMBUDSMAN'S PRIORITY: THE PATIENT'S GOALS

Ombudsmen are dedicated to reinforcing patient rights. They investigate to gather the facts, but their first priority and primary goal is always to resolve the problem to the patient's satisfaction. While patients are provided with information regarding their rights during the nursing home admission process, the Ombudsman is there to support the patient over time as he or she adjusts to the nursing facility, continually reiterating those rights and helping the patient exercise those rights when real-life problems arise.

Federal regulations require facilities to provide Ombudsmen with immediate access to the patient. If the patient consents, the state Ombudsman will disclose patient-identifying information to the proper agency or agencies for regulatory oversight; to protective services; to gain access to administrative, legal, or other remedies; and to law enforcement agencies concerning the alleged abuse, neglect and/or exploitation, if necessary.

However, patient-identifying information *cannot* be disclosed without the consent of the patient or the patient's representative, except with a court order. Thus, the Ombudsman programs are prohibited from being mandatory reporters of suspected abuse or neglect.

Ombudsmen can receive and respond to complaints from individuals other than the patient (e.g. family members or the patient's legal representative), but the Ombudsman still needs patient permission to investigate or share information. If someone other than a patient contacts the Ombudsman program with a concern or complaint, the Ombudsman will visit with the patient to determine if the patient shares the same concerns and wants to pursue the complaint. If so, the Ombudsman will investigate the complaint and continue to communicate with the patient throughout the investigative process.

The Ombudsman will also determine the patient's capacity to make decisions. If the patient is incapable of providing consent, the Ombudsman will work with the patient's legal representative, or follow their state's procedure when the patient doesn't have a legal representative. While complaints may be made on behalf of patients by other individuals, Ombudsmen always take care to ensure that complaints accurately reflect the concerns of the patient.

Importantly, the Ombudsman program is not limited to patients who have no guardians or other representatives to advocate for them. It's available to *every* patient. The Ombudsman's complaint investigation and resolution authority *also* applies to patients with guardians or other patient representatives.

Ombudsman programs are not limited to existing patients, their families or their legal representatives. They may also be utilized by individuals and families who are considering long-term care placement. Ombudsmen may also be utilized by nursing home staff, such as an administrator or employee with a concern about a facility patient, and by any individual or citizen group interested in the welfare of nursing home patients.

When the patient's goals can often be achieved by disclosing information to a nursing home facility representative, the Ombudsman program will assist the patient in contacting the appropriate facility representative to ensure that they fulfill their responsibilities to patients.

OMBUDSMAN SUCCESS STORIES

Ombudsmen handle many, many complaints each year. Following are some specific examples of complaints investigated and resolved by Ombudsmen in San Luis Obispo County, California (LTCO Services of San Luis Obispo County, CA, 2016)…

"During a visit to a nursing home, an Ombudsman noticed that the filters on several residents' oxygen concentrators were clogged and failing to provide the proper amount of clean oxygen. The Ombudsman was able to ensure that the facility staff cleaned the filters, avoiding several potentially life-threatening situations."

"Frances had been living in a nursing home for one year. Due to a stroke, she was unable to move her body and she was mostly bed-bound. Frances told her Ombudsman that another resident was coming into her room and hitting her, grabbing her arms and legs and yelling at her. The Ombudsman was able to ensure that the facility staff protected Frances from any future abuse."

"Jennifer, a 73 year old female who has resided in a residential care facility for the elderly since 1999, used all of her savings to pay for the care facility. She contacted our office for help to avoid being evicted to a nursing home. We were able to help Jennifer qualify for state and federal programs that helped to pay for her care. In addition, we provided the care facility with the licensing regulations that stopped them from evicting her."

"Mildred, who has Alzheimer's Disease, has lived in a nursing home for the past six months, following the death of her husband who was her caregiver. Mildred's daughter was in charge of her money, but unfortunately, the daughter was using the money to pay for her own personal items. She was not paying for Mildred's nursing home care. The facility staff contacted our local Ombudsmen because they didn't want to evict Mildred. We were able to work with law enforcement to stop Mildred's daughter from spending Mildred's money. Other family members are now taking care of Mildred's bills."

Typically, complaints revolve around issues such as patients' rights violations, patient dignity, and accommodation of individual needs. Following are a few examples of complaints investigated and resolved by Tennessee state Ombudsman programs (Tennessee Commission on Aging & Disability, 2016)…

Dignity Issues:

Complaint: *Resident must use a Foley catheter urine bag, which is visibly hooked to resident's wheelchair while in the dining room and all public areas.*

Ombudsman resolution: Facility implemented policy that all catheter urine bags are to be placed inside a no-see through bag/container.

Complaint: *Resident is transported in wheelchair through a public hallway to shower in the communal bathroom without clothes, only a linen sheet draped over her.*

Ombudsman resolution: Immediately, facility mandated that all residents are to be transported in full clothing and some type of footwear when leaving their rooms.

Resident Rights Violations:

Complaint: *Wheelchair bound resident with long history of mental health issues was involuntarily discharged by a nursing home facility to a homeless shelter without medications, follow up psychiatric services, income, or long term care shelter.*

Ombudsman resolution: Immediate referral to Department of Health regulatory agency for investigation; facility cited with an immediate jeopardy citation for immediate/potential harm to resident.

Complaint: *Residents with cognitive impairment and physical limitations are required to eat each meal in their rooms versus receiving meals in the formal dining room (denied social interactions, stimulus, etc.).*

Ombudsman resolution: Facility coordinated with residents and their responsible parties to identify those interested in integrating into the formal dining program. Facility implemented a schedule to accommodate the significant increase in residents attending meals outside of their rooms and in the formal dining program.

Accommodation of needs:

Complaint: *A cognitively aware, disabled, quadriplegic biochemical engineer in early his early 50's with an inoperable brain tumor and slow/limited verbal skills, wished to use his personal computer which has sip and puff technology (set up in his room upon admission 5 months earlier) and eat in the formal dining room where he could interact with equally alert and oriented residents. (While being fed in the assisted dining room with cognitively impaired residents, this resident had little social interaction, and on several occasions, one of the cognitively impaired residents pulled off his sheet, revealing him wearing only running shorts.)*

Ombudsman resolution: Facility established a schedule that allows the resident to be positioned in front of his computer for one hour each day. Resident is now taken to dining room for all meals. (Ombudsman had to intervene to prevent facility staff from waking and transferring the resident into his wheelchair at 4:00am for breakfast. **Staff rationale**: *not enough staff on day shift to wait to get him up and ready to go to the dining room for the breakfast meal.)*

HOW MUCH AUTHORITY DO OMBUDSMEN HAVE?

The truth is that Ombudsmen don't have enforcement power of their own, but they do have the capacity to threaten escalation of complaints to state investigators and/or law enforcement. They do know how the nursing industry game is played, including knowing who is responsible for what. Thus, their real power comes in the form of being able to convince a nursing home to resolve the problem voluntarily to the patient's satisfaction or face greater scrutiny from government investigators and law enforcement who have the authority, responsibility and power to ensure corrective measures are taken. At the very least, Ombudsmen can make sure that patients' voices are heard and that their concerns receive the attention they deserve.

An Ombudsman can be a powerful ally when a patient feels powerless and vulnerable, is physically or emotionally unable to confront nursing home management, or wants to make management aware of a problem by way of an anonymous report. Ombudsman advocacy is generally effective in cases where the problem is small and relatively easy to fix. Unfortunately, as you'll learn in upcoming chapters, additional measures (e.g., filing complaints with state investigators, or filing civil lawsuits) may be needed to address severe and grievances that haven't been remedied.

CONTACTING AN OMBUDSMAN

If you have concerns about a nursing home patient, or just want to ask questions about a patient's rights and the nursing home's responsibilities, don't hesitate to contact your local Ombudsman program.

> **MYTH:** My nursing home doesn't have an Ombudsman.
>
> **REALITY:** *Every* nursing home patient has access to a local Ombudsman.

Here's how to contact an Ombudsman…

Local/Phone book:

- Look for the Ombudsman poster at your nursing home facility, which should include the local Ombudsman's office and phone number. If you can't find the poster, ask a staff member who the Ombudsman is and how to contact them.

- Each state in the U.S. has a Long-Term Care Ombudsman office, often located in the State Office on Aging, which should be listed in your local phone book.

- **Eldercare Locator:** Call 800-677-1116 and ask for the local Ombudsman program that serves your area, or find them on the Internet at www.ElderCare.gov. (Run by the U.S. Administration on Aging, the Eldercare Locator is the federal agency that oversees the Ombudsman Program.)

On the Internet:

- For a complete list of contact information for local Ombudsmen, organized by state, please visit: www.AbusesAndExcuses.org.

- Use the National Long-Term Care Ombudsman Resource Center's handy map to find state-by-state contact information (http://theconsumervoice.org/get_help).

- Visit The National Long-Term Care Ombudsmen Resource Center (http://ltcOmbudsman.org)

TIPS

- Consult an Ombudsman early on when you have a concern so that they can help you find a resolution before the problem becomes more serious.

- Inform the Ombudsman at the outset if you want to keep your complaint anonymous.

- Get to know your facility Ombudsman when they make regular visits to the facility.

11

YOUR RIGHT TO A STATE INVESTIGATION: FILING A COMPLAINT

The government has a responsibility to protect society, to help maintain society. That's why we have laws... The rule of law creates a set of standards for our behavior.

— Vint Cerf, Internet Pioneer

"I *had a case where I was in on survey [investigation] — pressure ulcers was one of the issues... there were like two or three complaints, and I did that. And then, I went for the follow-up survey to see if they were in compliance. Well, during that time, another complaint came in about a pressure sore. But the pressure sore, the lady was there when I did my first survey. They were supposed to fix the problem systemically, and they didn't. And she went in because she had a broken hip, and all of a sudden, we've got all these other problems going on. The very last nurse's note, Jeff, says the nurse was trying to do the dressing change, and the patient screamed and moaned during the whole treatment. And I'm like, 'What nurse would write that? Did she give her pain medicine?' It was within 45 minutes. She didn't give her pain medicine. She goes over to the hospital. They had to give her two doses of morphine because of the pain. She's 91 years old.*

"And this one man who was in a bicycle accident, an all-terrain bicycle, and he got like a fracture, and he ended up paralyzed from his neck down. And he was totally alert and oriented. You could go in and talk to him, but you talk to him, you could smell this...

it just smelled like a rotten smell. So I was in there at 4 o'clock one afternoon, and I asked him if we could turn him to see how good his skin was. And he said, "Yeah," because he was having concerns too. He wasn't quite sure what that smell was. So they turn him, and Jeff, it was a stage four [pressure ulcer], to spine. Now, this guy went through the rehab hospital and made it all this way — no pressure ulcers until he went to this place [the nursing home]. And it was like, I don't know if we're going to heal this thing. It's so bad right now."

— Interview with a former state nursing home investigator

When nursing homes ignore state and federal regulations meant to protect patients from abuse and neglect, they are *cheating*. Nursing homes that disregard the rule of law cheat the patients who deserve — and are entitled to — proper care and basic human dignity. They cheat the public, whose taxpayer dollars (via Medicare and Medicaid) are paid to nursing homes in return for promising to follow the rules and regulations necessary to protect patients. And they cheat the system by unfairly competing in the marketplace with other healthcare providers that actually do endeavor to follow the rules.

If we allow nursing homes to escape accountability for ignoring the rules and regulations that have been implemented for the patients' safety and well-being, we're tacitly giving our approval to nursing homes that are cheating for their own financial gain (by understaffing, for example). We have the power to hold these nursing homes accountable and to ensure that patients receive the care that the nursing home is being paid to provide.

But it's up to us to hold them accountable and to take steps that will prevent future abuse and neglect. One very important way to do that is to exercise your right to have your complaints investigated by the State agencies charged with enforcing regulations that were designed to ensure quality of care.

Filing a complaint with your State agency is the next step you can take if your Ombudsman has been unable to achieve satisfactory resolution of your concern, or a serious incident of abuse or neglect has occurred and you want to ensure an investigation. In this chapter, you'll learn how to file an effective complaint and what you can expect from the investigatory process.

WHY FILE A COMPLAINT?

There are several important benefits that can result from the complaint and investigation process. While there's no compensation associated with filing a complaint, taking this step can often help you get answers and accountability. And even though the fines and penalties assessed against the nursing home are typically relatively minor, state investigators have significant power to, for example, enter the facility without notice, pull and review patient records, interview staff, address the issue of concern, and in doing so, preserve important evidence. Inspections and investigations may be conducted at any time, including weekends, 24 hours a day.

> The average number of consumer complaints reported per home increased by 21 percent from 2005-2014 (GAO, 2015).

First and foremost, a State investigator can help put an immediate stop to an ongoing problem that's either harming a patient or has the capacity to harm a patient. In doing so, the investigator's actions can also help prevent similar harm to other patients. For example, let's say that you have a loved one in a nursing home who has pressure sores that you believe are associated with inadequate turning and repositioning at night due to understaffing… you can file a complaint with the State and have the situation investigated. And because of the likelihood that other patients in this nursing home may also be similarly harmed, a State investigation will likely take place within days of filing your complaint. If, in fact, the investigator can find evidence substantiating that the nursing home was understaffed and failing to properly turn and reposition its patients, the State will require the nursing home to prepare a Plan of Correction designed to correct the understaffing problem and subsequent failure to implement proper pressure sore prevention interventions. By filing your complaint, you have quite possibly intervened and effectuated changes at the facility that may not only prevent further harm to your loved one, but also help protect the facility's other patients.

42 CFR § 488.406 Available remedies.

General. In addition to the remedy of termination of the provider agreement, the following remedies are available:

- Temporary management.

- Denial of payment including –

    1. **Denial of payment for all individuals**, imposed by CMS, to a –

        a. Skilled nursing facility, for Medicare;

        b. State, for Medicaid, or

    2. Denial of payment for all new admissions.

    3. Civil money penalties.

    4. State monitoring.

    5. Transfer of patients.

    6. Closure of the closure and transfer of patients.

    7. Directed plan of correction.

    8. Directed in-service training.

    9. Alternative or additional State remedies approved by CMS.

Second, by filing a complaint with the State you can help hold nursing homes that allow and enable neglectful or abusive care accountable. All nursing homes that accept Medicare and/or Medicaid dollars promise that, in return for receiving these taxpayer funds, they will render care in a manner that ensures that patients' needs are met. Nursing homes that either cannot or will not render care in accordance with these required minimum standards should not be permitted to receive the same Medicare and Medicaid funding that other nursing homes, which *do* ensure their patients' safety and well-being, receive. By filing a complaint to alert State investigators of substandard care, you're helping to hold bad nursing homes accountable so that they're either forced to improve practices or face the prospect of losing their most significant revenue streams — Medicare and Medicaid.

Third, filing a complaint that results in a deficiency citation that forces the nursing home to develop a Plan of Correction means that the resulting Form HFCA-2567, *Statement of Deficiencies* (referred to as "2567") report will become a matter of public record. This report will be available online at the Nursing Home Compare website and, in many instances, other State nursing home sites. In addition, nursing homes are required by law to have their latest survey results available to the public for review. This information, which is made public within the nursing home and online, is arguably the most valuable objective information about the facility's track record that you can find. Though certainly not perfect, these reports tell you much more about the level of care being rendered within a facility than do the shiny marble floors and beautiful landscaping that the nursing home marketing directors like to point out to you. The problem is, these 2567 reports are only generated annually, at the time of the annual survey, unless interim complaints are filed by concerned families, patients, staff members, or others.

Fourth, filing a complaint with your State ensures that the investigation will generate and preserve evidence that may be required to successfully pursue a criminal action or civil lawsuit against the nursing home should those actions become necessary. Importantly, these 2567 reports can be used to establish that those responsible for the nursing home were put on notice of substandard care issues within the facility, had a duty to correct the problems, and despite promises to correct them (the Plan of Correction), ignored them and continued to conduct business as usual, which ultimately led to further neglect, abuse, and harm.

For example, if a nursing home has been cited multiple times within a year for failing to ensure that the proper policies and procedures were in place to prevent medication errors and a patient suffers a tragic death due to a misadministration of medication, the patient's family should be able to use the evidence from prior 2567 reports to demonstrate that the facility was put on notice of deficient care practices, promised to make the necessary corrections, but failed to do so. In addition, the filing of a complaint permits the State investigator to enter the nursing home without notice and preserve evidence by copying pertinent medical records, interviewing staff members privately, and obtaining information from other patients.

For example, in one recent case brought by the Powless Law Firm, a patient was allowed to develop a horrible, necrotic pressure sore on his tailbone area that drained purulent fluid indicating infection. This elderly patient needed to be turned and repositioned regularly in order to prevent pressure sores; however, the patient's medical records confirmed that the facility staff was not utilizing a turning and repositioning program at that time. It was suspected that the nursing home, as is so often the case, was not providing adequate staffing to allow for proper care, including making sure the patient was being turned and repositioned frequently enough. Close examination of the facility's 2567 reports found that the state investigator had indeed confirmed and documented compelling evidence of understaffing.

According to the investigator's 2567 investigation report:

> A female resident told the investigator she waited "a half hour...maybe longer" for staff to answer her call light, causing her to experience both urinary and bowel incontinence as a result of having to wait.

> Another female resident told the investigator that: "You have to wait half an hour to an hour for them to answer your light. It just seems like they don't have enough people to cover the care... I've had accidents [incontinence] ...I recently had a bowel movement... it's embarrassing. I don't care how old you are."

> A nurse aide told the investigator: "We can't always get everyone toileted like we'd like [due to staffing/not having enough help]... Sometimes there are three [residents] at a time [who require/request toileting assistance...]"

> Several nurse aides told the investigator that facility management, LPNs and RNs...did not assist CNAs in answering call lights, toileting residents, or with dining room/meal times. Each of the nurse aides told the investigator that they have expressed

concerns regarding staffing and nursing/management not assisting with resident care. Each nurse aide told the investigator that management was unresponsive to their concerns.

A female resident told the investigator: "We don't get enough ice water because there's not enough staff. The other night I said, 'Why am I not getting any ice water?' and they said it was because they only had three people here and one of them was with [another resident]."

Because someone took the initiative to file a complaint, the investigator was able to enter the facility, gather evidence and uncover evidence of systemic understaffing that was affecting the quality of care received by multiple patients within that facility.

In addition to helping demonstrate that those responsible for the nursing home were put on notice of a problem and chose to ignore it, 2567 investigation reports can help prove that a nursing home has a routine practice (pattern of behavior) of neglecting or abusing their patients. Generally speaking, the law in most states allows for evidence of an organization's routine practice to be admitted to prove that on a particular occasion, the organization acted in accordance with the routine practice. Thus, the 2567 reports can help demonstrate that nursing home is engaged in a routine practice that leads to the neglect of its patients, as reflected in the series of 2567 reports.

CULTURE OF COVER-UP

"The one that is very vivid where somebody called in... My supervisor was with me because it was a bad area of town. So he and I went in there — he went down one side, and I went down the other. And I'm having to turn the lights on, and we're looking, turning people and seeing what's going on here. And one lady was in bed and her sheet was so wet, the curtain was on the bed, on the linen, and the urine was going up the curtain... she had to have laid there for hours.

... "They'll say, 'Well, she's a frequent wetter,' or, 'She's a heavy wetter.' What a way to describe somebody. 'Okay, so she wets frequently, so I guess you have to look in on her a little more often, but why do you have a brown ring on this bottom sheet? How long did that take to get brown?' 'Well, if you take a glove, you can feel it's still warm,' they said. I said, 'That brown there is not warm. I can tell you right now. Don't even try to go there with me, but that brown area is not warm. She's been laying there for a while.'"

— Interview with a former state nursing home investigator

As you've learned, nursing homes often engage in cover-up tactics intended to conceal neglect, abuse and substandard care in order to escape liability. But even if a particular 2567 report is not admitted as evidence in court, the State investigation is helpful because the investigator has now secured evidence that may otherwise be falsified or intentionally "lost."

One benefit to having the State investigator enter the facility and obtain and preserve medical records at that point in time is that it can help prevent nursing homes from tampering with and falsifying the patient's medical records before the patient's family can obtain a copy. If the State investigator secures a copy of the pertinent medical records at the time he or she enters the facility unannounced, nursing facility management may be deterred from falsifying records because they know that any "alterations" could later be revealed if the two versions of the record were ever compared.

Nursing homes are not permitted to squirrel away their employees or hide them behind lawyers when State investigators enter the facility to investigate a complaint. That tactic, unfortunately, is too often used in civil cases in an effort to prevent the patient and his/her family's attorney from gathering damning information about abuse and neglect. An unannounced visit by a State investigator, resulting from your complaint, can be an effective countermeasure to cover-up tactics, as is illustrated by these excerpts from an interview with a former state nursing home inspector...

A: *I had a mother show me pictures — her son was paralyzed from the neck down from a motorcycle accident, and she showed me pictures where somebody did cigarette burn, a couple of cigarette burns, on his legs, and he was not a smoker. She equated that to staff.*

Q: Did the nursing homes acknowledge that in their records, or was it —?

A: No. They wanted to say he did it to himself. But he couldn't even feed himself.

As we've discussed, the inadequate care problems often result from understaffing...

"You go to talk to them and say, 'When was the last time you had a bath or a shower?' 'Well, I don't get one because they don't have enough staff.' So I would go to the aides and say, "Is that true?' 'Well, I cannot give seven showers in an eight-hour period.' So she said, 'I don't give them.' They just don't get it.' She's like, 'I cleaned them as good as I can,' but they just don't get it.' So they would say, 'Well, what's the role for staffing?' And I would say, 'Well, the role for staffing is that they have to staff to meet the patient needs."And they didn't know what that meant.'"

— Interview with a former state nursing home investigator

Some nursing homes of course attempt to conceal the fact that they understaff...

"And the families would say, 'Well, can't you see they're short-staffed?' And I'm like, 'No. As soon as I walk in, they're on that phone calling everybody in that they could call in.'"

— Interview with a former state nursing home investigator

You can see how filing a complaint creates a paper trail, ensures a State investigation and preserves evidence, all of which may thwart cover-up attempts by the nursing home.

WHEN SHOULD YOU FILE A COMPLAINT?

Many patients, families, and even nursing home employees are confronted with the question: Does this event that just happened justify filing a complaint with the State Survey Agency? The answer probably depends on whether the conduct or care practice caused harm, or has the potential to cause harm to a patient. If either is true, the answer is likely *yes*.

Every nursing home that accepts the guaranteed flow of money that comes from being licensed and certified to accept Medicare and Medicaid payments (most nursing homes), has agreed — that is, *promised* — to provide every patient with the best possible care. By law, these nursing homes are required to help each patient "attain or maintain the highest practicable physical, mental and psychosocial well-being."[3] Moreover, they must ensure that the patient's condition does not decline, unless it is *medically unavoidable*.[4] The law requires that care, treatment and therapies must be used to maintain and improve health to the extent possible,[5] subject to the patient's right to choose and refuse services.[6]

Unfortunately, as we've discussed, far too often, those responsible for caregiving in U.S. nursing homes break this solemn promise and fail to provide the standard of care required by law. If you're aware of a nursing home patient who is not receiving proper care — whether that patient is you, a loved one, or a total stranger — you're entitled to file a complaint to help ensure that the nursing home meets its obligations and performs the job it's being paid to perform. You have the right to complain to the nursing home staff, your State investigator, to Ombudsmen, or to any other individual or agency without fear of retaliation. And you have the right to have your complaint addressed promptly by the nursing home.

It's not necessary that you know exactly which law or regulation is being violated by the nursing home. You only have to notify your state agency of your concerns about the care provided (or care not provided that should have been) by the facility and they'll investigate.

While there's no formal, comprehensive checklist for each and every issue that one could possibly be concerned about, following are some examples of issues that are often the subject of complaints against, and citations of, nursing homes providing substandard care…

---

3   42 USC §1396r(b)(2)

4   42 CFR §483.25

5   42 USC §1396r(b)(4)

6   42 CFR 483.10(b)(4), Title 22 CCR §72527(4).

Accommodation of Needs

- *Did the nursing home deny a patient reasonable accommodations of individual needs and preferences?*[7] The facility should attempt to adapt schedules, call systems, staff assignments and room arrangements to accommodate patient preferences, desires and unique needs.[8] For example, if a patient refuses a bath because he or she prefers a shower, prefers bathing at a different time of day or on a different day, does not feel well that day, is uncomfortable with the aide assigned to help, or is worried about falling, the staff should acknowledge that the patient is not refusing to be clean, but refusing the bath under the circumstances and make the necessary adjustments.[9]

- *Did the facility manage language or communication barriers between patients and staff?* The facility is required to use interpreters or other measures to ensure adequate communication.[10]

Adequate Staff

- *Did the nursing home fail to have sufficient staff to meet the needs of each patient in the nursing home at all times?*[11] The facility must have on hand an adequate number of licensed nursing and certified nursing assistants. Some states require a minimum number of hours of nursing care per patient day. The facility must post daily, for each shift, the current number of licensed and unlicensed nursing staff directly responsible for patient care.

Signs to look for:

- Are call lights not answered in a timely manner?

---

7   42 CFR 483.15(e).

8   Surveyor's Guideline to 42 CFR §483.15(e), Appendix PP to CMS State Operation Manual.

9   42 CFR 483.10(b)(1).

10   42 CFR 483.10(b)(1).

11   42 CFR §483.30.

- Are patients with mobility problems not being turned and repositioned at least every two hours while in bed, and at least once per hour while in a wheelchair?
- Does the staff complain that the facility is understaffed?
- Are patients getting the assistance they need to eat meals?
- Do you have trouble finding a staff member when a patient needs assistance?
- Do staff respond to bed and chair alarms quickly enough to prevent patients from falling?

Care Planning

- *Did the facility fail to establish a comprehensive, individualized care plan for the patient?*[12] The care plan should detail the patient's specific care needs and how they will be met.

Continence & Toileting Help

Did the nursing facility staff:

- *fail to ensure that a patient with bladder or bowel control problems was promptly assessed and effectively treated to improve the condition?*[13] Incontinence and inadequate toileting assistance can cause many serious problems, including discomfort, skin rashes, pressure sores, falls, sense of isolation and psychological harm.

- *use catheters without valid medical justification?*[14] Nursing homes are not allowed to use a catheter for the convenience of staff or to compensate for not hiring sufficient staff to ensure that patients receive toileting assistance when they need it. Catheters cause discomfort, limit mobility and increase the risk of infection, bladder stones and cancer.[15] For catheter users, facilities must act to prevent

---

12   42 CFR §483.20
13   42 CFR §483.25(d)(2).
14   42 CFR §483.25(d)(1).
15   CMS' Patient Assessment Instrument Version 2.0 Manual, Appendix C, §6 (Urinary Incontinence & Indwelling Catheter), Page C–30, revised December 2002.

urinary tract infections and restore as much normal bladder function as possible.

- *fail to provide toileting assistance for a patient who needs it?* Many nursing home patients need help with toileting, even if they're not incontinent (e.g., a patient who has limited mobility; or a patient with dementia who may need reminders. Nursing homes must help these patients use the toilet as often as needed).[16]

Feeding Tubes

Did the nursing facility staff:

- *use a feeding tube for its own convenience rather than as a last resort?* Feeding tubes can cause serious medical and psychological problems and lead to a loss of functioning, thus no tube should ever be used for a patient who can swallow and receive adequate nutrition orally, no matter how long it takes to feed the patient.[17] Lack of staff is no excuse.[18] A feeding tube can be used with the patient's consent when there's a demonstrated medical need to prevent malnutrition or dehydration. But even then, all possible alternatives should be explored first.[19]

- *fail to provide a patient fed by tube with the appropriate treatment and services to prevent aspiration pneumonia, diarrhea, vomiting, dehydration, and other adverse symptoms?*[20]

- *fail to do all it could to help a patient with a feeding tube take food by mouth again as soon as possible?*[21]

---

16   42 CFR §483.25(a)(1).

17   42 CFR §483.25(g)(1).

18   CMS' Resident Assessment Instrument Version 2.0 Manual, Appendix C, §13 (Feeding Tubes), Page C–68, revised December 2002.

19   CMS' Resident Assessment Instrument Version 2.0 Manual, Appendix C, §13 Feeding Tubes), Page C–68, revised December 2002.

20   42 CFR §483.25(g)(2).

21   42 CFR §483.25(g).

Food and Nutrition

- *Did the nursing facility staff fail to provide a patient a nourishing, palatable, well-balanced diet that meets daily nutritional and special dietary needs?*[22] Nursing homes are required to:

  ○ serve at least three meals daily, at regular times, with no more than a 14-hour span between the evening meal and breakfast;[23]

  ○ offer snacks at bedtime;[24]

  ○ reasonably accommodate patient food and mealtime preferences;[25]

  ○ offer a food substitute of similar nutritional value if a patient refuses food;[26]

  ○ serve food attractively, at the proper temperature, and in a form to meet individual needs;[27] and

  ○ prepare and follow menus that meet national dietary standards.[28]

- *Did the nursing home fail to:*

  ○ *ensure that a patient's ability to eat was not diminished unless it was medically unavoidable?*[29]

  ○ *provide individualized help to a patient who needs meal assistance, including enough time to enable the patient to finish meals?*[30]

  ○ *provide special eating utensils to a patient who needs them?*[31]

---

22   42 CFR §483.35.
23   42 CFR §483.35(f).
24   42 CFR §483.35(f).
25   42 USC §1396r(c)(1)(A)(v), 42 CFR §483.15(b)(1).
26   42 CFR §483.35(d)(4).
27   42 CFR §483.35(d).
28   42 CFR §483.35(c).
29   42 CFR §483.25(a)(1)(iv).
30   42 CFR §483.25(a)(1)–(3).
31   42 CFR §483.35(g.

- *provide table service (at a table of appropriate height) to a patient who desired it?*
- *store, prepare, distribute or serve food under sanitary conditions?[32]*
- *establish an individualized care plan to maintain the patient's ability to eat food orally if the patient's ability to eat is compromised?[33]*
- *notify a patient's physician immediately of signs of malnutrition (e.g., weight loss of 5 lbs. or more within a 30-day period)?* Federal guidelines urge nursing homes to reassess nutritional status whenever a patient experiences unplanned or undesired weight loss of 5% or more in one month, 7.5% or more in three months, or 10% or more in 6 months.[34]

Infection Control

Nursing homes are required to have an organized infection control program that prevents diseases and infections from developing and spreading.[35]

Did the nursing home fail to:

- *ensure that staff members wash their hands after each direct contact with a patient?*
- *prohibit staff who have communicable diseases or infected skin conditions from having direct contact with patients or their food?*
- *clean and disinfect contaminated articles and surfaces?*

---

32 42 CFR §483.35(h).

33 CMS' Resident Assessment Instrument Version 2.0 Manual, Appendix C, §12 (Nutritional Status), Page C–63, revised December 2002.

34 Surveyor's Guideline to 42 CFR §483.25(i), Appendix PP to CMS State Operation Manual.

35 42 CFR §483.65.

Medications

Did the nursing home staff:

- *fail to ensure the patient and his/her legal representative's right to consent to or to refuse any treatment, including use of medications?*[36]

- *fail to ensure that the patient's medication was prescribed (whether routine, emergency, or on as-needed basis) in a timely manner? (This requirement is not met if late administration of a prescribed drug causes the patient discomfort or endangers his or her health and safety.*[37]*)* Doses must be administered *within 1 hour of the prescribed time* unless otherwise indicated by the prescriber. Nursing homes are required to have 24–hour arrangements with one or more pharmacies.[38]

- *overprescribe or allow the patient to use any unnecessary drugs?* An unnecessary drug is any drug given: (1) in excessive dose; (2) for an excessive period of time; (3) without adequate monitoring; (4) without adequate justification; or (5) in the presence of adverse consequences that indicate the dose should be reduced or discontinued.[39]

- *allow for the use of restricted drugs (such as sedatives, tranquilizers and similar drugs) when the medical need was not clearly documented?*[40] Federal guidelines discourage nursing homes from using drugs with a high potential for severe adverse outcomes in older individual.[41]

---

36   42 CFR §483.10(b)(4).
37   42 CFR §483.60, Surveyor's Guideline to 42 CFR §483.60, Appendix PP to CMS State Operation Manual, See also Title 22 CCR §72355.
38   42 CFR §483.60.
39   42 CFR §483.25(l).
40   Surveyor's Guideline to 42 CFR §483.25(l), Appendix PP to CMS State Operation Manual.
41   Surveyor's Guideline to 42 CFR §483.25(l), Appendix PP to CMS State Operation Manual.

- *administer an antipsychotic drug to a patient without making sure it was necessary to treat a mental illness that has been diagnosed and documented in the resident's clinical record?*[42]

- *fail to attempt discontinuation of antipsychotic drugs by substituting behavioral interventions and gradual dose reductions, unless clinically contraindicated?*[43]

- *allow for the use of drugs to treat behavioral symptoms?* Except in emergencies, it is generally illegal to chemically restrain a patient; i.e., control a patient's behavior through drugs when other forms of care and treatment would be more appropriate.[44]

- *sedate the patient to cover up behavioral symptoms caused by any of the following:* (1) environmental conditions such as excessive heat, noise, overcrowding; (2) psychosocial problems such as abuse, taunting, or ignoring a patient's regular routine; or (3) treatable medical conditions such as heart disease or diabetes?[45]

- *allow medications to be administered by someone other than licensed nurses or medical personnel?* Unlicensed staff may administer certain laxatives, non-prescription lotions, medicinal shampoos and baths, subject to specific training, demonstrated competence and direct supervision by licensed nursing or medical personnel.

- *fail to ensure that the person who administered the drug or treatment recorded the date, time, and dosage in the patient's individual medication record?*

- *fail to prevent a significant medication error?* Nursing homes must keep medication error rates under 5% and ensure that patients are free of any significant medication errors.[46] A medication error

---

42   42 CFR §483.25(l)(2)(i).

43   42 CFR §483.25(l)(2)(ii).

44   42 USC §1396r(c)(1)(A)(ii), 42 CFR §483.13(a).

45   Surveyor's Guideline to 42 CFR §483.25(l), Appendix PP to CMS State Operation Manual.

46   42 CFR §483.25(m).

is a discrepancy between the facility's actions and either physician's orders, manufacturer's specifications, or accepted professional standards.[47] A medication error is considered "significant" when it causes the resident discomfort or jeopardizes his or her health and safety.[48]

- *allow "medication sharing," or give a medication to someone other than the patient for whom it was prescribed?*

- *fail to obtain services from a licensed pharmacist to assess its medication system and to review the drug regimen of each resident on a monthly basis?*[49] The pharmacist is required to report any irregularities to the patient's attending physician, the administrator and director of nursing, who must act on the reports.[50]

Personal Care

Did the nursing home fail to:

- *provide care to maintain clean, dry skin on the patient?*

- *change soiled linens, clothing and other items to keep a patient's skin is free from urine and feces?*

- *provide needed personal care services including bathing, shampooing and grooming of hair, oral hygiene, shaving or beard trimming, and cleaning and cutting of fingernails and toenails?*

- *ensure that patients are free of offensive odors?*

- *answer call signals for personal care promptly?*

- *ensure privacy during treatments and personal care?*

---

47   Surveyor's Guideline to 42 CFR §483.25(m), Appendix PP to CMS State Operation Manual.

48   Surveyor's Guideline to 42 CFR §483.25(m), Appendix PP to CMS State Operation Manual.

49   42 CFR §483.60(b)&(c).

50   42 CFR §483.60(c)(2)

Physician Services

Did the nursing home fail to:

- *ensure that the patient's care was supervised by a physician chosen by the patient or the patient's representative?*[51] Nursing homes may not place obstacles in the way of patients choosing their own physicians. For example, if a patient does not have a physician, or if the patient's physician becomes unable or unwilling to continue treating the patient, the facility must help the patient exercise his/her choice in finding another physician.[52]

- *ensure that the patient was seen and evaluated by a physician at least every 30 days, or more often if needed?*[53]

- *ensure that the physician had face-to-face contact with patients and reviewed the patient's total program of care during required visits?*[54] "Total program of care" means all care the facility provides, including medical services, medication management, therapy, nursing care, nutritional interventions, social work and activity services.[55]

- *ensure that a patient's attending physician:*[56]
  - ○ *Participated in the patient's assessment and care planning?*
  - ○ *Monitored changes in the patient's medical status?*
  - ○ *Reviewed the patient's total program of care at each required visit?*
  - ○ *Prescribed new therapy and treatments as needed?*

---

51   42 CFR §483.40, 42 CFR §483.10(d)(1)

52   Surveyor's Guideline to 42 CFR §483.10(d)(1), Appendix PP to CMS State Operation Manual.

53   42 CFR §483.40(c).

54   42 CFR §483.40, Surveyor's Guideline to 42 CFR §483.40, Appendix PP to CMS State Operation Manual.

55   42 CFR §483.40, Surveyor's Guideline to 42 CFR §483.40, Appendix PP to CMS State Operation Manual.

56   Surveyor's Guideline to 42 CFR §483.40, Appendix PP to CMS State Operation Manual.

- ○ *Ordered a patient's transfer to the hospital?*
- ○ *Supervised nurse practitioners or physician assistants when follow-up visits were delegated to them?*
- ○ *Provided consultation or treatment when contacted by the facility?*
- ○ *Recorded the patient's progress and problems in maintaining or improving their health status?*

- *carry out doctors' orders and arrange all necessary diagnostic and therapeutic services recommended by the patient's physician, podiatrist, dentist or clinical psychologist?*
- *help the patient arrange transportation to and from a service location if the patient needed services that cannot be brought into the facility?*
- *notify the patient's attending physician promptly of significant changes, such as:*
  - ○ a sudden or marked adverse change in signs, symptoms or behavior;
  - ○ an unusual occurrence involving the patient;
  - ○ a change in weight of five pounds or more within a 30-day period;
  - ○ an untoward response to a medication or treatment;
  - ○ a life threatening medication or treatment error; or
  - ○ a threat to the patient's health or safety caused by the facility's inability to obtain or administer prescribed drugs, equipment, supplies or services in a timely fashion.
- *ensure that substitute doctors were available to provide supervision and emergency medical care whenever the patient's physicians were unavailable?*[57]

---

57   42 CFR §483.40.

Pressure Sores

Patients who lie or sit in one position for long periods are at risk of developing pressure sores,(also known as *bedsores* or *decubitus ulcers*), which occur when pressure on the skin shuts off blood vessels, depriving skin tissue of oxygen and nutrients. If proper care is not given, large, deep sores can develop, sometimes exposing the muscle or bone beneath the skin. Untreated pressure sores can lead to infection, severe pain and death. Generally, pressure sores can be prevented with proper care.[58]

Did the nursing home staff:

- *let a patient who is bed-bound and cannot reposition himself/herself lie in the same position for more than 2 hours?*

- *let a patient in a wheelchair who cannot reposition himself/herself sit without being repositioned for more than 1 hour?*

- *allow a patient who entered the facility without a pressure sore to develop a pressure sore?*

- *allow a patient with a pressure sore to go without treatment to promote healing and prevent infection?[59]*

- *fail to keep a resident's skin clean and dry?*

- *fail to consistently use pressure relieving devices, such as pads and special mattresses*

- *fail to ensure that a bed-bound patient had his/her heels elevated off the mattress?*

- *fail to notify the patient's family and physician when a pressure sore first developed?*

- *fail to relieve pressure from a pressure sore, once it developed, in order to allow the wound to heal?*

- *fail to ensure that a patient received proper nutrition and hydration necessary for healthy skin?*

---

58   CMS' Resident Assessment Instrument Version 2.0 Manual, Appendix C, §16 (Pressure Ulcers), Page C–84, revised December 2002.

59   42 CFR §483.25(c).

• *fail to promptly notify the resident's physician if a pressure sore treatment order was not effective*

Preventing Accidents

Falls and accidents are a serious concern for nursing home patients and facilities have a responsibility to take measures to prevent them. Approximately 50% of nursing home patients fall annually, and 10% of these falls cause serious injury, especially hip fractures.[60]

Did the nursing home fail to:

   ◦ *identify a patient as a fall risk and develop a plan of care with interventions to help keep him/her safe?* If a patient has fallen, been injured, or is considered at risk for falling, his/her care plan must individually address this concern and identify steps to be taken to improve safety.

   ◦ *keep a patient's environment as free of accident hazards as possible (e.g., tripping hazards, slick floors, cords and tubing, etc.)?*

   ◦ *provide a patient with adequate supervision to prevent accidents?*

   ◦ *provide adequate assistive devices to help improve resident safety?*[61]

   ◦ *provide adequate lighting?*

   ◦ *provide sufficient staff to safely assist the patient with transfers?*

   ◦ *use a gait belt to safely assist a patient when one was needed?*

   ◦ *ensure that bed rails were in their proper position?*

   ◦ *answer call lights when patients needed assistance getting up?*

   ◦ *provide sufficient staff to respond to personal alarms in a timely fashion?*

---

60   CMS' Resident Assessment Instrument Version 2.0 Manual, Appendix C, §11 (Falls), Page C–59, revised December 2002.

61   42 CFR §483.25(h).

- ○ *provide bedside mats for a patient at risk of falling from his/her bed?*
- ○ *ensure that the bed was in a lowered position for a patient who is at risk of falling out of bed?*
- ○ *take into account the patient's personal risk factors in assessing their fall risk?*
- ○ *lock a patient's wheelchair wheels when they were supposed to?*

Special Services

Did the nursing home fail to ensure that a patient received proper treatment and care for:[62]

- *injections?*
- *IV fluids?*
- *a colostomy?*
- *a ureterostomy?*
- *an ileostomy?*
- *a tracheostomy?*
- *tracheal suctioning?*
- *respiratory care?*
- *foot care?*
- *a prostheses?*

Federal law requires that these services be provided if a patient needs them, regardless of whether they're covered by Medicare or Medicaid.[63] For services not covered, a nursing home is required to assist the patient in securing any available resources to obtain the needed services.

---

62   42 CFR §483.25(k).

63   Surveyor's Guideline to 42 CFR §483.25(k), Appendix PP to CMS State Operation Manual.

Therapy Services
(Therapies, Restorative Care and Range of Motion):

Nursing home patients often need specialized rehabilitative services to restore lost abilities caused by strokes, broken bones or other conditions. The nursing home must provide needed therapy services, no matter who's paying for the nursing home stay.[64]

Did the nursing home staff:

- *fail to ensure that a patient received the therapy needed to reach his/her highest practicable level of functioning?*[65] (Includes therapy services such as, but not limited to, physical therapy, occupational therapy, speech–language pathology and mental health rehabilitative services.[66])

- *improperly shorten therapy by claiming that a patient is not improving or has plateaued?* Medicare rules say that improvement is not necessary. Therapy services can be covered if they're needed to prevent further deterioration or preserve current capabilities.[67]

- *illegally halt formal therapy services when a patient exhausted Medicare skilled nursing facility coverage?* Specialized rehabilitative services are a covered Medicaid service and must be provided to patients who need them without charge.[68]

- *fail to ensure that, as formal therapy services were ending, the therapist established a care plan that continues needed exercises and other services with the help of facility nursing staff ("restorative care")?* For example, a patient recovering from a fractured hip may need assistance with daily walking, which should continue as long as needed without any extra fee if Medicare is paying for the patient's nursing home care.

---

64   42 USC §1396r(c)(4)(A).
65   42 USC §1395r(b)(4)(A)(i).
66   42 CFR §483.45(a).
67   42 CFR §409.32.
68   Surveyor's Guideline to 42 CFR §483.45(a), Appendix PP to CMS State Operation Manual.

- *fail to ensure routine care for "range of motion exercises" with the hands, arms, legs and feet so the patient didn't lose joint mobility or develop contractures (freezing of the joint in a contracted position), unless it was medically unavoidable? Did the facility offer appropriate treatment and services if the patient has limited range of motion?*[69] Preventive care may include exercise of the joints performed by the patient, with or without assistance by staff. Range of motion exercises, however, should never be used as a substitute for patients who need specialized therapies from licensed therapists.

Vision, Dental and Hearing Care

Did the nursing home fail to:

- *ensure that a patient's care plan comprehensively addressed his/her dental, vision and hearing services needs?*
- *assist a patient in obtaining routine (annual exam) and emergency dental care?*[70] An "emergency" involves pain or other dental problem that requires immediate attention.[71]
- *make a prompt referral to a dentist and to aggressively work at replacing lost or damaged dentures?*[72]
- *arrange treatment to maintain a patient's ability to see or hear?*[73]
- *make necessary appointments and arrange transportation for services received away from the facility for a patient who needed hearing or vision care or assistive devices?*[74] Assistive devices includes glasses, contact lenses, magnifying glasses and hearing aids.[75]

---

69   42 CFR §483.25(e).

70   42 CFR §483.55.

71   Surveyor's Guideline to 42 CFR §483.55, Appendix PP to CMS State Operation Manual.

72   42 CFR §483.55, Surveyor's Guideline to 42 CFR §483.55, Appendix PP to CMS State Operation Manual.

73   42 CFR §483.25(b).

74   42 CFR §483.25(b), Surveyor's Guideline to 42 CFR §483.25(b), Appendix PP to CMS State Operation Manual.

75   Surveyor's Guideline to 42 CFR §483.25(b), Appendix PP to CMS State Operation Manual.

- *help the patient and family locate and utilize any available community resources or payment programs, including Medicare and Medicaid?*[76]

WHAT TO EXPECT WHEN YOU FILE A COMPLAINT

What happens after a complaint is filed?

Once a complaint about a nursing home is registered, investigations are conducted. Investigations of complaints that result in health deficiency citations are reported to Centers for Medicare and Medicaid Services (CMS) and included on the Nursing Home Compare website.

While each State has its own agency that investigates nursing home complaints, the process is more or less the same in each state. Regardless of which communication method you choose to file your complaint (e.g, email, fax, etc.), you'll typically be notified within 7-10 days that your complaint has been received and that an investigation will follow. You may be given a general (and often vague) timeline as to when the complaint will be investigated. Because investigators do not want the nursing homes to know when they'll be entering the facility, the exact date and time will likely not be provided.

Typically, once the investigator arrives at the facility to begin the investigation, he or she will contact the complainant to obtain additional information. You may be asked for specific details about your issues of concern, names of any witnesses, photographs evidencing neglect or abuse, etc. The investigation may take several days to complete. During a typical investigation, the investigator:

- reviews patient charts;

- speaks with patients and staff members;

- reviews hospital records if a hospitalization resulted from the neglect or abuse; and

---

76   Surveyor's Guideline to 42 CFR §483.25(b), Appendix PP to CMS State Operation Manual.

- reviews the facility's policies and procedures, staffing schedules, and other documentation that may help the investigator substantiate the complaint or determine if there are any care deficiencies for which the facility may be cited.

If investigators find that a nursing home doesn't meet a specific standard, they issue a *deficiency citation*. The federal government may then impose sanctions or penalties on a nursing home for serious deficiencies, or for deficiencies that the nursing home fails to correct for a long period of time. For example, Centers for Medicare and Medicaid Services (CMS) has the authority assess a fine, deny payment to the nursing home, assign a temporary manager, install a State monitor, or even terminate Federal payments to a nursing home facility.

State governments may also impose penalties on nursing homes. (These citations aren't listed on Nursing Home Compare, but information about them may be available on your State website.)

If the facility is cited for deficiencies, the facility is given 10 calendar days in which to respond with a Plan of Correction (PoC) for each cited deficiency. The PoC identifies the ways in which the facility promises to remedy the deficiencies. It's not uncommon for the State to reject the nursing home's initial Plan of Correction and require another one that better addresses the problems. If the facility does not comply with all conditions or requirements within the time period accepted as reasonable, the State agency certifies "noncompliance."

Once the investigation has been completed, any deficiencies cited, and any required plans of correction approved, the agency issues a Form HFCA-2567 report, which identifies the citations and the Plan of Correction. Incidentally, every nursing home that provides Medicare- or Medicaid-funded services is required to make the results of its last full inspection available at the nursing home for the public to review. The Nursing Home Compare website gives you access to all reports from the last year.

The State investigator will send a copy of the 2567 report to you, typically, within 30 days or so after filing the complaint. This timeline may vary from complaint to complaint, and from State to State. Some types of complaints take longer to investigate than others. Also, nursing home complaints are typically investigated in order of severity. For example, complaints involving immediate threats to a patient's health care and safety receive top priority, as do complaints involving widespread problems that affect a number of patients.

State investigators have the authority to review all records (not just those of the complainant), which allows them to spot trends in care deficiencies as is illustrated by the following excerpt from an interview with a former state nursing home investigator…

> *Q: Are there any fall cases that stick out in your mind —?*
>
> *A: I have a lot, yeah. And sometimes, the staff would call in complaints. So I went there, and they said, "Well, it was all about staffing." And I'm thinking, "Well, no, they told me falls and broken legs." So I thought, "Okay, so we'll kind of go around, see what's going on here." And it was a big facility. …So I start looking at these charts, and I must have had ten spiral fractures. Easily.*
>
> *Q: And those are bad, or you know they're caused from--…?*
>
> *A: Their feet don't turn. And I was able to track it down, it was the same aide. It was either evening shift or night shift, and all these spiral fractures. So then, I said, "Well, didn't you think this was odd?" And they said, "Well, they all have osteoporosis." And I said, "Well, we didn't have a problem with spiral fractures before we came in and before this one person started working. Don't you think there's a problem here?" They never even threw red flags, nothing. Nothing.*
>
> *Q: And how — a fairly short period of time that all those happened in —?*
>
> *A: Yeah, probably within a two-week period.*

How to Interpret the Investigation Report (Form 2567)

Your investigation report (2567) will include a cover letter that identifies the investigator's key findings, what will happen if the nursing home does not achieve substantial compliance, and a list of the essential elements required for an acceptable Plan of Correction. The 2567 report will consist of several forms or pages and include a summary statement of the deficiencies found and the regulation that applies to each deficiency.

> **MYTH:** Only a patient or a patient's family can file a complaint with state investigators.
>
> **REALITY:** Anyone, including visitors to the facility and employees of the nursing home can file a complaint, anonymously if desired.

In the next chapter, *Researching Nursing Homes*, you'll find a sample 2567 report, as well as a complete guide to interpreting the investigator's findings. While reading a 2567 report, you must bear in mind that it's only a one-time snapshot of the quality of care that a nursing home is providing. The quality of care can grow much better or much worse in a short period of time. When a nursing home's administrator, ownership, or finances suddenly change, the quality of care can change dramatically, as well. The next chapter will show you how to conduct deeper research into the quality of care a particular nursing home provides.

HOW TO FILE A COMPLAINT

Who can file a complaint?

Anyone with knowledge or concerns about the care of a nursing home patient may file a complaint with their State Survey Agency, including the patient herself/himself, family members, guardians or other patient representatives, persons who are simply visiting the nursing, and even the nursing home facility staff, for example.

The complainant's name and any specific medical information provided in the complaint is confidential. In fact, complaints can be filed anonymously.

Where do you file the complaint?

File the complaint with your State Survey Agency, which has regulatory responsibility for all the nursing homes in your State. You may file a complaint by any means available to you; typically, one of the following methods:

- calling a complaint hot line
- mailing a complaint
- emailing a complaint
- using an online form
- faxing a complaint

Some states provide their own complaint forms. Here you'll find a complete list of all State Survey Agencies with contact information:

https://www.medicare.gov/NursingHomeCompare/Resources/State-Websites.html.

Some states provide online complaint forms on their websites. If your state doesn't have its own complaint form, you may use the template available at www.AbusesAndExcuses.org. However, you're not required to use any particular template, or to limit your information to only the information requested on that template.

Your state's complaint form will be a tool to assist you in identifying information helpful to the investigator in evaluating the care issue, but the form is not required. You may simply send an email, fax or letter that includes all the pertinent information. If you call the Toll-free Complaint Line, the intake specialist taking your call will likely ask similar questions.

What details should the complaint include?

Prior to contacting your State investigatory agency, it's helpful to prepare a summary and logs of events related to the problem. Take time to make notes on what occurred in order to fully document your complaint. Provide investigators with as many details as possible to ensure that they can effectively investigate your complaint.

The following list reflects the types of questions that the investigator will ask during the complaint intake process. Although it's not mandatory to provide all the information listed below, it will be helpful for the investigative process:

- **Your Contact Information.** Include complete contact information so that the investigator can contact you for additional information and provide you with survey results.

- **Facility Name & Location**

- **Dates of Incident(s)** (if a specific date is applicable) If there is no specific date, include time period information (e.g., weekdays, weekends, within the last week, within the last month, etc.).

- **Time of Day (or shift)** during which the problem was observed or was most prevalent (e.g., 7 a.m., day shift, evening shift, night shift, etc.).

- **Individuals/Caregivers Involved.** List individuals (or departments) involved in the concern you're reporting (e.g., nursing staff, certified nurse aides, dietary staff, etc.) and how each individual was involved.

- **Specifics of the Concern.** Be as specific as possible — this greatly increases the likelihood that the problem will be discovered and confirmed by surveyors. Example: If you're dissatisfied with meal service, describe the aspect you are dissatisfied with (e.g., food temperature, presentation, taste, wrong diet, etc.). If you think the facility is unsanitary, specifically identify what conditions make it unsanitary (e.g., dust, debris, soiled floors, etc.).

- **Timely Reporting.** File your complaint as soon as possible following the initial occurrence of a problem. It's difficult for investigators to effectively gather information surrounding an incident that occurred months before.

And remember, your local Ombudsman program can provide guidance and answer questions about filing complaints and the investigation process.

TIPS

The following tips will help ensure that investigators have all the information they need...

1. Often, people who file complaints later realize that they forgot to include critical details. So, take a few minutes to organize your thoughts before contacting the State. Write your list of concerns and complaints and organize them, if possible, from the most pressing concerns to the least. This list will help ensure that you don't forget any important issues when filing your complaint. If the State is unaware of one of your complaints, it likely won't be investigated.

2. Try to provide investigators with the names of all employees or other witnesses who may be able to provide additional information. If you only know a first name, include a description of the individual to help investigators locate those who may have the most knowledge about your area of concern. Nursing home employees should wear identification badges that will provide you with at least partial names.

3. If the problem is occurring on a particular shift, be sure to advise the investigators of when the incidents are occurring. For example, if you notice that employees are not turning and repositioning patients on the third shift, it's helpful for the investigator to be able to observe what's going on during the time period in question.

4. Provide the investigator with the dates on which the problems have occurred if you can. For example, if your complaint involves the patient suffering several falls, try to provide the dates on which the falls occurred. Unfortunately, nursing home staff don't always record incidents that may pose liability problems. In other cases, while they may have recorded an incident, the particular page on which the incident was recorded may have been removed from the chart by facility management. By providing dates, the investigator can review the patient's chart and speak with individuals who would have been present at that time in an effort to determine what really transpired.

5. If possible, provide photos of any patient injuries (such as a pressure sore or unexplained bruise) to the investigator. Sometimes injuries or wounds are not properly recorded by staff in the patient's chart. If the patient's chart doesn't accurately depict the severity of the injury, photographs can help the investigator prove it.

6. If you need to include many details, it may help to type your summary and offer to email or fax it to the investigator. If your State accepts complaints by email or fax, this method of registering your complaint may be more efficient and ensure that all details are included. It's not necessary to provide the investigator with a short novel, but it is important to make sure you include the critical facts of each concern you have.

7. Be sure to provide accurate contact information (including the best time to reach you) so that the investigator can follow up with you. It's not uncommon for investigators to struggle to reach complainants to obtain additional information. If investigators can't get the information they need, it can impact their ability to properly evaluate the complaint in a timely fashion.

8. Don't wait too long to file your complaint. It can negatively impact the investigator's ability to conduct the review in several ways. First, the longer a problem goes unaddressed, the more potential that problem has to harm the same or other patients. If there are serious issues within the facility that need to be addressed, the issue should be addressed as soon as possible. Second, the longer one waits to file a complaint, the greater the odds that the nursing home employees with knowledge of the problem may no longer be employed at the facility. Nursing homes are notorious for their high turnover rates. If the investigator cannot interview a key witness, that can certainly impact the investigation. Third, memories tend to fade over time, so it's important to allow the investigator to access important witnesses while the recollections of the events is fresh in their minds.

ADDITIONAL RESOURCES

- Templates for filing a complaint: www.AbusesAndExcuses.org
- Nursing Home Compare website: https://www.medicare.gov/nursinghomecompare/search.html?

12

RESEARCHING NURSING HOMES

Whoever wishes to foresee the future must consult the
past; for human events ever resemble those of preceding
times. This arises from the fact that they are produced by
men who ever have been, and ever shall be, animated by
the same passions, and thus they necessarily have the
same results.

— **Niccolò Machiavelli**

What's the best strategy for preventing abuse and neglectful care of you
or your loved one? Choose a nursing home that doesn't allow these gross care
failures to happen in the first place. Of course, that's easier said than done.

Most of us don't take much interest in monitoring the quality of care
provided by our local nursing homes until it becomes necessary to place
ourselves or a loved one in one of these facilities. This need often arises rather
suddenly, with little warning. Here's how it can happen…

A patient suffers a fall, injury, or the onset of an acute illness, which
necessitates surgery or other treatment, which, in turn, necessitates either
a short-term nursing home admission for recovery and rehabilitation,
or perhaps even long-term residency. This moment in time represents a
major life change, yet the patient and his or her family typically have little
experience or information to guide them during this critical time. What's
more, the decision as to which nursing home facility should be chosen must
often be made quickly, and unfortunately, usually against the backdrop of
the physical and emotional exhaustion of coping with the precipitating
injury or illness itself, with hospitalization or other stressful interventions
and the possible long-term ramifications of these events.

It's not uncommon for families to be approached at the hospital around the time of discharge by nursing home representatives attempting to sell their facilities. The problem is that glossy brochures and slick, engaging sales presentations by nursing home marketers provide very little factual information about the quality of care that the facility actually provides. Neither does the meticulous landscaping, the stylish, designer-decorated lobby, or the swanky dining room they point out during your tour. While a nursing home should be capable of providing all of those amenities too, they're just window dressing. The issue that really matters is: What is the *quality of the patient care* that this nursing home provides?

While the information available to the public is much more limited than it should be, there *is* information available that will provide clues as to the quality of care a facility provides if you know where to look and how to interpret what you find. At the very least, being armed with this knowledge will enable you to ask facility representatives and marketers the hard but critical questions about the level of care the facility has provided in the past and steps that are being taken to ensure that the care provided to you or your loved one in the future meets acceptable quality standards.

In this chapter, you'll learn how to research nursing homes in your chosen geographic area to obtain critical information about not only the size of the facility, types of payment they accept, and who owns and operates the facility, but most importantly, information about staffing, the results of government inspections, and the quality of care these facilities provide.

HOW TO RESEARCH NURSING HOMES WITH *NURSING HOME COMPARE*

Every nursing home that provides Medicare- or Medicaid-funded services is required to make the results of its last full inspection available at the nursing home for the public to review. When visiting a nursing home, you should be able to view, upon request, the nursing home's most recent Form HFCA-2567, *Statement of Deficiencies* investigation report (referred to as "2567"). It can be an invaluable research tool. In fact, if the nursing home doesn't make it readily available for review, that may be a red flag.

You can also review a facility's past 2567 reports online on Medicare. gov's website Nursing Home Compare, which is funded and managed by the U.S. Centers for Medicare & Medicaid Services. (The special section at the end of this chapter, "How to Interpret the Investigation Report (Form 2567)," will discuss the 2567 in depth.)

To begin researching nursing homes in your area, visit Nursing Home Compare at:

https://www.medicare.gov/nursinghomecompare/search.html. (Includes a Spanish language option.)

In addition to publishing 2567 reports, Nursing Home Compare provides information on:

- 5-star quality ratings of overall and individual star performance on health inspections, quality measures, and hours of care provided per patient by staff performing nursing care tasks.

- Health and fire-safety inspections with detailed and summary information about deficiencies found during the three most recent comprehensive inspections (conducted annually) and the last three years of complaint investigations.

- Staffing information about the number of registered nurses, licensed practical or vocational nurses, physical therapists and nursing assistants in each nursing home.

- A set of quality measures that describe the quality of care in nursing homes, including percentage of patients with pressure sores, urinary incontinence and more.

- Penalties imposed against a nursing home.

You'll be greeted with an initial "Find a nursing home..." search box (pictured below) that enables you to enter a geographic location or the name of a specific nursing home facility to begin your search.

The search results allow you to explore multiple facets of any nursing home. For example, following are partial results from a search for nursing homes in the 46202 zip code in Indianapolis, Indiana, which found 90 nursing home facilities located within 25 miles of the center of the 46202 area code:

On the search results page, you can view the location of the facilities on a map by clicking "Go to map view" at the top of the right sidebar. Here, you can also filter or further refine your search by location, overall ratings or other characteristics.

Click the green "Add to Compare" buttons that appear within each facility's listing to compare up to three facilities that you want to examine more closely.

The search results page provides summary location and distance, as well as the five-star ratings for each facility in four separate categories (Overall, Health Inspections, Staffing, Quality Measures) that we discussed in *Chapter 2: Tip of the Iceberg.*

MYTH: All information posted on the Nursing Home Compare website has been verified as being accurate.

REALITY: Some of the data, such as information related to staffing levels and quality measures, are derived from data reported by the nursing home.

According to the Nursing Home Compare website, the star ratings are calculated as follows:

- **Health inspections rating:** Health inspection ratings are based on the 3 most recent comprehensive (annual) inspections, and inspections due to complaints in the last 3 years. More emphasis is placed on recent inspections.

- **Quality measures (QM) rating:** The values on 16 QMs are combined (a subset of the 24 QMs listed on Nursing Home Compare) to create the QM star-rating. Like staffing levels, QMs are derived from clinical data reported by the nursing home.

- **Staffing rating:** Staffing ratings are based on 2 measures: 1) Registered Nurse (RN) hours per patient per day; and 2) total staffing hours per patient per day. Total staffing includes: RNs; Licensed Practical Nurses (LPNs) or Licensed Vocational Nurses (LVNs); and Certified Nurse Aids (CNAs). Staffing data are submitted by the facility and are adjusted for the needs of the nursing home patients. Keep in mind that any data that is self-reported by the facility may be subject to manipulation to boost their ratings, and thus suspect.

- The **overall 5-star ratings** are assigned by following these five steps:

- Start with the health inspections rating.

- Add 1 star if the staffing rating is 4 or 5 stars and greater than the health inspections rating. Subtract 1 star if the staffing rating is 1 star.

- Add 1 star if the quality measures rating is 5 stars; subtract 1 star if the quality measures rating is 1 star.

- If the health inspections rating is 1 star, the overall rating cannot be upgraded by more than 1 star based on the staffing and quality measure ratings.

- If a nursing home is a special focus facility, the maximum overall rating is 3 stars.

DRILLING DOWN FOR MORE INFORMATION

On the facility results page, click the name of a particular nursing home and you'll see a screen that looks like this:

General Information

In addition to showing the five-star ratings, the "General Information" screen will provide additional information including:

- The number of "certified beds" indicates how many beds have been approved by the federal government to participate in Medicare or Medicaid funding.

- The type of ownership (e.g., "private for profit corporation," "non-profit corporation," "religious affiliated organization," or "government entity"). It should be noted that these designations can be complicated and misleading. For example, in Indiana, county hospitals are purchasing nursing homes and are technically considered the "owners;" however, many hire private for-profit corporations to "operate" the nursing home and essentially oversee every aspect of the business. You can click the "Get More Ownership Information" link at the bottom of the page to obtain more detailed information about who is directly involved in the operation and management of the facility. You'll see a screen like this one:

Ownership Information

NORTH CAPITOL NURSING & REHABILITATION CENTER
2010 N CAPITOL AVE
INDIANAPOLIS, IN 46202
(317) 924-5821

Ownership: Government - City/county
Legal Business Name: THE HEALTH AND HOSPITAL CORPORATION OF MARION COUNTY

Owners and Managers of NORTH CAPITOL NURSING & REHABILITATION CENTER

5% OR GREATER DIRECT OWNERSHIP INTEREST
THE HEALTH AND HOSPITAL CORPORATION OF MARION COUNTY (100%), since 12/01/2003

OPERATIONAL/MANAGERIAL CONTROL
AMERICAN SENIOR COMMUNITIES, since 12/01/2003
DAVENPORT, EDNA, since 11/19/2012
JACKSON-KENNY, TORON, since 03/24/2012
PATEL, SONIA, since 11/01/2015

OFFICER
GUTWEIN, MATTHEW, since 12/02/2002

MANAGING EMPLOYEE
JACKSON, MARK, since 09/15/2015

- Whether the facility has automatic sprinkler systems in all areas to protect the patients.

- Whether the nursing home has a patient and family council to help facilitate communications with staff and resolve problems. You can speak with council patients to find out what they perceive to be the strengths and weaknesses of the facility. If the facility doesn't have a patient or family council, ask the administrator why not, since the law requires nursing homes to allow them.

In addition to exploring the "General Information" about a facility (as shown in the above screenshot), you can click the other four tabs at the top for a wealth of information about "Health, Fire, and Safety Inspections," "Staffing," "Quality Measures," and "Penalties."

Staffing

Click the "Staffing" tab to learn more about: total number of licensed nurses; the number of RN, LPN/LVN and CNA hours per patient per day, as well as the physical therapy staff hours per patient per day. If, in place of data representing the staff statistics, you encounter "not available" or "not enough data available to calculate a star rating," make it a point to ask representatives of prospective facilities these questions.

Quality Measures

Click the "Quality Measures" tab for statistical percentages (and graphs) of patients with the following conditions…

Long-stay patients:

- **% who experienced one or more falls with major injury.** This information may indicate whether the facility has developed and implemented effective fall prevention strategies. Nursing homes can and should take many preventive measures not only to prevent falls, but also to prevent injuries from falls. Yet tragically, too many patients are allowed to fall needlessly, and one third of falls among nursing home patients results in injury, often serious injuries such as bone fractures, joint dislocation, head trauma or subdural hematomas, which can be life-threatening. A high percentage of falls may be indicate a facility that is understaffed, and cannot provide adequate assistance for, and supervision of, its patients.

- **% who have a urinary tract infection.** This information may indicate whether the nursing home facility has effectively implemented policies and procedures to reduce the risk of UTIs and other infections. Poor hygiene, improper catheter care, and failing to ensure patients receive adequate hydration, among other things, can put patients at unnecessary risk of developing a UTI. Early recognition and effective treatment of a UTI can prevent the infection from becoming more serious or causing further, and potentially life-threatening, complications.

- **% who self-report moderate to severe pain.** This information may indicate whether the facility has effectively implemented pain management strategies. Inadequately managed pain may lead to other problems in that if pain isn't properly treated, a patient may not be able to perform daily routines, may become depressed, or have an overall poor quality of life.

- **% who are high-risk patients with pressure ulcers.** Pressure ulcers (also known as pressure sores and decubitus ulcers) are very serious injuries which can be indicative of substandard nursing care. Most pressure sores are avoidable if proper pressure sore prevention measures are taken. Pressure sores can be indicative of a nursing home that is understaffed, because one of the key interventions to prevent them is to turn and reposition the patient diligently, which takes nursing time.

- **% who are low-risk patients who lose control of their bowels or bladder.** Loss of bowel or bladder control is not merely "a normal sign of aging" and can often be successfully treated. It's the nursing home's responsibility to assess the cause of loss of bladder or bowel control and properly treat the underlying condition to prevent infections and pressure ulcers, as well as restore dignity, quality of life and social interaction. High percentages of patients with bladder or bowel control problems may indicate negligence in treating conditions such as: constipation, muscle weakness, bladder infection; toilet location problems (the bathroom is too far away); adverse reaction to medication; limited ability to walk or move around; improper diet and fluid intake; toilet routine problems; lack of mobility assistance; failure to assess certain associated medical conditions such as, diabetes, dementia, spinal cord injury, or neurological disease.

- **% who have/had a catheter inserted and left in their bladders.** This information may shed light on whether the facility is understaffed or is otherwise providing substandard care. A catheter should only be used when medically necessary, never for the convenience of the nursing home staff. Too often, nursing homes catheterize patients because they don't have sufficient staff to assist their patients with their toileting needs. Catheter use can result in complications such as urinary tract or blood infections, physical injury, skin problems, bladder stones, or blood in the urine. Over many years, indwelling catheters may increase the rates of bladder cancer in patients with spinal cord injuries.

- **% who were physically restrained.** This information may also be indicative of an understaffed facility. Some facilities have used restraints as a substitute for implementing proper fall precautions, including adequate supervision, simply because they did not provide sufficient staffing to carry out those interventions. Restraints should only be used when they're necessary as part of the treatment of a patient's medical condition (and only on a doctor's orders), never for the convenience of the nursing home staff, or to punish a patient. Restrained patients can become weak, lose their ability to go to the bathroom by themselves, develop pressure sores or other medical problems, and suffer severe injuries and even death due to the restraint.

- **% whose ability to move independently worsened.** It's the nursing home's responsibility to maintain a patient's independence in moving as much as possible. Patients who experience a decline in their ability to move independently also require more staff time than those who are more independent.

- **% whose need for help with daily activities has increased.** Nursing home staff must encourage patients to do as much as they can for themselves, which fosters better health and enhances quality of life.

- **% who lose too much weight.** A loss of 5% or more of body weight in one month is typically considered unhealthy. Too much weight loss may mean that the patient is depressed, isn't being properly fed or the facility has a poor nutrition program, their medical care isn't properly managed, or they have a medical problem that makes eating difficult and require special assistance that they may not be receiving.

- **% who have depressive symptoms.** Depression lessens quality of life and can lead to other health problems. While nursing home patients are at a high risk for developing depression and anxiety for many reasons, it's the facility's responsibility to provide proper prevention and treatment (e.g., medication, therapy, social support) measures.

- **% who received an anti-anxiety or hypnotic medication.** This information may be indicative of a nursing home that is inadequately staffed to provided necessary supervision, and thus compensates by overusing medications to keep patients "manageable." Nursing homes may appropriately use anti-anxiety or hypnotic medications for a limited period of time to treat acute symptoms, but high use rates of these medications may point to inadequate or incompetent assessment of patients and/or overuse of medications. Ask facility staff about their approach to managing patient behavior. Interventions that don't require medications, such as higher staffing ratios and offering many and varied activities, are often successful at reducing the use of psychotropic medications.

- **% who were assessed and given, appropriately, the seasonal influenza vaccine.** Patients are to be given a flu shot during the flu season (October through March). People who are 65 and older are at higher risk for developing serious life-threatening medical complications from the flu.

- **% who were assessed and given, appropriately, the pneumococcal vaccine.** Patients should be asked if they've been vaccinated for pneumonia, and if not, should be given the pneumococcal shot unless there's a medical reason why they shouldn't receive it. It may help prevent or lower the risk of becoming seriously ill from pneumonia caused by bacteria.

- **% who received an antipsychotic medication.** Ask facility staff about their approach to managing behavior. Interventions that don't require medications, such as higher staffing ratios and many and varied activities, have been shown to be successful at reducing the use of antipsychotic medications in many cases. Antipsychotics tend to have side effects and, according to the FDA, are associated with an increased risk of death for elderly patients with dementia; thus, these medications must be administered appropriately.

Short-stay patients:

- **% who made improvements in function.** Short-stay patients generally have limitations in physical functioning because of illness, hospitalization, or surgery. It's the nursing home's responsibility to improve functioning and increase independence so that patients can be discharged.

- **% who were re-hospitalized after a nursing home admission.** If a nursing home sends many patients back to the hospital, it may indicate that the nursing home isn't properly assessing or taking care of patients.

- **% who have had an outpatient emergency department visit.** If a nursing home regularly sends many patients to the emergency room, it may indicate that the staff isn't properly assessing or taking care of patients to prevent the development of conditions that require emergency treatment. It may also be indicative of a facility that has inadequate staffing and supervision to prevent falls, accidents, and the development of serious conditions such as pressure sores.

- **% who were successfully discharged to the community.** High rates of successful discharge, or a patient remaining in the community for at least a month, may indicate that the nursing home is restoring a patients' functioning so that they may successfully return to the community.

- **% who self-report moderate to severe pain.** (See insights under "Long-stay patients")

- **% with pressure ulcers that are new or worsened.** (See insights under "Long-stay patients")

- **% who were assessed and given, appropriately, the seasonal influenza vaccine.** (See insights under "Long-stay patients")

- **% who were assessed and given, appropriately, the pneumococcal vaccine.** (See insights under "Long-stay patients")

- **% who newly received an antipsychotic medication.** (See insights under "Long-stay patients")

Health, Fire and Safety Inspections

Click the "Health, Fire and Safety Inspections" tab for a summary of the most recent health inspection reports, which includes information about recent complaints filed, the number of deficiencies found in recent inspections and more.

To read a complete 2567 report, click the "View full report" link to view the most recent 2567 report. To read past health inspection summaries and view the associated 2567 reports, click the "View all health inspections" link.

HOW TO INTERPRET THE INVESTIGATION REPORT (FORM 2567)

Your Form 2567 investigation report will include a cover letter that identifies the investigator's key findings, what will happen if the nursing home does not achieve substantial compliance, and the essential elements required for an acceptable Plan of Correction, which states how and when the deficiency will be corrected.

The report will include several forms or pages and include a Summary Statement of Deficiencies found, along with the regulation(s) designed to prevent each deficiency.

The 2567 report will look like this…

(X4) ID PREFIX TAG	SUMMARY STATEMENT OF DEFICIENCIES (EACH DEFICIENCY MUST BE PRECEDED BY FULL REGULATORY OR LSC IDENTIFYING INFORMATION)	ID PREFIX TAG	PROVIDER'S PLAN OF CORRECTION (EACH CORRECTIVE ACTION SHOULD BE CROSS-REFERENCED TO THE APPROPRIATE DEFICIENCY)	(X5) COMPLETION DATE
F000314 SS=D	483.25(c) TREATMENT/SVCS TO PREVENT/HEAL PRESSURE SORES Based on the comprehensive assessment of a resident, the facility must ensure that a resident who enters the facility without pressure sores does not develop pressure sores unless the individual's clinical condition demonstrates that they were unavoidable; and a resident having pressure sores receives necessary treatment and services to promote healing, prevent infection and prevent new sores from developing.			

Sample 2567 Report

Understanding F-Tags

Once your complaint has been investigated, each deficiency will be assigned an ID Prefix Number — a F tag number (known as a "F-tag"). The numerical F-XXX tags (e.g., F000314, etc.) correspond to federal nursing home regulation identifiers. (For a list of F-tags, see www.AbusesAndExcuses. org.)

Each F-tag in your report will be assigned an alphabetical ranking or *SS ranking* of *A* through *L* (e.g., *SS=D*), listed directly under the F-tag number, which describes the Scope and Severity (SS) level of each deficiency. *Scope* describes how many patients are affected by the deficiency. *Severity* indicates the level of harm to health and/or safety.

The scope and severity of deficiencies are reflected in this Federal Scope and Severity Grid, which is explained below…

	ISOLATED	PATTERN	WIDESPREAD
Level IV Immediate Jeopardy to Resident Health or Safety	J	K	L
Level III Actual Harm that is not Immediate Jeopardy	G	H	I
Level II No Actual Harm with Potential for More than Minimal Harm that is not Immediate Jeopardy	D	E	F
Level I No Actual Harm with Potential for Minimal Harm	A	B	C

Here's how to interpret the SS rankings in terms of assessing the severity and scope of a deficiency:

- *A* means the deficiency is *isolated*, resulted in *no actual harm* but has the *potential for minimal harm* (Level I Severity), and the facility was found to be in *substantial compliance*.

- *B* means the deficiency is *part of a pattern*, resulted in *no actual harm* but has the *potential for minimal harm* (Level I Severity), and the facility was found to be in *substantial compliance*.

- *C* means the deficiency is *widespread*, resulted in *no actual harm* but has the *potential for minimal harm* (Level I Severity), and the facility was found to be in *substantial compliance*.

- *D* means the deficiency is *isolated*, resulted in *no actual harm* but has the *potential for more than minimal harm that is not immediate jeopardy* (Level II Severity), and the facility was found to be in *noncompliance*.

- *E* means the deficiency is *part of a pattern*, resulted in *no actual harm* but has the *potential for more than minimal harm that is not immediate jeopardy* (Level II Severity), and the facility was found to be in *noncompliance*.

- *F* means the deficiency is *widespread*, resulted in *no actual harm* but has the *potential for more than minimal harm* that is *not immediate jeopardy* (Level II Severity), and the facility was found to be in *noncompliance*.

- *G* means the deficiency is *isolated*, resulted in *actual harm* that is *not immediate jeopardy* (Level III Severity), and the facility was found to be in *noncompliance*.

- *H* means the deficiency is *part of a pattern*, resulted in *actual harm that is not immediate jeopardy* (Level III Severity), and the facility was found to be in *noncompliance*.

- *I* means the deficiency is *widespread*, resulted in *actual harm that is not immediate jeopardy* (Level III Severity), and the facility was found to be in *noncompliance*.

- *J* means the deficiency is *isolated*, resulted in *immediate jeopardy to patient health or safety* (Level IV Severity), and the facility was found to be in *noncompliance*.

- *K* means the deficiency is *part of a pattern*, resulted in *immediate jeopardy to patient health or safety* (Level IV Severity), and the facility was found to be in *noncompliance*.

- *L* means the deficiency is *widespread*, resulted in *immediate jeopardy to patient health or safety* (Level IV Severity), and the facility was found to be in *noncompliance*.

Understanding Scope and Severity of Deficiencies

Severity Levels

- **Level I:** A deficiency that has the potential for causing no more than a minor negative impact on the patient(s).

- **Level II:** Noncompliance that results in minimal physical, mental and/or psychosocial discomfort to the patient and/or has the potential to compromise the patient's ability to maintain and/or reach his/her highest practicable physical, mental and/or psychosocial well-being as defined by the patient assessment, plan of care, and provision of services.

- **Level III:** Noncompliance that results in a negative outcome that has compromised the patient's ability to maintain and/or reach his/her highest practicable physical, mental and psychosocial well-being as defined by the patient assessment, plan of care and provision of services.

- **Level IV:** Immediate jeopardy, a situation in which immediate corrective action is necessary because the provider's noncompliance with one or more requirements has caused, or is likely to cause, serious injury, serious harm, impairment or death to a patient receiving care in a facility. This facility practice establishes a reasonable degree of predictability of similar actions, situations, practices or incidents occurring in the future.

Scope Levels

The definitions of scope are as follows:

- **Isolated:** The scope is *Isolated* when one or a very limited number of patients are affected and/or one or a very limited number of staff are involved and/or the situation has occurred only occasionally or in a limited number of locations.

- **Pattern:** The scope is a *Pattern* when more than a very limited number of patients are affected and/or more than a very limited number of staff are involved, and/or the situation has occurred in several locations, and/or the same patient(s) have been affected by repeated occurrences of the same deficient practice. The effect of the deficient practices is not found to be pervasive throughout the facility.

- **Widespread:** The scope is *Widespread* when the problems causing the deficiencies are pervasive in the facility and/or represent systemic failure that affected or has the potential to affect a large portion or all of the facility's patients. Widespread scope refers to the entire facility population, not a subset of patients or one unit of a facility. In addition, widespread scope may be identified if a systemic failure in the facility (e.g., failure to maintain food at a safe temperature) would be likely to affect a large number of patients and is, therefore, pervasive in the facility.

WHAT INVESTIGATION RESULTS MEAN

Inspections or investigations determine whether the nursing home meets certain "minimum standards." If a nursing home has no deficiencies, it means that it met the minimum standards at the time of the inspection.

But remember, any 2567 report is only a one-time snapshot of facility compliance with established standards and the quality of care that a particular nursing home provides. The quality of care may grow much better or much worse in a short period of time. To more fully assess the quality of care provided by a facility, it's important to review both recent and past survey reports.

Following is a summary of what the investigation results mean in terms of compliance and follow up actions that the nursing home is required to take:

- SS rankings of A, B or C mean that the facility is in substantial compliance on a deficiency.

- Even though a SS ranking of D, G, or J means that the care deficiency was found to be isolated, the practice must be corrected before a determination of substantial compliance can be made and continued certification recommended to the CMS.

- All F-XXX (tags) that are scored B through L require the facility to submit a written Plan of Correction (PoC), which must address the points listed in the cover letter accompanying the report. The PoC is reviewed by a state designated healthcare professional to determine if it will correct the deficiency in a manner that will assure substantial compliance at all times.

- SS rankings of J, K, or L mean that the deficiency poses immediate jeopardy to patients and immediate corrective action is necessary.

When reading a report, bear in mind that the length of a report (number of pages) has nothing to do with the severity or scope of the findings. The F-XXX tags and SS rankings have more gravity.

In order to receive Medicare and Medicaid payments, nursing facilities are required to comply with the requirements for Long-Term Care Facilities set forth in 42 CFR Part 483, Subpart B, and State Survey Agencies are responsible for visiting these facilities to determine whether they are, in fact, "in compliance" with these Federal requirements. These surveys (or investigations) are surprise visits — they're not supposed to be announced to the facility, and they may be conducted at any time, including weekends, 24 hours a day.

If facilities are found to be in compliance with Federal requirements, they receive a "certification of compliance." As long as the facility is found to be in substantial compliance with respect to a particular care deficiency, it is eligible for continued certification as a participant in the Medicare/Medicaid benefit program.

But when the facility is not in compliance, the state surveyor/investigator can recommend appropriate enforcement actions to the State Medicaid agency for Medicaid and to the regional office for Medicare. Centers for Medicare and Medicaid Services (CMS) can actually terminate its agreement to pay a nursing home facility if they determine that the facility:

- is not complying substantially with the terms of the agreement, the provisions of title XVIII of the Social Security Act, or regulations promulgated thereunder;

- refuses to permit examination of fiscal and other records (including medical records) necessary for the verification of information furnished as a basis for claiming payment under the Medicare program;

- refuses to permit photocopying of any records or other information necessary to determine or verify compliance with participation requirements; or

- has failed to supply information necessary to determine whether payments are or were due and the amounts of such payments.

In other words, if enough people complain and the facility fails to correct the deficiencies found, State investigators can effectively shut down a nursing home since, after all, losing Medicare/Medicaid payments represents a loss of their most significant revenue streams.

What Does "Substantial Compliance" Mean?

The investigation goal of *substantial compliance* is not the same as *total compliance*. The fact that a 2567 report states that a facility is in *substantial compliance* does not necessarily mean that the facility is providing high-quality care. Current government regulation of nursing homes allows too many marginal or substandard nursing homes to continue to operate. Why is this allowed to happen?

Regulatory history is part of the problem. When the federal government became directly involved in nursing home regulation after 1965, few nursing homes could even meet the federal standards. Strict enforcement of federal standards would have barred most nursing homes from participating in the

Medicare program at all, and therefore prevent many Medicare patients from receiving much-needed services. The Department of Health, Education, and Welfare then decided to certify nursing homes that were only in "substantial compliance" with Medicare standards. And, for better or worse, the *substantial compliance* standard has stuck.

So, from the very beginning, the goal of enforcing federal nursing home regulations was to allow some substandard facilities to participate in the program while encouraging them to achieve compliance, rather than barring these facilities until they came into compliance. The emphasis was — and in many states still *is* — improving substandard facilities rather than kicking them out of the program.

Another problem is that federal regulations are inadequately enforced. The Institute of Medicine Committee on Nursing Home Regulation found that large numbers of marginal or substandard nursing homes are chronically out of compliance when inspected, may or may not be subject to mild sanctions, temporarily correct their deficiencies under a Plan of Correction, and then quickly lapse into noncompliance again until the next annual survey (Committee on Nursing Home Regulation, 1987).

In other words, substandard nursing homes often come into compliance just long enough to be recertified, without penalty, but in subsequent annual inspections, are again, chronically, found to be out of compliance with the same or similar standards. The Committee dubbed these repeat offenders "roller-coaster," "yo-yo," "in-and-out," or "borderline" nursing homes (Committee on Nursing Home Regulation, 1984).

This noncompliance recidivism happens because federal procedures for dealing with noncompliant facilities are oriented more toward *helping facilities improve,* rather than *enforcing the certification standards.* While this stance may offer some long-term benefits, it allows states to continue certifying facilities that provide poor or marginal care.

Current federal survey policies and procedures encourage states to consult and coerce facilities into compliance, not to punish them. The state agency does not have the authority under federal regulations to punish a violation immediately. The survey agency must issue a notice to the operator of a substandard nursing home, giving the facility a period of time (usually 30 to 60 days) in which to correct deficiencies. The state survey agency is instructed to try to resolve cases before referring them to the formal administrative or law enforcement system (Health Care Financing Administration, 1981). The agency may apply formal sanctions *only* if the facility remains in violation beyond the deadline set for compliance.

Thus, the facility is not punished for violations directly, but rather for failing to carry out an administrative order to correct violations by a certain date. Resorting to formal sanctions therefore becomes the last step in a long series of follow-up visits and Plans of Correction. In practice, in the interest of eliminating the hazard as quickly as possible, nursing home regulators typically continue their efforts to gain compliance well after the point at which they could resort to formal sanctions (Health Care Financing Administration, 1981).

Now, it's important to note that just one condition out of compliance provides grounds for starting decertification procedures — that is, at least one complaint which results in deficiencies found by investigators. But even when facilities are decertified, they're still able to reenter the program too easily, then revert to the same patterns of substandard care all over again (Committee on Nursing Home Regulation, 1984).

STRENGTHS AND LIMITATIONS OF THE 5-STAR RATING SYSTEM

The Nursing Home Compare website acknowledges that its 5-star rating system has limitations. No rating system can address every consideration that goes into deciding which nursing home may be best for a particular person. For example, the ratings may not fully address the extent to which specialty care is provided (such as specialized rehabilitation or dementia care), or how easy it will be for family members to visit the nursing home patient.

The best advice is to weigh the information provided on the Nursing Home Compare website in conjunction with other sources of information about nursing homes in your area, such as your State Ombudsman program and other local advocacy groups, interaction with the resident and family councils if they exist at the nursing home, and personal visits to the nursing home.

Following is an analysis of both strengths and limitations of the 5-star rating system to keep in mind as you compare nursing homes.

Health Inspection Results

Strengths:

- *Comprehensive:* The nursing home health inspection process evaluates all major aspects of care in a nursing home (about 180 different items).

- *Onsite visits by trained inspectors:* This is the only source of information that comes from a trained team of objective surveyors (inspectors) who visit each nursing home to check on the quality of care, inspect medical records, and talk with patients about their care.

- *Federal quality checks:* Federal inspectors check on the state inspectors' work to make sure they're following the national process and that any differences between states stay within reasonable bounds.

Limitations:

- *Variation among states:* There are differences in how states carry out the inspection process, even though the standards are the same across the country.

- *Medicaid program differences:* There are also differences between state licensing requirements that affect quality, as well as differences in-state Medicaid programs that pay for much of the care in nursing homes.

Staffing

Strengths:

- *Overall staffing:* Quality ratings examine the overall number of staff compared to the number of patients and how many of the staff are trained nurses.

- *Adjusted for the population:* The ratings consider differences in how sick the nursing home patients are in each nursing home, since that impacts how many staff are needed.

Limitations:

- *Self-reported:* Staffing data are self-reported by nursing homes, rather than collected and reported by an independent agency.

- *Snapshot in time:* Staffing data are reported just once a year and reflect staffing over a two-week period of time.

Quality Measures

Strengths:

- *In-depth look:* The quality measures provide an important in-depth look at how well each nursing home performs important aspects of care. For example, these measures show how well the nursing home helps people maintain their ability to dress and eat, or how well the nursing home staff prevents and treats skin ulcers.

- *National measures:* The quality measures used in the 5-star rating are used in all nursing homes.

Limitations:

- *Self-reported data:* The quality measures are self-reported by the nursing home, rather than collected and reported by an independent agency.

- *Just a few aspects of care:* The quality measures represent only a few of the many aspects of care that may be important to you.

Overall

A nursing home's Overall score will be subject to all of the strengths and limitations of each of the three other categories. It's also important to remember that much of this data is self-reported by the nursing homes, thus, in some cases, may be suspect. We can only hope that there will be sufficient political willpower to ensure that the detail and accuracy of this information improves over time.

Regardless, Nursing Home Compare is a good place to start your nursing home research. If you're faced with making this all-important decision about which nursing home to choose for yourself or a loved one, knowledge and information will help empower the right choice.

TIPS

Quality is generally better in nursing homes that have more staff available to work directly with patients. It's important to ask nursing homes about their true staff levels, the qualifications of their staff, and the rate at which staff leave and are replaced (i.e., their "turnover rate.")

Discuss the quality measures with the nursing home staff. Ask what else they're doing to improve the care they give their patients. Consider the things that are most important to you and ask about them specifically, especially if none of the quality measures focus on your main concerns.

The most accurate comparisons are made by comparing nursing homes within the same state. Be cautious when comparing nursing homes in different states.

13

FILING A CRIMINAL COMPLAINT

The safety of the people shall be the highest law.
— **Marcus Tullius Cicero**

At 83 years old, unable to speak, unable to fight back, she was even more vulnerable than she was as a little girl fleeing her homeland. In fact, she was as vulnerable as an infant when she was raped. The dignity which she always displayed during her life, which was already being assaulted so unrelentingly by Alzheimer's disease, was dealt a final devastating blow by this man. The horrific irony is not lost upon me… that the very thing she feared most as a young girl fleeing her homeland happened to her in the final, most vulnerable days of her life."

— Statement of Maya Fischer, daughter of nursing home sexual assault victim Sonja Fischer

Maya Fischer offered this statement in court at the 2015 sentencing of 76-year-old nursing assistant George Kpingbah, who raped her mother at Walker Methodist Health Center in Minneapolis, Minnesota. She recounted how her mother had fled Indonesia as a young girl with her family to escape the rape and killing of young girls by Japanese soldiers, only to fall victim, decades later, to Kpingbah, a man who had been entrusted with her care. Kpingbah ultimately pled guilty to third-degree criminal sexual conduct with a mentally impaired or helpless victim and was sentenced to eight years in prison (Ellis & Hicken, 2017a).

Police had previously investigated allegations that he had engaged in sexual intercourse with a 65-year-old multiple sclerosis patient and an

83-year-old blind and deaf woman who was raped multiple times, always at midnight — the latter of which was investigated by police just seven months before Sonja Fischer was raped, but the victim was unable to identify her assailant. In fact, neither of the previous allegations were found to be substantiated by police, the facility or the state investigators.

For years, Kpingbah continued to work the overnight shift at Walker Methodist until December 2014, when another employee finally caught him in the act of raping Sonja Fischer. Kpingbah was finally fired. But since Walker Methodist had previously provided Kpingbah with the required abuse training, the facility was not cited for any wrongdoing by the state; only Kpingbah was held accountable for the assault.

Unfortunately, Maya Fischer didn't know about the previous allegations against Kpingbah, according to CNN investigators. When they reached out to family members of other residents who had earlier reported sexual assaults at Walker Methodist during the time Kpingbah worked there, they said nursing home officials were quick to dismiss the residents' claims as "hallucinations or fantasies."

The victims were easy prey for predators. It was only a matter of time.

Some wrongful conduct committed in nursing homes is not only an administrative violation of state and federal regulations, it's also a violation of criminal code. *Crimes committed in nursing homes are still crimes.*

We've established that nursing homes too often hire convicted criminals — whether knowingly or unknowingly. So it's no surprise that criminal nursing home employees commit crimes against these most vulnerable citizens: the patients. But it's not just the convicted criminals who abuse patients. Assault, theft and other crimes are committed every day in this country by nursing home caregivers with no previous criminal record, and even by, as you'll see, other troubled patients as well as predators who are merely visiting the nursing homes and are provided easy access to the patients by the nursing home staff.

If you suspect that a crime has been committed against a nursing home patient, you have the right to contact your local law enforcement officials. This right is in addition to, and not in place of, the other rights that we've discussed in previous chapters. And there are certainly plenty of examples of criminal charges being brought against individuals who abused nursing home patients, a few of which we've highlighted in previous chapters. Many of these crimes fall within two categories in particular: assault (including sexual assault) and theft of property. Consider these examples...

Assault, Sexual Assault, Sexual Exploitation

- In March 2017, a male certified nursing assistant (CNA) in an Indiana nursing home, Arbors in Michigan City, was charged with felony voyeurism after videotaping an 85-year-old female patient taking a shower and uploading naked photographs to social media (Maddux, 2016).

- In July 2016, Gary D. Stinger confessed to charges of rape and sexual battery of a female patient at Covington Manor Nursing Home in Indiana who, after being struck by a vehicle, functioned at the level of a 3-year-old, able to speak only in single syllables. While visiting a relative at the nursing home, Stinger was believed to have performed sexual acts on this patient on 10 occasions, and was ultimately reported by a facility nurse, who witnessed the final incident (Krieg, 2016).

- Across northeast Ohio, police and state inspection reports describe egregious crimes committed in nursing homes (Lenhoff & Livingston, 2012):
  - three sexual assault cases in a dementia unit at a Canton, Ohio facility
  - a 90-year-old woman was beaten with a clothes hanger at a Stow facility
  - At a nursing home in Canton, Ohio, an 80-year-old resident allegedly sexually assaulted a female resident repeatedly, was ultimately charged with gross sexual imposition, but found incompetent to stand trial

A well-publicized case in Waynesville, North Carolina highlights how some nursing homes deal with repeat offenders. According to reports, at this nursing home, a female patient suffering from chronic obstructive pulmonary disease and congestive heart failure was repeatedly sexually assaulted by a nursing aide, who had been employed by at least five other nursing homes (Ellis & Hicken, 2017b). In October 2015, the facility's director of nursing (DON), dismissed the victim's story, telling her to "go live under a bridge, because nothing like that happened" in her facility. The police showed up… but not to investigate the allegation of sexual abuse. Instead, an officer delivered the victim to the psychiatric ward in a nearby hospital, where no one there believed her either. Discharged after a few days, she had no choice but to return to the same nursing home. She ended up homeless at one point before finally landing at her current residence. She was dismissed as a complainer, troublemaker, attention-seeker. But she wasn't the first nursing home resident to complain about the nursing home aide, and she wouldn't be the last…

A month later, in February 2016, a nurse willing to risk her job, reported the rape of a resident to police after the DON failed to call police the day before when the victim reported the rape; the DON told this concerned nurse that she would "handle everything." She didn't, of course, and the nurse aide was allowed to continue working. Another of his victims called 911 herself to report her own sexual assault. Two more victim-patients emerged — they, too, had reported the assaults to the DON to no avail, and would tell their stories to police. Police ultimately learned that allegations of sexual assault had been made against the nurse aide at several other nursing homes, too, including one in 2011. When detectives accessed the nurse aide's official record on file with the state, they were surprised to discover that it was completely clean.

The accused nurse aide is currently awaiting trial on two counts of forcible rape and sexual activity by a custodian. The DON was fired. Her boss, the administrator, also left the facility. Neither faced criminal charges.

State investigators fined the nursing home $110,402.50 and cited the facility for a long list of violations. The facility temporarily lost Medicare/Medicaid funding for new residents, and would risk losing it permanently unless it could prove that it had taken steps to prevent such failures in the future.

Theft, Identity Theft, Fraud, Forgery

- A CNA at a Boardman, Ohio nursing home was charged with two felony assaults of dementia patients (ages 96 and 80); meanwhile, she was still listed in "good standing" on the Ohio Department of Health's Nurse Aide registry months later. Three months before being hired at the Boardman nursing home, the nurse aide was arrested on a felony drug charge, sentenced to six months of probation and ordered to pay fines. She had been hired at this nursing home while still on probation (Lenhoff & Livingston, 2012).

- A former Georgia nursing home worker pled guilty to stealing the identities of nursing home residents and using them to file fraudulent income tax returns, reaping more than $460,000 in refunds. She was sentenced to 27 years in prison and ordered to pay more than $493,000 in restitution (Mullaney, 2014).

- Brian Frawley, the former business manager of Clifton Care Center, a nursing home in Ohio, was sentenced to four years in prison for stealing more than $173,000 from over 100 residents — funds that should have been used for the residents' well-being. He stole cash from resident trust fund accounts and made false entries in trust fund ledgers in an attempt to cover up his crimes. Frawley was also ordered to pay $60,000 restitution; the remainder was covered by insurance (Norwalk Reflector, 2017).

- In June 2015, a former employee at Hickory Creek nursing home in Indiana, was charged with forgery, theft, and two counts of fraud on a financial institution. According to a police report, the employee allegedly forged signatures of residents and the administrator on more than 30 occasions in amounts ranging from $12 to $1,000. The accused was suspected to have written forged checks to withdraw a total of $9,700 from Hickory Creek's resident trust account, a single bank account into which residents' Medicare checks were deposited (Ladwig, 2015).

Law enforcement agencies in some states, such as Maryland, have acknowledged the scope of criminal activity in nursing homes and have made a concerted effort to develop policies and procedures specifically for responding to allegations of criminal activity in nursing homes. In their relentless attempts to fill beds, many nursing homes are admitting younger patients for short-term rehab stays, which has increased the incidence and prevalence of illegal drug activity, theft and aggressively violent behavior. Some of these patients bring with them problems that are too complex and dangerous for nursing homes to handle. Deaton, a large Baltimore nursing home, was closed and decertified because this younger population made daily operations unmanageable (Maryland Health Care Commission, 2004).

But as you can see in the case of 76-year-old George Kpingbah and the 80-year-old Canton, Ohio patient, criminal activity in nursing homes is certainly not confined to the younger generation. In the latter case, the nursing home failed to protect vulnerable residents from another predatory resident; in the former, they failed to protect the victims from a predatory employee. If not for criminal charges being brought in these cases, who knows how many other helpless victims would have been ravaged by these predators.

POTENTIAL HURDLES

Filing a criminal complaint sometimes requires perseverance. As you've seen, victims and families are sometimes failed at various stages of the investigative process.

The Elder Justice Act of 2009 requires owners, operators, employees, managers, agents, and contractors of nursing home facilities in nursing facilities to report *any reasonable suspicion of crimes* committed against a resident of that facility to the appropriate entities (law enforcement agencies) (Section 6703(b)(3) of the Elder Justice Act of 2009). But, as you might imagine, nursing homes are often slow to investigate, report, or cooperate in criminal allegations, either out of a desire to conceal them or a reluctance to believe them. They certainly don't want the negative publicity that may follow a criminal investigation and prosecution because it may impact the number of new admissions, and thus the bottom line. Criminal complaints also often prompt investigations by state agencies, which may result in findings of deficiencies and citations that will be made public on websites used by prospective patients such as Nursing Home Compare.

Second, police are sometimes skeptical of claims at the outset, dismissing victims who have cognitive deficits, such as disorganized thinking and memory impairment, and who are perhaps unable to effectively identify the perpetrator and articulate what happened. Also, since police are not healthcare providers, they may be reluctant to label substandard care as *criminal*. Law enforcement officers are often qualified to determine whether an automobile accident is caused by the negligence of a particular driver or not — following the rules of the road is within their scope of expertise. However, in abuse cases where the harm is alleged to have been caused by improper provision of healthcare, if they cannot see obvious indicators of abuse in a nursing home patient, they're often not comfortable — or necessarily qualified — to determine whether caregivers are criminally at fault. Thus, police often rely upon state investigators to determine whether or not the patient's care was appropriate.

And finally, because of the high bar set for *substantiating* complaints of patient abuse and loopholes in the laws, it can be difficult for facilities to flag patterns of repeated allegations against a particular caregiver.

But shouldn't repeated complaints at a facility cause grave concern among nursing home administrators and state inspectors who investigate those complaints? Shouldn't nursing home personnel at least search for past state complaints against caregivers before hiring them, whether substantiated or not? Yes, of course they should.

But under the current reporting system, CNN investigators found that any facility or investigator screening the Waynesville, North Carolina nurse aide discussed earlier would have seen a record reflecting a longtime nursing aide with no history of problems, despite the many complaints that had been made involving him (Ellis & Hicken, 2017b). As it stands today, nursing aides can rack up any number of complaints, and even continue working, as long as the claims against them haven't been "substantiated." And for that matter, even after claims *have* been substantiated, as in some of the cases we've discussed, some CNAs may still retain their licenses.

It is these colossal systemic failures that can make it harder for victims to find justice, and easier for perpetrators to get away with their crimes.

And there's another problem: Those at the top, who have the power to stop these predatory criminals in the first place usually go scot-free…

Typically, a criminal case is brought against the low-level employee who committed the crime (theft, sexual assault, etc.) That's laudable, of course, and as it should be. But this does little to address the prevailing conditions, means and motives — the perfect storm — that created an environment in which this criminal act could happen in the first place. The fact that this lone perpetrator will receive some relatively light sentence that may or may not include prison time does nothing to address the lack of oversight, lack of employee screening, inadequate training, and understaffing that results in burnout and a suboptimal pool of workers willing to work in this industry for low pay.

The result is clearly foreseeable, but the cost to nursing home corporations and those who operate the nursing home is minimal. As long as nursing home profiteers can get off the hook by simply paying administrative fines that amount to a slap on the wrist and nursing home decision-makers can escape criminal charges, these perfect-storm environments that enable foreseeable criminal acts to be perpetrated against innocent, vulnerable patients will persist.

Proving a crime against the owners, operators and managers who are ultimately responsible for these conditions can often be time-consuming, expensive and difficult for prosecutors. Unlike low-level staff who are charged with a crime, those at the top are typically able to mount a well-funded defense. And that top-notch defense team will challenge the prosecution's ability to prove *mens rea*. Mens rea ("guilty mind" in Latin) is the intention or knowledge of wrongdoing that constitutes one element of the crime. Most crimes require that prosecutors must prove that the accused did so purposefully, intentionally, knowingly, willfully, etc.

Those responsible for the circumstances which led to criminal acts being perpetrated upon the patients will typically claim they did not intend or know that their actions, or failures to act, would lead to a crime being committed.

So, prosecuting the perpetrator is important, of course, and may even deter others from committing similar crimes. But the problem is, this alone has a limited capacity to deter corporate decision-makers from knowingly allowing, if not *creating*, circumstances whereby the lack of properly screened, trained, and supervised staff results in an environment ripe for criminal misconduct — effectively committing what could be described as premeditated neglect and abuse at the highest levels. Only prosecuting decision-makers and/or impacting the corporate bottom line (thus also their job security, bonuses, etc.) by way of a civil lawsuit or other means (such as public exposure and subsequent accountability) are likely to have a meaningful, lasting impact on the safety of those residing in our nursing homes.

As renowned publisher Joseph Pulitzer said:

"There is not a crime, there is not a dodge, there is not a trick, there is not a swindle, there is not a vice which does not live by secrecy. Get these things out in the open, describe them, attack them, ridicule them in the press, and sooner or later public opinion will sweep them away. Publicity may not be the only thing that is needed, but it is the one thing without which all other agencies will fail."

Though it's relatively rare, prosecutors have in some instances sought to hold high-level employees accountable for their actions. Take for example the recent criminal case filed in Indiana against two top executives of one of the largest nursing home chains in the state. In that case, prosecutors brought charges against CEO James Burkhart and COO Daniel Benson of American Senior Communities, LLC (ASC). According to prosecutors, evidence shows that Burkhart, Benson, and others engaged in a vast fraud, kickback, and money laundering scheme, personally pocketing more than $16 million in illegal kickbacks and fraudulent overcharges, which they spent on vacation homes, private plane flights, golf trips, expensive jewelry, gold bullion, casino chips and political contributions. According to public statements made by U.S. Attorney Josh Minkler, evidence shows that, in some instances, vendors paid kickbacks to these co-conspirators in exchange for doing business with ASC. In others, it's alleged that they intentionally overcharged the facility's parent company for products and services that vendors provided, then funneled the overcharged amounts back to themselves through a complex web of more than 20 shell companies and bank accounts. For example, according to allegations, they directed a landscaping vendor to artificially inflate its invoices to ASC by 45%, defrauding ASC and Health & Hospital out of over $2.3 million on landscaping services alone. But these alleged schemes reportedly encompassed a vast array of other services, too, including pharmacy, nurse call systems, food supplies, medical supplies, patient lifts, patient therapies, interior decorations furniture, office supplies, scent products, American flags, patient discharge packages, uniforms, and even Alzheimer's Memory Walk t-shirts. Nothing was sacred.

But this time, these alleged acts of financial fraud were investigated by federal agencies (including the FBI, DHHS, OIG, IRS), and the Indiana Attorney General's Medicaid Control Fraud Unit. In October 2016, four individuals were indicted on charges of conspiracy to commit mail, wire, and health care fraud, along with multiple other counts of mail fraud, wire fraud, and money laundering. Three were also charged with conspiracy to violate the federal Anti-Kickback Statute (U. S. Attorney's Office, Southern District of Indiana, 2016). So far, one defendant, Dave Mazanowski, founder of landscaping company Mainscape, pled guilty to one felony count of conspiracy to commit mail, wire and healthcare fraud. According to the indictment, $1.5 million in facility funds were paid to Mainscape for fictitious consulting services (Andrews, 2016).

U.S. Attorney Josh Minkler stated in media releases, these individuals "took advantage of a system entrusted with the care of this state's elderly, sick and mentally challenged, allowing them to live a lifestyle of gratuitous luxury, fraught with unbridled greed."

As of this writing, the remaining individuals continue to maintain their innocence and the criminal case is still pending. In addition, my law firm has brought a civil case against American Senior Communities and these individuals, alleging they diverted funds that should have been spent on resources (staffing, supplies, equipment etc.) needed to provide proper care for all of the nursing home's patients, including our client, an elderly gentleman who as a result of the facility's negligence, suffered advanced pressure sores, osteomyelitis (bone marrow inflammation), sepsis, and respiratory distress, and ultimately died from septic shock and gangrene.

THE BOTTOM LINE

When should you contact law enforcement? The simple answer is that if you think the misconduct is something that *should* be criminal, it probably is, and it should probably be reported to law enforcement officials, as well as to state investigators. If the safety or well-being of a patient is at stake, the police will likely respond quicker than state inspectors, and their presence may help protect the patient and others from being harmed, preserve evidence, and notify other agencies that need to be involved. Law enforcement may call upon state investigators to help substantiate claims, who may be more familiar with investigating neglect and abuse in nursing homes.

Even if law enforcement agencies don't always vigorously investigate and pursue criminal neglect and abuse of nursing home patients today, and even if the laws in their state make it difficult for them to prosecute the cases they do investigate, the fact that more people report criminal conduct can only serve to increase and prioritize the resources devoted to pursuing criminal activity in nursing homes.

If someone commits a crime against you or a loved one in a nursing home, it's understandable that you may feel that this predator should be imprisoned, that it's not enough to file a complaint with state investigators or pursue compensation in civil court. But you may ultimately find that the only remedy that ensures both investigative power and a financial consequence — which strikes at the heart of what nursing home corporations care about most (money) — is a civil lawsuit. And it's not an either-or situation. A perpetrator who has committed crimes can both be sued in civil court for damages *and* tried for his/her crimes in criminal court.

Throughout this book, we've discussed different tools and strategies, each of which can be effective for accomplishing different goals. But while Ombudsman have some limited investigative powers, they cannot enforce financial consequences. State surveyors have investigative powers, but can only enforce limited financial consequences. Law enforcement have investigative powers, but, in addition to their lack of clinical knowledge, they're often reluctant to use their investigative powers because of the difficulty in proving the *mens rea* element of the criminal violation. But the investigative powers afforded by both criminal and civil lawsuits can be crucial to bringing perpetrators to justice.

As you'll learn in the next chapter, the only mechanism through which victims of neglect and abuse can be compensated for the economic impact and human loss that nursing home greed has caused is a civil lawsuit. A civil lawsuit is the solution that ensures that the patient's (or patient's family's) attorney can subpoena witnesses to testify under oath, request the production of pertinent documents, empower a jury to evaluate all of the facts (that are admissible), and force the wrongdoer to compensate the victims for the harm caused by preventable neglect or abuse.

TIPS

- Be on the lookout for evidence of crimes and abuse and request immediate investigation by police. Learn the names of the caregivers who provide hands-on care to your loved one and keep a log of relevant dates and times. Research these employees on social media to look for anything that may be cause for concern. The following indicators, for example, may warrant investigation:

  - reports of abuse by the patient or by the patient's room-mate

  - mysterious or unexplained injuries, such as skin tears, bruises, bone fractures, or contusions

  - indications that the patient has become fearful of staff when they come in the room

  - missing personal property, such as electronics, jewelry, or patient trust funds.

- Report the incident(s) promptly while witnesses memories are fresh and evidence is still accessible.

- Be sure to provide police with as many details as possible — the who, what, where, when, and how — and take care to preserve all evidence. Provide police with complete witness names, medical records or other documents that provide details relating to the injury or incident of abuse.

- Provide photo or video documentation, if possible. Photograph any physical injuries from multiple angles and at varying distances. Consider installing hidden video cameras if your state laws allow it.

- Look for evidence that pain patches have been removed and replaced.

- Be alert to the patient reporting pain after supposedly receiving their ordered pain medications — this may indicate the patient's pain medication is being stolen.

- Keep an inventory and photographs of all personal property belonging to the patient and kept in the patient's room. Check on your loved one frequently and at different times of the day so the staff cannot anticipate when you will or won't be around.

- Follow up with the police to ensure that the matter was thoroughly investigated.

14
FILING A CIVIL LAWSUIT

The social purpose of tort law is accident and injury prevention. It is only when we fail in our initial purpose that we move to the secondary purpose, compensation for the victim.

— Henry Philo, renowned plaintiff trial lawyer

If you have not been successful at holding a nursing home fully accountable for neglect or abuse through the strategies discussed in previous chapters, take heart. You may have the right to file a civil lawsuit to help find the answers and accountability you deserve.

Since the dawn of our nation, Americans have held dear the right to have a jury composed of ordinary citizens like each of us serve as the conscience of our communities. This is not just true of criminal cases brought by the state against a person accused of a crime, but of civil cases as well. In 1791, our forefathers ratified the 7th Amendment to the Constitution as part of the Bill of Rights, which recognized the right to impanel a jury to decide civil cases.

Civil cases include those brought by individuals alleging that another individual, corporation or other entity has failed to meet their legal responsibilities and caused harm. Such civil cases include *torts*. A tort is a wrongful act causing damage or injury, usually done intentionally, knowingly, or negligently, for which a civil suit can be brought and a court may impose liability. Examples of torts include negligence (e.g., "medical malpractice"), fraud, battery, conversion (commonly known as theft), and invasion of privacy.

Though civil lawsuits and the tort system are under attack by corporate special interests seeking to avoid accountability, these American institutions are vital to the fabric and wellbeing of our society. Civil lawsuits help hold wrongdoers accountable and compensate victims who have been harmed by the recklessness, negligence or misconduct of others.

> **7th Amendment — United States Constitution:**
>
> In Suits at common law, where the value in controversy shall exceed twenty dollars, the right of trial by jury shall be preserved, and no fact tried by a jury, shall be otherwise re-examined in any Court of the United States, than according to the rules of the common law.

But perhaps even more importantly, there's this benefit: The fear of a potential lawsuit can discourage unsafe nursing homes from neglecting or abusing their patients, and that fear can function as an economic incentive to become more safe and responsible. In cases where laws and regulations are violated but the meager penalty is not sufficient to deter wrongful conduct, the fear of a civil lawsuit can actually become a more effective deterrent than regulatory penalties because nursing homes exist to make a profit.

This is the power you have by exercising your right to file a civil lawsuit. The nursing home industry is driven by profit — just like drug companies, auto manufacturers, and insurance companies. The economic bottom line, above all else, drives corporate decisions, including those involving safety.

Civil lawsuits — whether filed against a neglectful nursing home, a careless product manufacturer, or other corporate wrongdoer — protect us all by operating as a financial incentive that can keep corporations from running amok and sacrificing safety for profit. And something else, too: they provide a forum where evidence of misconduct can be forced out into the light. In fact, the Economic Policy Institute found that "virtually every study conducted, covering a variety of consumer products, shows that the quality, variety, and safety of products made in the United States has improved dramatically in recent decades, in large measure as a result of the tort system" (Chimerine & Eisenbrey, 2005).

Civil lawsuits have dramatically improved U.S. consumer safety in so many ways. Following are a few examples of tort cases that made a difference.

Incidentally, in many of these cases, you'll notice the culture of cover-up operating at full throttle.

Prescription Drug Safety and Healthcare:

- **Propulsid's Fatal Side Effects.** From 1993 to 1998, pharmaceutical manufacturer Johnson & Johnson generated over $1 Billion in sales from the heartburn medication, Propulsid, even as the company knew hundreds of patients were dying from lethal side effects. Children were at high risk, so federal regulators would not approve the drug for pediatric sales. Johnson & Johnson agreed not to market Propulsid directly for children, but side-stepped the agreement by pushing so-called "educational efforts" that advocated the drug's use for pediatric patients. Documents revealed that Johnson & Johnson knew that 90% of the company's cherry-flavored liquid Propulsid went to children, while claiming it was aimed at geriatric patients. The FDA proposed major changes to Propulsid's warning label, but didn't have the power to order Johnson & Johnson to change the label. The company's analysis estimated that the changes would cost over $250 million a year in lost sales, and so rejected almost all of the proposed changes. Over the next three years, over 100 infants were injured and at least 24 died. In all, at least 300 people died and around 16,000 were injured. In 2004, Johnson & Johnson agreed to pay $90 million to injured patients and the families of those who died. Propulsid has been discontinued in the U.S. (Harris & Koli, 2005; Moore et al., 2002).

- **Humana Insurance Fraud.** Mark and Barbara Chipps' four-year-old daughter, Caitlyn, who was born with cerebral palsy, was terminated from the Humana "medical case management" program, a special Humana program for chronically ill patients. There was no medical diagnosis supporting the termination, and it clearly violated the terms of the family's insurance agreement. When the Chipps family appealed to Humana, their daughter's speech, occupational and physical therapies were terminated, as well. Ultimately, the family exhausted their financial resources trying to continue Caitlyn's care and filed a lawsuit. The ensuing litigation uncovered widespread fraud at Humana; they had unlawfully denied coverage to more than 100 catastrophically ill and injured children in Florida in order to boost profit. They even went so far as to send a letter to a child — not the parent — who had been in a coma for 14 years, advising him that he had improved to such an extent that he no longer needed medical case management. All this while paying incentive bonuses to physicians and nurses based on the number of medical claims denied each month. The jury found that Humana intentionally disregarded its insureds' health and safety, and awarded Caitlyn and her family restitution equal to the $78.5 million Humana sought to save by terminating these childrens' coverage. Humana fought the award and the Chipps' later settled for $2.2 million. But Caitlyn was accepted back into the medical case management program, and Humana's fraudulent behavior was exposed to the world (*Chipps v. Humana Health Insurance Co. of Florida, Inc.*).

- A baby suffered permanent brain damage after an obstetrician ignored a nurse's concerns over abnormalities on the fetal monitor. After this verdict, North Carolina hospitals adopted a new protocol that allows nurses to intervene on behalf of patients without risking their jobs (*Campbell v. Pitt County Memorial Hospital, Inc.*).

- A newborn suffered permanent brain damage after being left alone in a hospital's pediatric unit for 35 minutes, 10 to 15 of which he stopped breathing. After this lawsuit, the corporation changed its policy on staffing pediatric units throughout its chain of hospitals (*National Bank of Commerce v. HCA Health Services of Midwest, Inc.*).

Unsafe Auto Design:

- **Toyota & Lexus Runaway Cars.** Many defect petitions were filed with the NHTSA (National Highway Safety Administration) from 2002 to 2009 regarding Toyota and Lexus models' tendency to unintentionally accelerate, but most were deemed to be caused by "user error." Toyota issued a minor fix by switching out floor mats to prevent "pedal entrapment." Then in 2009, California Highway

Patrol officer Mark Saylor was traveling with his family in a loaner Lexus ES350 when the car lost all brake function and accelerated out of control. Everyone in the vehicle died, and the crash generated national media coverage. Toyota issued 7 separate recalls that included around 10 million vehicles, for which they switched out floor mats and carpet covers that they claimed caused pedal entrapment. But the problem wasn't fixed. In 2013, a former Toyota employee released a personal statement that accused Toyota of covering up facts and tricking government officials. The Justice Department investigated and handed Toyota a $1.2 billion penalty for issuing misleading statements to the NHTSA and another $1.2 billion dollar penalty in a class action lawsuit brought by Toyota drivers who complained that their vehicles lost value as a result of the scandal (*U.S. v. Toyota Motor Corp*).

- **The Exploding Pinto.** Who can forget the infamous 1970s cases involving the Ford Pinto, a favorite of business ethics professors. The Pinto had a controversial safety record due to a fuel system that was found to be defective by the NHTSA, rupturing into deadly fuel-tank fires when met with rear-end collisions. The NHTSA also found that not only did Ford know about this problem, they deliberately neglected to engineer a redesign after conducting a cost-benefit analysis that determined it was cheaper to pay off possible lawsuits than to fix the problem. The result was a massive recall of 1.5 million Pintos and several lawsuits against Ford Motor Company, including *Grimshaw v. Ford Motor Company*, in which the plaintiffs were awarded significant compensatory and punitive damages, as well as a 1973 Indiana criminal case alleging criminal recklessness and reckless homicide when three teenage girls died (Leggett, 1999; *Grimshaw v. Ford Motor Co.*).

- **Corvair: Unsafe at any Speed.** The investigation and lawsuits of the highly publicized mid-1960s rear-engined Chevrolet Corvair, which consumer protection activist Ralph Nader dubbed "unsafe at any speed," were primarily related to the Corvair's unstable swing-axle suspension design, ultimately triggering over 100 lawsuits against General Motors and resulting in the creation of the federal safety agency that became the NHTSA (National Highway Safety Administration) (Nader, 1965; *Nader v. General Motors Corp.*).

*   **The Ford Firestone Fiasco.** Ford's use of Firestone 500 15-inch radial tires, which had a tendency toward tread separation, caused 271 deaths and thousands of injuries, ultimately resulting in the recall of 2.8 million tires. Internal company documents revealed that both Firestone and Ford had been aware of the deadly tread separation and associated rollover problems for years but had done everything they could to hide it (Winerip, 2001).

Other Examples:

*   **Mega Bloks' Magnetix.** The plastic parts of a Magnetix toy, manufactured by Mega Blok, broke open, spilling small, powerful magnets onto the carpet, which were swallowed by 22-month Kenny Sweet, who fell ill shortly after and became unable to hold down solid food. Nine tiny magnets had attached together in Kenny's intestines and were gradually cutting off the blood supply to parts of his bowels, causing the tissue to die and allowing gangrene to set in. He died that night. The Sweets filed a complaint with the Consumer Product Safety Commission (CPSC). The manufacturer, Mega Bloks, claimed it had "no record or knowledge of a similar occurrence involving this toy." Eventually, the CPSC received at least 1,500 reports of Magnetix magnets coming loose. The toys were eventually recalled, but not before 34 children were injured, at least 15 of whom were hurt after Kenny's death. Although the corporation denied knowledge of other injuries caused by the toys, the law suit revealed they were aware of the life-threatening dangers. The Sweets filed suit, seeking not only restitution for the loss of their child, but also a permanent injunction to keep Mega Bloks from further manufacture or distribution of the toys. The CPSC implemented a new safety standard test that toys with small magnets must pass before hitting the shelves (*Sweet et al v. Rose Art Industries Inc et al*).

- **Defective Pool Drain.** In a well-known North Carolina case, 5-year-old Valerie Lakey lost 80% of her intestines after being sucked into a pool drain outlet whose cover had been removed. Four adults were unable to free her until, finally, the pool's pumps were turned off. Valerie spends 12 -14 hours daily being fed by a tube in her chest dripping nutrients into her body, an expensive procedure that will likely be required for the rest of her life, in addition to other medical treatments. Her parents sued the recreation club that owned the pool, the county, the maker of the pool's circulation pump and Sta-Rite Industries, the manufacturer of the missing drain cover. The first three defendants settled, pre-trial, for a total of $5.9 million. Sta-Rite offered $100,000. The Lakeys declined and the case went to trial. Then their attorneys discovered that 12 other children had suffered similar injuries from Sta-Rite drains; Sta-Rite increased its offer to $1.25 million, which the plaintiffs rejected. Two weeks into trial, Sta-Rite increased their offer to $8.5 million. The Lakeys rejected the offer and asked the jury for the insurance policy limit of $22.5 million; Sta-Rite countered with $17.5 million which was again rejected. The jury found Sta-Rite liable for $25 million in economic (compensatory) damages. The case caused Sta-Rite to change its warnings and instructions regarding the safe use of its drain covers and triggered an industry-wide recall of pool drain covers (*Lakey v. Sta-Rite Industries Inc.*).

Thanks to determined and courageous individuals like those who filed these lawsuits, an inestimable number of lives have been saved and the rest of us are a little bit safer.

We have an obligation to protect, and seek justice for, the least among us, including the elderly, the sick, and the disabled who are typically not capable of protecting themselves. In acting as the conscience of the community, a jury has the power to decide what the acceptable standard of care is in a nursing home. Is it okay for a patient to lie in bed for hours on end without being turned, resulting in the development of an advanced, necrotic, life-threatening pressure sore? Is it okay for a nursing home to skimp on staffing, which all but guarantees that call lights will go unanswered for a prolonged period of time, resulting in a foreseeable fall for a patient who was forced to attempt toileting without assistance?

Too many nursing homes claim that such events are simply unfortunate incidents that did not result from any wrongdoing. They like to call these tragedies "unavoidable." But until nursing homes are held accountable for neglectful care, they have no incentive to *avoid* these care failures and change their ways. If nursing homes aren't held accountable, those that cut corners are allowed to compete for new patients on the same playing field as those that endeavor to provide high quality care.

Filing a lawsuit ensures that patients and families have an opportunity to present neglectful care issues to a jury, which has the power to decide whether the nursing home is failing to meet its legal obligations under state and federal law. If a jury decides that this type of care violates the patient's rights, the jury is deciding what the acceptable level of care is in their community. The jury is setting the standards. And juries tend to take this responsibility seriously.

If you're considering filing a civil lawsuit against a nursing home, this chapter will help you weigh the pros and cons, and should you decide to consult a lawyer, provide guidance on how to choose the right lawyer, and help gather evidence to build your case.

WHEN CIVIL LAWSUITS CAN BE HELPFUL

The other rights and remedies we've discussed are important, and each can help you achieve a particular objective. For example, by requesting a copy of your medical records, you can discover information about what care was (and was not) provided, and by whom. By contacting an Ombudsman, you're enlisting a trained advocate to address an ongoing problem in short order in hopes of avoiding greater or further harm. By asking your state survey agency to conduct an investigation, you can help expose quality of care problems at the facility and cause the nursing home to develop and submit a Plan of Correction to address the problem(s).

Each of these are very important tools. Yet, none of these tools alone can substantially impact nursing homes with respect to the thing they too often care about most: the financial bottom line. That's where civil lawsuits come in.

We expect children to understand the concept of being accountable for their actions. Kids who are goofing around and throw a baseball through a neighbor's window are expected to own up to their mistake and pay to replace the broken window. But of course, accountability is not just a societal expectation of children. We all know that adult drivers who run a stop sign and hit another driver are expected to accept responsibility for the damage they've caused.

Unfortunately, this basic concept of fairness and accountability often escapes those corporate nursing home profiteers whose choices and actions injure and kill the patients whose lives and well-being have been entrusted to them in exchange for monetary payment. We live in a society whose rules revolve around accountability. And our court system is designed to ensure just that — enforcement of accountability.

To achieve the objective of holding nursing homes fully accountable (or at least to the extent the law allows) for the harm they cause due to abuse and neglect, your most powerful tool is likely a civil lawsuit. By filing a civil lawsuit, you can seek to hold those who are responsible for abusive and neglectful care financially responsible for the medical bills, funeral and burial expenses, and most importantly for the needless human suffering their misconduct has inflicted. Your lawsuit can seek *compensatory damages,* which include compensation for the actual losses and harm sustained. Compensatory damages include reimbursement for economic damages (money expended or lost due to the negligence, such as medical bills), but more significantly, also for other important harms, such as: pain, human suffering, embarrassment, humiliation, disfigurement, disability, loss of another's love and companionship, loss of quality of life, and the like.

In some circumstances, one may also seek *exemplary damages* (also known as *punitive damages*) for particularly egregious conduct to deter the defendant nursing home or any other defendant from allowing such conduct again. The goal of punitive damages is to address conduct that's considered to be so dangerous, so egregious, or to represents such disregard for others' safety or welfare that it is deemed by lawmakers to warrant special damages sufficient to send a message that such conduct is intolerable.

Importantly, while proceeding with a civil lawsuit, you and your attorney can typically obtain a greater understanding of the circumstances that led to the harm because the procedural rules that govern your lawsuit likely allow you access to information about the care at issue, the facility policies and procedures which were (or were not) in place to prevent the neglect or abuse, corporate decisions to understaff the facility, and the use of parent and shell corporations to siphon money from care, and so on. An attorney who is experienced in handling nursing home neglect and abuse cases can utilize powerful strategies and tactics, including: issuing subpoenas to compel witnesses to testify under oath and conducting discovery to force those responsible for the nursing home to disclose key documentation that will expose the egregious misconduct that caused the injuries or death at issue.

In addition, the public nature of a civil lawsuit can bring community attention to a local healthcare problem that could affect *many* nursing home patients. The public spotlight upon even just one jury verdict against a neglectful nursing home corporation can often do more to alert the public about the problems plaguing not just that one facility, but also the problems associated with that nursing home chain and even the entire nursing home industry, in general, and in doing so, bring about needed changes more effectively than any other strategy.

In the same way that lawsuits prevented Ford from continuing to sell Pintos and compete in the market with other automakers that chose to put safety ahead of profits, patients and their families can help clean up the nursing home industry by forcing bad nursing homes to take responsibility for their actions and either change their ways or stop selling their defective product.

WHAT YOU SHOULD KNOW ABOUT FILING A CIVIL LAWSUIT

In order to establish a viable case that can prevail in court, you must meet the criteria necessary to prove a *cause of action*. The following section will give you an idea of the elements typically involved in building a solid case, as well as other practical realities and limitations to be aware of when filing a civil lawsuit.

A lawsuit is typically initiated by the plaintiff filing a written pleading (usually called a *complaint* or *petition* depending upon the jurisdiction). The defendant(s) then are typically required to file a responsive pleading that admits or denies the various allegations in the plaintiff's complaint.

When a civil lawsuit is filed, the complaint or petition typically must state a *cause of action*, which has been defined as: *the basis of a lawsuit founded on legal grounds and alleged facts which, if proved, would constitute all the "elements" required by the law.*

In a civil case, a cause of action can be understood as the grounds recognized under the law that entitle the plaintiff to compensation. There are several possible causes of action that can support a lawsuit against a nursing home. These causes of action often include, but are not limited to:

- *breach of contract* (not performing the services they promised to perform)

- *fraud* (intentionally misrepresenting the care they will provide)

- *negligence* (failing to provide a reasonable level of care under the circumstances)

Again, these are just a few examples, and there are other causes of action that can be pled in some jurisdictions. Therefore, you should consult an attorney familiar with the laws of your state, which set forth which causes of action you may pursue and what must be proven in order to prevail.

Let's discuss the negligence cause of action in more detail because it tends to be the most common cause of action pled in a nursing home case. Negligence is generally defined as: *the failure by the defendant to use a reasonable amount of care under the circumstances, and thereby causing harm to another.*

Foreseeability

Typically, in order for the defendant to be found liable or responsible for the harm, the type of harm that was caused by the negligence must have been *foreseeable*. Here are some examples of foreseeable harm that may result from negligence in the nursing home setting:

- Failing to turn and reposition a bed-bound patient frequently can foreseeably cause that patient to develop painful pressure sores.

- Failing to respond to a bed alarm for a patient who is a fall risk can foreseeably result in the patient trying to leave his/her bed without the needed assistance, then falling and causing an injury.

- Failing to ensure that a patient is provided sufficient liquids will foreseeably cause dehydration and other illnesses.

- Administering the wrong medications (or *not* properly administering physician-prescribed medications) to a patient can foreseeably result in the patient experiencing harmful effects.

- Failing to ensure that the entrances or exits to a unit housing dementia patients are properly secured can foreseeably result in a dementia patient wandering away from the facility and suffering harm while out in the community.

- Not providing a patient with limited function of his/her arms with assistance when drinking coffee can foreseeably result in the patient spilling the hot coffee on himself/herself and suffering painful burns.

These are just a few examples that help illustrate the concept of negligence causing foreseeable harm. Now, if you're thinking that these examples seem "obvious," you're right. They are. Foreseeable harm is often a matter of the nursing home staff simply failing to use common sense.

Yet nursing homes, which are supposed to be staffed and managed by professionals trained in caring for people who require special care, often pretend that the harm they cause could not have been foreseen. They tell the patient or the patient's family that the harm was "unavoidable." If nursing home staff has given you this excuse, don't simply accept that explanation at face value and assume that the nursing home "would know best." If your gut tells you something's wrong, or that common sense could have prevented the injury or harm, you should speak to a qualified nursing home neglect attorney before concluding that the incident was unavoidable and that the nursing home staff was not negligent.

Harm Required

Generally speaking, whether a lawsuit alleges that the nursing home was negligent, breached a contract with the patient, or otherwise failed to uphold a duty it owed to a patient, it must be demonstrated that the conduct complained of caused harm. As a practical matter, in most cases, it must be shown not just that the complained-of conduct caused harm, but that it caused *substantial* or *significant* harm.

It's important to understand that these lawsuits can be time-consuming, complex, and expensive for an attorney to bring. If it would not be expected that, at the end of the case, a jury would award a significant amount of money that would cover the costs of pursuing the case, it's unlikely that a lawyer will find the case viable. It's unfortunate, because the care complained of may be egregious. But if the negligence only caused minimal harm or no harm, it's unlikely that a jury could award an amount large enough to justify the expense of bringing the case.

For example, if a nursing home employee gives a patient the wrong medication, but there's no demonstrable harm to the patient, it's quite possible that this care failure would not serve as a viable claim to pursue by way of a civil lawsuit. Instead, this scenario may be better handled by a complaint to the state survey agency. State investigators don't need to find actual harm in order to cite the facility for providing deficient care and require the facility to develop and implement a Plan of Correction.

Similarly, if a patient who requires a two-person assist with transfers is assisted by only one nursing home aide and, as a result, falls back into her bed, landing safely and without injury, there's no clear harm that resulted from the negligent act. A jury in a civil suit would be unable to award significant, or perhaps any, damages at all. However, because the nursing staff clearly violated the patient's Plan of Care, which required a two-person assist for the purpose of safety, the conduct of the nursing home aide would represent substandard care and could support a finding of a quality of care deficiency if the matter were brought to the attention of the state survey agency.

On the other hand, in a circumstance whereby a patient is given the wrong medication and as a result, suffers an allergic reaction and requires a lengthy hospitalization or dies, these facts would certainly support the filing of a civil lawsuit. One could expect a jury to award substantial damages to compensate for the clear harm that would have directly resulted from the negligent act.

In a similar vein, using our prior example of the patient being transferred without adequate assistance, if that patient were to fall to the floor and strike her head, causing a subdural hematoma that resulted in death or a significant hospital stay, a civil lawsuit would be an appropriate vehicle to hold the nursing home accountable for the foreseeable harm that resulted from this negligent care failure.

It's important to keep in mind that every state has a different set of laws that apply to civil cases, including laws pertaining to nursing homes. The preceding discussion of damages is a general overview of the law in most jurisdictions; however, before deciding whether or not to pursue a civil case, you should consult an attorney in your state who's familiar with and experienced with your state's laws.

The Harm Exception: Qui Tam

One important exception to the general requirement that a civil suit requires the showing of substantial harm to a patient as a result of the nursing home's misconduct is a *qui tam* action or lawsuit. A qui tam action is a civil lawsuit in which one or more individual whistleblowers (also referred to as *relators*) provides information to the government which exposes the nursing home or defendant for charging the government for services that were not provided. This is actionable fraud.

These actions are typically brought under the Federal False Claims Act or similar state or local laws that forbid nursing homes or other healthcare providers from filing claims to receive government funds (e.g. Medicare, Medicaid, etc.) for healthcare services that were not actually provided as promised. The complaint is filed "under seal" for at least 60 days while the government investigates the allegations.

In qui tam cases, a whistleblower does not need to show that a particular patient suffered an injury, but rather that the government was defrauded out of taxpayer funds. As an incentive to the whistleblowers for exposing such misconduct, the Act allows for the whistleblower to receive a share (up to 30%) of the recovery from the government's recovery and attorney fees.

Whistleblowers in nursing home cases can be not only the patient or a patient's family, but anyone, including an employee of the nursing home corporation or a contractor who works within the facility.

Here are some examples of successful qui tam cases brought under the Federal False Claims Act:

- Extendicare Health Services Inc. agreed to a $38 million settlement for billing Medicare and Medicaid for substandard nursing services that were so deficient as to be relatively worthless and billing Medicare for medically unreasonable and unnecessary rehabilitation services (*United States ex rel. Lovvorn v. EHSI, et. al.; United States ex rel. Gallick et al.*).

- Plaza Health Network in Florida agreed to a $17 million Medicare fraud settlement for creating false records to cover up almost $130 million in improper Medicare and Medicaid payments between 2008 and 2011, and for violating the Anti-Kickback Statute when it paid physicians to pose as medical directors in exchange for Medicare patient referrals to its facilities (Whistleblower CFO Stephen Beacon, received $4.25 million of the settlement.)(*United States ex rel. Beaujon v. Hebrew Homes Health Network, Inc., et al.*).

- In 2016, the U.S. government filed suit against six Vanguard Healthcare LLC nursing home facilities, headquartered in Brentwood, Tennessee, alleging they submitted claims to Medicare and Medicaid for services that were either nonexistent or grossly substandard, and for submitting required nursing facility Pre-Admission forms with forged physician and nurse signatures. The alleged substandard care at the Vanguard facilities included: chronic understaffing, medical supplies shortages, failure to provide standard infection control, failure to administer medication as prescribed, failure to provide wound care as ordered by physicians, failure to adequately manage residents' pain and administering unnecessary and excessive psychotropic medications to residents and using unnecessary physical restraints on residents. As a result of these care failures, Vanguard residents allegedly suffered pressure ulcers, falls, dehydration and malnutrition, among other harms. (*United States vs. Vanguard, et. al.*) This case is still pending.

Statutes of Limitation

It's crucial to understand that you don't have unlimited time in which to file a lawsuit. Most, if not all states, have "statutes of limitation," which allow a limited period of time for a plaintiff to file a claim, or be forever barred from doing so. Determining the applicable statute of limitations or time frame can be exceedingly complicated in some states, depending upon the state and circumstances of the claim. It's critically important that you don't simply rely upon information that you may find on the Internet that purports to set forth the applicable statute of limitations in your state. Consult a qualified attorney to help determine the applicable statute of limitations in your specific case, and if necessary, whether any exception may apply to extend or shorten the period of time in which you can file suit.

There are typically exceptions which can either lengthen or shorten the time period to take action, depending on specific circumstances. For example, in some states, a statute of limitations may be extended if the victim is under a disability or is legally incompetent. In some states, the statute of limitations may be extended if the defendant fraudulently concealed facts which give rise to the claim from the plaintiff. Both of these exceptions, if they apply in your state, could be critical in cases involving nursing home neglect and abuse. Depending on the type of claim, there are other exceptions, as well, that may apply in certain jurisdictions. For example, statutes of limitation for negligence causes of action are usually shorter than those for breach of contract or fraud.

There may be important deadlines that pertain to your case, in addition to the statute of limitations. Generally speaking, in Indiana, for example, the statute of limitations is 2 years from the date of the negligent act for a case brought against a non-government-owned nursing home. But, unfortunately, the time frame for taking some action may be shortened in some circumstances. For example, in Indiana, there's been a trend towards county-owned hospitals purchasing a license to operate nursing homes in order to take advantage of certain Medicare/Medicaid loopholes that allow for higher reimbursement. Indiana law, however, requires, in some cases, that claims brought against a government-owned entity be preceded by the issuance of a *tort claim notice,* which must be sent to various related entities within *months* (180 days) of the incident of negligence, rather than within the time frame allowed for by the statute of limitations. The effect of this tort claim notice could be to bar claims that are brought within the statute of limitations, but for which the required notice was not sent within the shorter time frame allowed for by the tort claim notice requirement.

This means that it's imperative for you to do two things:

- Do not delay in seeking counsel if you have a claim that you *may* want to pursue by way of a civil lawsuit; and

- When you do consult counsel, make sure that the attorney you select has significant experience and is well-versed in handling nursing home abuse and neglect claims. (More about this later in this chapter.)

Finally, bear in mind that the statute of limitations sets forth the period of time you have to ensure that your case is *filed*, not concluded. Although a case may take years to work its way through the court system, the requirements of the statute of limitations have been met as long as the case is filed within the period of time prescribed by the statute of limitations, regardless of how long the case may take to conclude.

Should the Patient Be Removed From the Facility?

Often when families express concern about a patient's treatment, they're told: "If you didn't like the care we were providing, you could have taken the patient out of here." Problem is, in some cases, even when a patient has clearly suffered confirmed or suspected neglect or abuse, it's not feasible for the patient to be moved from the nursing home facility. While it may technically be feasible, it may not be in the patient's best interests. For example, in some smaller communities, there may only be one nursing home facility within miles of the patient's family. If the family is unable to visit a nursing home many miles away as frequently as they would otherwise be able to (e.g., due to work, school, or other family obligations), not only would a relocation be detrimental in that it would reduce the time that the patient can spend with his/her family and vice versa, it also reduces the amount of time that the family will have to monitor the care being provided to the patient.

In other cases, the level of care that the patient requires may only be available at a particular facility within a community, even if there are other nursing homes located in that community. For example, if only one nursing home in a community provides tracheotomy care, there may be no reasonable alternative for the family other than to leave the patient in the original facility, despite concerns about previous negligence or abuse that occurred.

This "no reasonable alternative" scenario can create a difficult dilemma for the family and/or patient. For example, if a patient is neglected and suffers a fall that results in a broken hip and subsequent surgery and hospitalization, the family is left with significant medical bills related to the harm caused by the nursing home's neglect. The patient may have no other options in terms of nursing facilities that can provide the necessary care, particularly after suffering such a fall. Nonetheless, the patient and/or the family is suddenly faced with significant and unexpected medical bills that are the sole result of the nursing home negligently allowing the patient to fall and suffer the injury.

Should the family be unable to seek compensation from the nursing home for the substantial medical bills that they incurred as a result of the negligence simply because they have no other option but to leave the patient at the facility? The technical answer is no. The law does not prevent, generally, a patient from bringing a civil lawsuit against a facility in which they still reside.

But a more difficult problem arises from concern that the nursing home facility may inflict some sort of retribution upon the patient for filing the lawsuit. There's also concern that the nursing home staff could exert some sort of undue influence upon the patient that would affect decisions being made with respect to the lawsuit.

There is no single universal answer as to how to best handle this type of circumstance; however, attorneys experienced in handling nursing home claims have likely dealt with this scenario before and may be able to offer some guidance. You should bring these issues to the attention of your attorney when you first discuss a potential claim with him or her. It's best to discuss the range of possible placement solutions at the outset before steps are undertaken to investigate the case, such as requesting medical records.

SHOULD YOU FILE A CIVIL LAWSUIT?

Sunlight Is the Best Disinfectant

If you're reading this book, chances are, it's because you have concerns about a nursing home's treatment of you or a loved one and you want answers, but are having trouble getting them from the nursing home facility.

Here's the reality: We see too often acts of nursing home neglect or abuse, and when the family expresses concern, the facility very rarely, if ever, voluntarily discloses what really happened, much less ever apologize or accept responsibility. In fact, nursing homes often respond with an arrogant defense to the effect of: "If you didn't like the care we were providing, you could have taken the patient out of here."

Too often, when the family asks for medical records, they have trouble getting them. Too often, when the state investigates their complaint, nothing comes of it because the records have been falsified, are incomplete, misrepresent what actually happened, or the staff witnesses have been coached into repeating a prepared narrative. The result is that the investigator can't prove the deficiency and the family receives a letter that contains language similar to this, which may vary from state to state:

> *"Each concern of your complaint was investigated. The evidence obtained by the investigation failed to support a violation of the Federal or State regulation. This does not mean that your complaint was unjustified, simply that there was not sufficient supporting evidence to substantiate a violation of the Federal or State regulations at the time the surveyors were present in the facility. With this investigation being completed, your complaint is now closed."*

The family now feels powerless to rectify the problem and hold the nursing home accountable.

Filing a lawsuit enables you to reclaim power. A lawsuit, executed properly, forces all parties to explain and account for what happened. Staff members still lie and medical records are still doctored, but the adversarial legal system, which includes the ability to subpoena records and witnesses, puts those involved in the care failures under oath. The right to cross-examine witnesses tends to expose the truth, and often, much more effectively than any other remedy a victim or a victim's family may have at their disposal.

The byproduct of using the legal system to get answers and shine a light on the dirty details of the neglect or abuse is often the payment of money to compensate for the harm that was inflicted by the exposed misconduct. Until the lawsuit is filed, the nursing home holds all the power... the power to hide records, hide witnesses, hide the truth. But after the lawsuit is filed, the patient (and patient's family) and the nursing home are — to the greatest extent allowed by law — put on equal footing. The civil lawsuit is the great leveler. And as we'll discuss in the next chapter, too many states still have laws that serve to protect bad nursing homes, but nursing homes can't entirely run and hide when a lawsuit has been filed against them.

Here's an example of a tragic case that demonstrates what filing a lawsuit can accomplish in terms of getting answers and accountability...

Carl was born during the depression in rural Kentucky. His mother died when he was 10 years old, his father when he was 13. Carl and his siblings were forced to raise themselves and each other. At age 18, he taught himself to read. At age 21, he met and married his wife with whom he raised three children. After his wife of 43 years passed, Carl remained active and involved in his children's and grandchildren's lives.

After undergoing successful surgery to repair a fractured leg at the age of 75, Carl was admitted to a local nursing home for rehabilitative therapy so that he could return home to independent living.

One morning, while in the care of the nursing home staff, Carl exhibited classic early signs and symptoms of a heart attack. He first reported dizziness and shortness of breath. He was then noted by staff to look pale and complained of indigestion, telling the nurse, "I don't feel well. My chest feels like it's filling up." Despite these ominous red flags, the nursing staff took no vital signs, performed no further assessment, and chose not to notify Carl's physician or family.

But 45 minutes later, Carl appeared anxious. Still no assessment or call to his physician or family. Fifteen minutes later, nursing staff observed that Carl was unable to stand even with two people assisting him, who heard him complain of "chest discomfort" and noticed him having trouble breathing. Nursing staff later testified that they knew these were basic signs and symptoms of a heart attack, yet they still chose not to notify Carl's physician or family.

As Carl was complaining of chest pain another 20 minutes later, nursing finally called Carl's physician, who ordered that Carl be sent to the emergency room immediately. Nursing still chose to wait for at least another 20 minutes before calling an ambulance to transport Carl. A few minutes later, Carl was unresponsive. By the time the ambulance arrived, it was too late. Carl's children and grand children would never enjoy his company again.

Carl's death didn't have to happen. For more than one hour and forty-five minutes, it was entirely foreseeable that Carl was having a heart attack and needed emergency attention. Had the nursing staff called the ambulance when they should have, Carl would have been alive when he arrived at the hospital and could have still received treatment for his heart attack.

After Carl died, his family had questions about what had transpired. The nursing home callously and arrogantly chose to ignore the family's questions and refused to offer the answers they were entitled to.

In an effort to ensure that they received the answers and accountability they deserved, Carl's family decided to file a civil lawsuit. Their decision was driven in significant part by a concern for the care that others were receiving — now and in the future — at this nursing facility. If their very legitimate questions and concerns were being ignored, what incentive would the nursing home have to correct their mistakes, do what was necessary to ensure it never happened again, and be accountable to other patients and their families?

The nursing home claimed that staff did not delay significantly in getting Carl to the ER after Carl's doctor ordered immediate transport to the hospital, but the doctor's testimony would reveal otherwise. The doctor didn't want to be involved in pointing the finger or affixing blame — he also just happened to be the medical director of this small town nursing home, making him responsible for developing and implementing policies and procedures for care.

But once the lawsuit against the nursing home was filed, we subpoenaed the doctor, requiring him to testify in a deposition. The doctor's testimony revealed the nursing home administrator's arrogant defiance, lack of empathy and sense of responsibility, as this deposition excerpt demonstrates…

> **Q:** *When did you speak with her [the administrator] about it [patient's heart attack], or him [the patient]?*
>
> **A:** *When it happened.*
>
> **Q.** *What did you talk about?*
>
> **A.** *That she needs to call the family. And she wouldn't.*
>
> **Q.** *What do you mean by that? She needs to call the family and advise them of the death?*
>
> **A:** *Things at the nursing home did not happen very smoothly. The family had a lot of questions. The family was not happy with the care at the nursing home. I really felt that if the administrator were to have called, you know, and talked to the family and consoled them, I thought the family would be satisfied with that.*
>
> **Q:** *What did the administrator say?*
>
> **A:** *There's no way she's calling them.*
>
> **Q:** *Did she say why?*
>
> **A:** *She was rather nasty about it.*
>
> **Q.** *You mentioned that the administrator said that — just said she wasn't calling the family, as sort of a matter of fact — in sort of a matter of fact way. Do you remember, did she say why she wouldn't call the family and talk to them?*
>
> **A:** *She wasn't a compassionate person. So — yeah, I think she just wasn't compassionate.*

Carl's doctor felt that if the nursing home explained the care failure (not sending Carl to hospital after clear, multiple symptoms that he was having a heart attack until it was too late) and apologized for the errors, the family would have forgiven what happened and moved on. Instead, the arrogant nursing home administrator refuses to give Carl's family answers and access to his medical records, and the family must ultimately filing suit to get both, as this excerpt of the doctor's testimony illustrates…

> **A:** *And then I think the family wanted to see the charts. And she made them go get an attorney and everything. Which they're*

going to see the chart, anyhow. And I just really think this could have just, you know...

Q. *So the family wanted to see the chart, and the nursing home administrator denied access?*

A. *Yeah. That was one of the main things.*

The doctor's testimony also revealed his belief that the nursing home had later falsified Carl's medical records to cover up their errors.

Q. *Was it appropriate for the nurse to take those vitals at that point in time?*

A. *She felt that — she felt it necessary to check it at that time, I guess. Do those vital signs jump out at you as being extremely bothersome?*

A. *You know, is the heart rate 78 or 98? I can't tell. It looks like it's been, you know, altered.*

When nursing home staff called the doctor back to notify him that Carl was en route to the hospital, the doctor was shocked that they had not already sent Carl sooner. The following excerpt from the doctor's deposition revealed some of the nursing home staff's blatant care failures...

A. *I've only had five patients who died in the emergency room — less than that — who survived going to the hospital after they had been dead in the nursing home, and they were brain dead. So the answer for your peer review, yeah, his outcome was already done. He was already to the critical stage. And you had a 15-minute ambulance ride, to boot, on top of that. But if he would have been sent out and he was in the emergency room, heart beating, blood pressure and everything, could it have been different? The answer is yes, it could have been. So that's my point.*

I have one thing that bothers me the most. Why did not my patient get sent out when I said to send him out? Because I've got a question. Six years has elapsed. I still remember being in my bedroom when I got that telephone call that we finally got him in an ambulance and he doesn't look real good. Why does that stick in my head six years later?

Q. How much time had elapsed between those two calls?

A. I don't know. Enough to sit there and say, are you for real, he hasn't been shipped yet? You know, it's like, really, that's why I was on my way to the emergency room, because I really thought I would catch him at the emergency room.

Q. Your order, telephone call with the facility, happened at 8:35 --

A. Correct.

Q. -- a.m. Is that 20-minute gap consistent with your expectation of what was going to happen at the nursing home?

A. No.

Q. Would you agree with me that a 20-minute gap between your conversation and the nursing home calling 9-1-1 is a breach in the standard of care?

A. I'm not sure what a standard of care is. I don't think it's reasonable.

Q. It's not what should have happened?

A. No.

Q. And having been medical director at the facility, are you confident that the nursing staff at the facility should have known better than to wait 20 minutes to make a 9-1-1 call after it's been ordered?

A. Yes.

Q. Okay. And the same would be true if it were 15 or 10 minutes; right?

A. If I get a telephone call, almost right away.

Q. Within a minute or two?

A. It actually would have been the first thing done.

Q. And again, I know this sounds like a silly question, but why is it important to carry out an order to call 9-1-1 immediately, when a physician says to do that?

A. We need to get into a location that we can deal with the medical situation.

Q. Goes back to the "minutes matter" thing?

A. Minutes matter.

As you can see, the nursing home's defense that they acted promptly is undercut by their own medical director's testimony that they didn't. If not for this lawsuit, these facts would never have been exposed.

Civil Lawsuits Do Take Time

It's important to keep in mind that filing a civil lawsuit is just one of the first steps. It can take time to conclude the case and achieve your goal. While we in the United States have what may be considered the greatest justice system in the world, it's important to recognize at the outset that civil lawsuits can take time. It's not uncommon for a civil lawsuit to take years to conclude, depending upon the complexity of the suit.

Typically, medical records and other information must be gathered prior to filing suit in order to assess the merits of the claim and the viability of proceeding with a lawsuit. Once the lawsuit is filed with the court, the procedural rules that will govern the lawsuit allow for the parties to conduct *discovery* of facts and information relevant to the claims being made. Discovery can take several forms…

Interrogatories are a form of discovery that allow the parties to send written questions to the other side which require answers. *Requests for production* are a form of discovery that allows parties to request documents and other tangible items from the other side. Parties may also send a *request for admission* to the other side, which requests the other side to admit or deny certain facts. In addition to these written forms of discovery, the parties can typically conduct oral *depositions* of witnesses, experts, and other parties to the litigation. This typically involves conducting a question and answer session before a court reporter and/or videographer, depending upon the rules of the particular jurisdiction.

Depending upon the complexity of the case and the number of parties, the scheduling and completion of discovery can take months, or in some cases, years. If there are disputes concerning discovery, those disputes may have to be addressed by the court in the interim. Discovery disputes can further delay the prosecution of the case. Eventually, if the case is not settled, the court will set the case for trial. The scheduling of the trial date can sometimes be delayed depending upon the schedule of the court.

The bottom line is that nursing home cases are often complex and time consuming cases for the attorneys, if the case is properly prosecuted. While many cases are settled by the parties prior to trial — in some instances, either prior to filing the suit, or within a reasonably short period of time after the case is filed — one should always be prepared for the long haul if a trial is necessary to bring about justice.

But don't let this discourage you from seeking counsel from a qualified attorney. An attorney experienced in handling nursing home neglect and abuse cases will be more likely to recognize and avoid potential pitfalls that can delay and hinder the case. An attorney familiar with the issues that arise in these cases will also likely be better able to recognize, for example, whether a settlement offer is truly and fairly reflective of the egregiousness of the conduct and the extent of the harm. It's also true that a quick settlement that undervalues a claim not only fails to adequately compensate the victim(s), but also fails to adequately hold the defendant nursing home accountable and undermines the ability of the lawsuit to serve as a deterrent for future misconduct.

HOW TO HELP BUILD YOUR CASE

In addition to consulting a qualified attorney as soon as you believe you may have reason to file a civil suit, there are additional steps you can take to help ensure that your attorney has the information and documentation necessary to provide you with the best evaluation, investigation, and prosecution of your case.

Keep Every Document Related to the Nursing Home.

It's wise to keep every document you've received over the course of your interaction with the nursing home. You never know what may be important to your attorney in terms of prosecuting your case. This may include the following items:

- Any marketing brochures or materials that were used to market the facility to you.

- Nursing home personnel business cards.

- All billing statements from the nursing home and evidence of payment.

- Patient admission agreement and all authorizations signed at the time of admission.

- Any contract that the facility may have required you to sign, including a forced arbitration clause.

- Patient rulebooks or handbooks of any kind.

- Medical records you provided to, or received from, the nursing home.

- Complaints or grievance forms that you filed relating to the nursing home's care.

- Any documentation that may have been received from the resident or family council.

- Any policies and procedures documents that the nursing home may have provided to you.

- Any powers of attorney or guardianship papers that may have been provided to the nursing home.

Provide Photographs If Possible.

As the saying goes, a picture is worth a thousand words. If you observe any visible indications of neglect or abuse, photograph these physical signs, if you're comfortable doing so. Take photographs from multiple angles and at varying distances.

Visible evidence could include (but is not limited to):

- pressure sores

- open wounds, skin tears, bruises, scratches, rashes

- markings indicating that restraints were used

- excoriation to the groin or other areas

- unexplained scabs
- dirty or unkempt fingernails or toenails, dirty ears, dirty or sore mucus membranes in the mouth or nose, dirty or greasy hair
- evidence of bug bites
- undergarments or bedding that appears to be evidence of urine or feces having been there for a prolonged period of time, dirty catheters or catheter bags

These are only examples, so try to be vigilant and photograph *anything* that indicates that the patient is not receiving proper and timely care. Because different states may have different laws related to taking photographs inside a healthcare facility, it may be advisable to discuss the matter with a nursing-home-neglect attorney, if there's time to do so, before taking photos. In any event, it's always important to make sure that you do not photograph other patients or particulars that would violate their privacy.

Take Names.

Nursing homes are notorious for having extraordinarily high turnover rates. In six months, a patient may have virtually all new health care providers caring for them. To avoid forgetting or losing track of caregiver names that you may not remember later, it's wise to write down the first and last names of the nursing staff and physicians who are seeing the patient and keep a time/date log of when these caregivers saw them to the extent possible. If those staff members later leave the facility for other employment, your attorney can attempt to locate them if he or she knows their first and last names. Former employees can be critical witnesses in the prosecution of a nursing home neglect and abuse case.

If you meet other patients and their family members, it's also advisable to keep track of their names. Often, families of nursing home patients exchange contact information if they come to know each other through their visits to the facility. It could prove to be extraordinarily helpful for your attorney to have contact information for any of the patient's roommates, or the roommate's family members who would have been present and would have observed events pertinent to your case. Certainly these other patients and their family members can speak to issues of understaffing, unanswered call bells, and other indicators of neglectful care. Nursing home staff are often resistant to providing contact information for a patient's roommate after a case has been filed, citing privacy concerns. However, the over-riding reason for this refusal is more likely that they know these individuals can provide revealing information related to the case. So by obtaining other patients' (and their families') contact information directly from them early on, you won't have to rely upon the nursing home to provide it when once they've decided it's in their best interest not to.

Other Issues.

If the patient at issue has since passed away, it's helpful to obtain a copy of the death certificate and an autopsy report, if any. All medical bills and funeral or burial expenses should also be provided to the attorney.

Not all of the materials discussed above may apply to your case, and others may be long lost. However, keeping what you have and providing it to your attorney will help expedite the process.

HOW TO CHOOSE A LAWYER

If you learned that you must undergo surgery, chances are, you'd endeavor to find the most qualified surgeon with experience in handling the particular procedure that you are to undergo. The reason for this is simple: experience and familiarity with subject matter are critical keys to success. This is true of most professions, and it's certainly true with respect to finding the right lawyer to handle a nursing home neglect or abuse case.

Medical negligence cases are a very specialized type of personal injury case and thus are very likely best handled by a lawyer with significant experience in prosecuting them. Healthcare negligence cases require deep knowledge of the applicable "standard of care" for the healthcare provider defendant (e.g. doctor, hospital, nursing home, etc.). In order to know whether the nursing home employee or physician was negligent, the lawyer must know how the healthcare provider was supposed to act under those particular circumstances. Specialized healthcare knowledge is not something that every attorney has. In addition, an attorney who handles a nursing home neglect and abuse case must be qualified, experienced, and prepared to vigorously navigate the case through the various legal hurdles imposed upon professional negligence cases and take the matter to trial, if necessary.

Not every attorney, or even every personal injury attorney, has this preparation and experience. Nursing home neglect and abuse cases are also often complex and expensive for the attorney to pursue due to the need to hire medical experts to consult and assist with the case. Not every lawyer or law firm is prepared to adequately devote the resources necessary to vigorously prosecute such a case. In short, there are many lawyers, and many law firms that advertise that they're "personal injury lawyers," but that doesn't mean they have the necessary experience and resources to prosecute the case in the manner you may desire. Be diligent in researching the lawyer or law firm that you're thinking of hiring to make sure they meet the criteria we've discussed.

It bears mentioning that, most experienced attorneys handle nursing home cases on a contingency fee basis (no fees required from the client until a monetary recovery is obtained). It should also be noted that a capable attorney experienced in nursing home matters will likely charge the same approximate contingency fee as one who is less qualified to handle your case.

Here are some important questions to ask:

- How many nursing home neglect and abuse cases have you handled?
- Are you financially prepared to devote the resources necessary to hire the proper experts and adequately present the case through trial?
- Will you be handling my case personally, or will you be referring it to another lawyer to handle with you?
- Will an attorney oversee my case or just a paralegal?
- Will I be responsible for any upfront expenses or fees?

Final Thoughts: Making An Impact

I've been fortunate to have worked with patients and families in litigating hundreds of nursing home neglect and healthcare negligence cases. Though it wasn't necessarily always easy, these patients and families have done what they could to help hold bad nursing homes and healthcare providers accountable by forcing them to make restitution (by way of jury verdict and/or pre-trial settlement), in some cases, multimillion dollar payments. Not every case results in a nursing home forking over multimillion dollar payments; however, every dollar paid by a nursing home to account and compensate for harm that they could have prevented serves as another incentive for them to ensure that the proper safety measures are put in place to avoid similar harm in the future, and similar payouts in the future. The patients and families who have had the courage stand up to bad nursing homes and careless healthcare providers have not only helped right the wrongs inflicted upon them, but have made a lasting impact that will help prevent the same thing from happening to someone else.

TIPS

- Keep *all* documents related to the nursing home and present them to your attorney. You never know what documents may be useful if you need to file a civil suit down the road.

- Obtain photographic evidence of neglect or abuse with documentation of the dates and time.

- Keep track of the full names of all nursing home employees involved in caring for the patient, as well as the contact information for other patients (and their families) who may be able to provide relevant information.

- In choosing an attorney, the key is find one who focuses his/her practice on — and has extensive experience in handling — nursing home cases, rather than simply choosing an attorney whose practice focuses on the broader category of medical malpractice cases.

15

WHAT TO EXPECT:
NURSING HOME EXCUSES & TACTICS

An excuse is worse and more terrible than a lie;
for an excuse is a lie guarded.

— **Alexander Pope**

Ninety-nine percent of the failures come from people who
have the habit of making excuses.

— **George Washington Carver**

If you've been forced to confront a nursing home for neglecting or abusing you or a loved one, this chapter will help you anticipate and prepare for the nursing home facility's response. Your efforts to hold the facility accountable will likely be met with one or more of the excuses and tactics you're about to read. But by the time you finish this chapter, you'll know them when you see them and be able to recognize them for what they are: shameless attempts to protect profit by shirking responsibility.

Nursing homes are quite skilled and practiced at making excuses because patients and their families so frequently have good reason to confront them, just as shady used car dealers can be highly skilled at dodging the many customers to whom they've sold a lemon. Nursing home administrators have a lot of experience — and often, actual training — in what they refer to as "risk management," which, in many contexts, is just a fancy term for *avoiding blame.*

But…

Don't let nursing home excuses and tactics deter or discourage you from pursuing accountability. In fact, often, these same outrageous excuses and tactics can actually be used to expose a nursing home for not only harming the patient, but also running from responsibility. They're the healthcare equivalent of a hit-and-run. It's one thing to run a stop sign and hit and injure a pedestrian; it's another thing to run a stop sign, hit and injure a pedestrian, then take off in an attempt to avoid responsibility for your actions. Yet, this is what many nursing homes effectively do to their patients.

This chapter is intended to level the playing field by enabling you to see through — and even anticipate — the excuses and defenses that the nursing home industry commonly employs so that you won't be deterred from your pursuit of accountability and can move forward with your attorney to help mount a successful offense. In reality, there are so many excuses used by nursing homes that it's beyond the scope of this book to cover them all. So we'll focus upon four common categories.

TOP 4 BOGUS NURSING HOME EXCUSES & TACTICS

Those responsible for operating the nursing home rarely acknowledge its care failures, or voluntarily accept responsibility for neglecting or abusing a patient. Instead, the nursing home industry playbook typically involves using one or more of these tactics: cover-up, denial, or deflecting blame.

Excuse #1: "The medical records prove that we provided good care."

In far too many nursing homes, patient care records are inaccurate, falsified or later doctored to reflect that care was properly provided when it wasn't. During "charting parties," as they're sometimes called in the industry, the nursing staff go back at the end of the week or month and document the medical record to "fill in the holes" in the chart. Those "holes" represent those times when the patient did not receive showers, grooming, turning and repositioning, skin inspections, medications, or other care that they were supposed to receive. The facility knows that leaving these "holes" in the chart may mean that it will be held accountable by state surveyors or found liable in civil suits for the failure to provide the care that the patient needed, and for which they are fraudulently billing Medicare, Medicaid, private insurance, or the patient or patient's family.

This willingness to falsify records pertains not just to instances when the nursing home failed to provide care. So many nursing homes permit — or even *encourage* — the staff to falsely document (or not document at all) *sentinel events*, which are unusual occurrences that result in an injury or harm to the patient. Take, for example, a situation where the nursing home staff recognizes that a patient fell. This is an unusual occurrence or sentinel event that should be documented because it has very serious implications for the patient's well-being and may necessitate a modification of the patient's care plan.

Too often, nursing home staff choose not to document known patient falls in the medical record at all, essentially whitewashing the medical record of evidence of possible neglect or abuse. For example, consider the case of Evelyn, whom we discussed in *Chapter 5: Falls*. Evelyn's fall was concealed, not documented in her medical record, but the 911 tape revealed that she had been allowed to fall.

In some instances, the nursing home will document the fall on a special form that's not included in the medical record, which they often claim is covered by a "quality assurance" or some other legal privilege that allows them to keep the contents of the document secret and private. So when the family requests a copy of the medical record, there's no mention of the fall. Bad nursing homes hope that if they simply document in their medical records that they provided good care, they will be immune from the obvious and undeniable reality of the harm their neglect has inflicted upon a patient.

But the failure to completely and accurately document the patient's record is a violation of federal regulations. It's also negligence in its own right. Why? Because a patient relies upon healthcare providers to accurately document the care they receive — it's an integral part of caregiving. It is a solemn responsibility. "Continuity of care" depends upon subsequent healthcare providers being able to determine from the medical records what care and treatments were administered to a patient and how it affected them so that they can properly assess the patient, provide care, and plan future care. Second, only the healthcare provider, through his or her documentation, can *account* for what he or she did to a patient. Patients, particularly in the nursing home setting, are at the mercy of the nursing staff being self-accountable for their own conduct. Often, there's no one else around to ensure that this critical information is being recorded.

Take, for example, the case of a patient who is bed-bound, immobile and at risk for developing pressure sores. It's important to accurately document when that patient was last turned and repositioned so other staff members will know when the patient next needs to be turned; to enable caregivers to assess the effectiveness of the turning and repositioning schedule thus avoiding dangerous prolonged pressure to vulnerable areas; and to develop the proper plan of care moving forward. If staff records that they properly turned the patient but didn't, they put the patient at risk of developing life-threatening pressure wounds. They also undermine the ability of staff to determine whether the patient's care plan needs to be modified to better protect the patient from developing pressure sores.

Response: While this unfortunate "defense" is common, it is also commonly defeated. There are a variety ways in which your attorney and his/her experts can expose, through meticulous analysis, this type of fraudulent medical record documentation. For example, by cross-referencing nursing home medical record entries with other evidence — such as employee time cards, signature sheets, work schedules, and other medical records — inconsistencies can be found, which demonstrate that the records were falsified. It's not uncommon to find instances where the nursing staff documented that they bathed and repositioned a patient on days when the patient was not even present in the nursing home because he or she had been admitted to another facility (e.g., a hospital) for treatment. It's also common to find nursing staff documenting that they provided care on days when they didn't even work, according to their time cards. Forensic examination of the paper records can also reveal forgeries and after-the-fact documentation. And, with the implementation of electronic medical record charting, it's now possible to extract electronic data and metadata from the medical record system that shows who altered or deleted records, and when.

Lies have a way of being exposed, especially during the litigation process. When nursing homes falsify and alter medical record evidence, as they often do, they risk the significant likelihood of compounding their troubles by having to explain this additional and intentional misconduct to a jury or judge.

Excuse #2: "Despite what the medical records say, we provided good care."

Even in cases where the patient's nursing home medical records either contain information that evidences neglect or abuse, or have been revealed to contain falsified information, the nursing home and their attorneys often still argue that the facility gave excellent care despite the "record problems." Nursing homes often argue that "there is a difference between *giving* care and *documenting* care," and that they would rather devote their resources to giving proper care than making sure the care they provide is documented properly. And, even in cases where the records unequivocally prove negligent care, the nursing home will sometimes argue that they should not be held accountable for those instances of negligence because, after all, if you look at the entire patient residency, they met the "overall standard of care."

Response: This type of defense can be dealt with and exposed for what it is: a self-serving attempt to ignore clear evidence of negligence. First, there is no such thing as an "overall standard of care." The bottom line is that if the nursing home is negligent and causes the patient harm, at any time — even *one time* — it is still negligent, and can be held accountable. Nursing homes are not entitled to a free pass even if they can show that they only neglected a patient on one day or several days of the patient's residency, rather than most days or every day.

The nursing home's argument that it has its staff focus on care rather than documentation is also revealing: By excusing yourself for something, you admit that you did it. Or, as 16th century French writer, Gabriel Merrier, put it: "He who excuses himself accuses himself." This excuse shows that the facility management recklessly puts its nursing staff in a position where they don't have enough time or staffing to render proper hands-on care while *also* properly documenting the medical record to ensure continuity of care.

Any nursing home that makes its staff choose between providing the hands-on care that the patient needs *or* properly documenting the patient's care in accordance with the law and accepted nursing standards of care is a nursing home that is knowingly and systematically neglecting its patients' needs. Documenting the medical record is not an optional, unnecessary task that can simply be ignored. Documenting the care that was actually provided and the patient's response to it is *part of* providing proper care because it indicates to all caregivers what care is still needed, how the patient is responding to each treatment, and whether a care plan modification is required.

Poor documentation is indicative of poor care, period. And that's exactly why the law requires nursing homes to accurately and completely document the medical record.

Excuse #3: "It was the patient's fault."

Blaming the victim is a common defense used by nursing homes. As if neglecting a patient and possibly falsifying records to hide it weren't bad enough, many nursing homes try to divert attention from their own misconduct by claiming that whatever harm befell the patient was his/her own fault. Unfortunately, in many cases, the patient is no longer alive or able to give his/her own version of events, so the nursing home staff are often the only witnesses to the incident or series of incidents that gave rise to the harm. When the patient is unable to tell his/her side of the story, it becomes all-too-convenient for the nursing home to blame the patient.

For example, nursing homes that allow patients to develop advanced, deadly pressure sores from unrelieved pressure to the skin often claim, after the fact, of course, that it was the patient's fault, arguing the patient "refused" to turn and reposition. It was the patient's refusal that caused the pressure sores to develop, they claim — the nursing home staff didn't do anything wrong.

If a patient is allowed to suffer falls that result in injury, the nursing home often tries to blame the patient, claiming that he tried to get out of bed alone to go to the restroom without assistance, instead of waiting for staff to answer the call light.

The nursing home may also try to blame the patient in a roundabout way by arguing that the patient's other medical conditions caused the harm, not their neglect. For example, in pressure sore cases, nursing homes will argue that the patient's medical conditions — such as diabetes, peripheral vascular disease, incontinence, or other conditions — were to blame, making the pressure sores "clinically unavoidable." They imply that pressure sores would have developed no matter how well the nursing home cared for the patient. In a similar vein, when the nursing home staff finds a patient lying on the ground with a broken hip, they often blames the patient's age and brittle bones. They claim that the hip broke "spontaneously," causing the patient to fall, rather than the patient breaking her hip because she was allowed to suffer a severe fall, landing on the hip.

Response: Blaming the patient for their own neglect is a shameless, desperate act on the part of the nursing homes that do it. It's not unlike the child abuser blaming the baby for crying too much. Blaming the victim is an attempt to divert attention from the truth. If the patients were perfectly healthy, they wouldn't be in a nursing home to begin with, and care is, after all, the service that the nursing is selling those patients.

Fortunately, there are strategies your attorney can use to combat these blatant attempts to avoid responsibility. Take the nursing home pressure sore arguments, for example. Most patients who can reposition themselves do so naturally, because it's uncomfortable and even painful to lie in the same position for a prolonged period of time, placing unrelenting pressure on the skin over a bony prominence, such as the tailbone area, the hips, the buttocks, and the heels. Whether we're consciously aware of it or not, our bodies, if able, will naturally shift positions to prevent this type of prolonged pressure and resulting injury. You've probably noticed this urge to self-reposition when lying in bed in one position for too long, or when lying in an MRI machine for even a relatively short period of time.

Just because a patient is physically incapable of repositioning himself doesn't mean he wouldn't still feel that urge to be repositioned to relieve pressure on affected areas, nor does it imply that he would have reason to refuse assistance from nursing staff. And even if a patient *did* resist the nursing staff's efforts to reposition him, it's still incumbent upon the nursing staff to determine *why* the patient is resisting and remove that obstacle. The facility is obligated to perform a nursing assessment and implement a plan of care that addresses any difficulty the patient may have in complying with the nursing staff's efforts. For example, if a patient is suffering from so much pain that he cannot bear to be repositioned, a proper assessment must be performed and the care plan needs to be modified to ensure that his pain is adequately controlled.

Similarly, in the fall example, it's not the fault of a patient who attempts to arise from bed and make it to the restroom in time without assistance because her call light went unanswered due to understaffing. Although nursing homes rarely document it, it's quite common for patients to report that they called for help to get out of bed, but no one answered their call. So their only two choices were to soil themselves or attempt to make it to the restroom alone.

Unanswered call lights are not the fault of the patient. *It's the fault of the nursing home.* Furthermore, it's the responsibility of the nursing staff to *anticipate* patients' toileting needs and ensure that those needs are met so that patients aren't forced to risk going to the restroom unassisted to avoid suffering the humiliation and indignity of soiling themselves.

Finally, it's almost always inappropriate and unfounded for a nursing home to blame a patient's medical condition for creating some "unavoidable" injury. The nursing home has an affirmative duty to demonstrate that they've implemented every appropriate precaution, and have implemented it *diligently*. For then, and only then, can the nursing home suggest that despite having given entirely proper care, the pressure sore, femur fracture, or other injury was somehow unavoidable.

Excuse #4: "It was the patient's family's fault."

Another tactic that those responsible for poor nursing care use to divert attention and avoid accountability is to bully or blame the patient's family, implying that they caused or contributed to the care failures.

Tactic: In cases where patients were not properly supervised or protected from falling and suffering serious injury, nursing homes often claim that "the family agreed that the patient was not going to be tied down with restraints, so they were taking the risk that this would happen."

Response: This argument, of course, ignores the fact that there are other fall prevention measures besides the use of restraints, which can and should be implemented according to the patient's needs. This tactic is like arguing that because bicyclists know that once they get on the road, they could be struck by a motor vehicle, a drunk driver who plows through a stop sign and kills that bicyclist should not be held responsible because the bicyclist "took the risk that this could happen."

Tactic: In some cases, nursing homes will argue that the family somehow "prevented" the nursing home from rendering proper care. For example, in a pressure sore case, a nursing home may argue that the family instructed them *not* to turn and reposition the patient.

Response: The problem is, if the nursing staff believed the family was preventing them from giving the care they felt the patient needed, they had a duty to document that issue in the nursing home medical record and to educate the family about the issue so that the family would understand and consent to the care. If the family still didn't agree after having been properly educated about this issue, it's still the nursing home's responsibility to protect the well-being of the patient, with or without the family's consent. It's simply not legitimate for the nursing home to hide behind the argument that the family stood in the way of providing necessary care, without seeking further intervention and/or education.

If you sense that the nursing home may be trying to use this disingenuous excuse for not providing proper care to your loved one, you should make your concerns known to a third party, such as state investigators or an Ombudsman as soon as possible so that you'll have credible witnesses who can rebut the facility's baseless claim.

Tactic: Nursing homes will often argue that the family attended, or had the opportunity to attend, patient care conferences and did not object to the care plan that was discussed at that time; therefore, the facility should not be held responsible because the care plan did not protect the patient from harm.

Response: This argument is bogus for any number of reasons. First, many nursing homes claim that they invite the patient's family to the patient care conference, but far fewer actually make a serious effort to inform the family of the date and time that the care conference will be held, or schedule the conference at a time that accommodates family member work schedules, child care and other obligations. And even in cases where the facility schedules the conference at a time that's convenient for the family, it's unlikely that the risks and benefits of the various care plan interventions will be fully explored with the family, assuming they're even discussed at all. But perhaps most importantly, those nursing home employees responsible for ensuring that proper care is rendered in the facility are the "experts" upon whom the patient and the patient's family must rely to develop and implement a care plan that includes the interventions necessary to keep the patient safe.

Families rarely, if ever, look forward to the day that they must acknowledge that the patient can no longer care for himself or herself and accept that they are unable to provide the necessary care that skilled professionals in a nursing home can provide. This is the service that nursing homes aggressively market to patients and their families. But they're required to have a sufficient number of trained, qualified, professional healthcare providers to ensure that the patient receives the necessary care and services to attain and maintain the highest practicable physical, mental, and psychosocial well-being.

Tactic: Nursing homes will often make after-the-fact arguments that they should not be held accountable for alleged abuse or neglect because the family made no complaint to the administrator or director of nursing while the care was being provided.

Response: This argument ignores the reality that many patients and families rarely (or never) meet the facility administrator or director of nursing; rather, they're accustomed to discussing problems directly with the nursing aides and floor nurses with whom they interact and who are directly responsible for the providing care to the patient. In such circumstances, families are routinely assured by staff that corrective measures will be taken, whether that turns out to be the case or not. Often, for example, family members express their concerns about finding the patient in soiled clothing or left lying in the same position for an extended period of time to the nurse aides who personally provide care to the patient and/or to the nurse aides' supervising nurses, rather than to the director of nursing or facility administrator whom they never see because they're tucked away in their offices and only in the facility during regular workday hours.

But this doesn't mean that the family didn't make their concerns known and attempt to rectify the problem at the time of the incident. It certainly doesn't let the facility off the hook. The facility can still be held responsible for providing substandard care that harmed a patient.

Tactic: Nursing homes often criticize families for holding a nursing home accountable for neglect or abuse when the family didn't file a complaint with the state investigative agency.

Response: While this book shows you how to file such a complaint, the reality is that many, if not most, families wouldn't have otherwise known how to go about requesting an investigation by the state surveyors. The fact that these families didn't file a complaint with the state agency, of course, has nothing to do with whether the nursing home neglected the patient or not. And, for that matter, it's also the responsibility of nursing home staff to notify the state of neglect and abuse; therefore, it would be reasonable for families to assume that the facility would have reported the incident themselves.

The argument that the family is to blame for not filing a complaint also ignores the fact that when a patient is harmed or killed due to the nursing home's negligence or abuse, the family's attention during this emotional time certainly may not be solely focused on the procedural mechanics of lodging a regulatory complaint. Some families are knowledgeable and do file a formal complaint, while, for a variety of reasons (e.g., fear of retaliation), others do not. Regardless, the nursing home's attempt to divert attention from their own misconduct by nitpicking the fact that a family did not file a regulatory complaint while in the throes of coping with the discovery that a family member was abused or neglected is desperate and despicable.

Tactic: To add insult to injury, nursing homes will also attempt to deflect attention from their own care failures or discourage families from pursuing a civil suit by taking jabs at the family members who are seeking to hold them accountable. These types of personal attacks may, for example, take the form of insinuating that the family filed the lawsuit because they felt guilty about placing the patient in the nursing home to begin with and that blaming the nursing home is a misdirected attempt to assuage their own guilt.

Response: Well, while placing a loved one in a nursing home can no doubt be a difficult decision, families don't sue nursing homes when the patient was placed in the facility and received the high-quality care they were promised. Families sue nursing homes because they failed to do what they were responsible for doing and harmed or killed a patient. Of course a family member, with the hindsight of realizing that the nursing home he or she chose has neglected or abused the patient, may feel remorse or regret about the choice of nursing home. But by accepting a patient into the nursing home, the facility is confirming that the patient needs the type of care they provide, and promising that it is capable of — and *will* — provide the care that the patient needs. Thus, the family's reason for filing suit has nothing to do with their guilt over placing their loved one in the nursing home. But it has everything to do with the nursing home's failure to deliver the care it promised the family it could provide.

Tactic: It's not uncommon for nursing homes to try to stir feelings of guilt in family members by questioning whether some family members "visited the patient often enough."

Response: Every family is different, has different additional obligations and responsibilities, and thus visit patients with varying frequency. This is an ugly accusation, not a legal argument. And it's irrelevant to the quality of care provided by the nursing home staff — ultimately, that's what matters when determining liability. The only purpose of such accusations is to divert attention from the neglect or abuse facts, to deter the family from proceeding with a civil suit. With the help of your attorney, these nursing home tactics can be exposed for what they are and even used to further infuriate a jury that disapproves of how the nursing home responded in the wake of harming the patient.

PLAYING THE CORPORATE SHELL GAME:

When All Else Fails, Hide The Money.

The nursing home industry hires an army of smart lawyers and accountants to ensure that their businesses are designed to avoid accountability. Many nursing home operators plot and plan strategies to avoid having to compensate victims of neglect and abuse, even when a judge or jury finds them liable for their neglect or abuse. These nursing home profiteers go to great lengths in structuring their business entities (corporations, limited liability companies, limited partnerships, etc.) to protect and hide the wealth that's generated from their corporation's operations.

Nursing homes are often operated by a chain of corporate entities that are strategically linked to each other in a way that's designed to maximize the generation and protection of wealth. They devise a master plan that maximizes profit by accomplishing several key goals, including maximizing the amount that can be charged to Medicare and Medicaid, tax avoidance, and protection from liability risk. As you're about to learn, nursing homes strategically and intentionally structure their legal entities with the goal of avoiding their liabilities, including paying civil suit judgments against them.

For example, let's establish a typical but rather basic corporate structure for operating a nursing home that we'll call "Pot of Gold Healthcare Center." We start by creating a corporation that will own the license to the nursing home and technically be considered the "operator" of the facility. This company will be called "Pot of Gold Healthcare Center, L.L.C." (L.L.C. stands for "limited liability company.") This will be the company likely registered with the state by a name similar to the nursing home's trade name, and thus likely named in any future lawsuit that seeks to hold the nursing home accountable for harming or killing a patient.

For purposes of maximizing the profits that could potentially be taken from the facility in a lawsuit, we'll create a separate company that will own the land and building and receive rent from Pot of Gold Healthcare Center, L.L.C. Since this second company will own significant assets (the building and land), which could be used to pay a judgment if the nursing home was found liable for neglect or abuse, we'll want to obscure the relationship between the two companies in hopes that anyone suing for neglect or abuse will not discover this relationship or the lease agreement in order to avoid having the assets seized to pay a judgment. So this second company will be discretely named POG Land, LLC. In order to siphon more profits from the operator entity, we'll establish a third company called POG Management, LLC to provide "management services" to Pot of Gold Healthcare Center L.L.C., and charge huge sums of money for those services. Again, this entity will be discretely named in hopes of obscuring the corporate relationship, should the nursing home be sued, because there will be significant cash flowing from the nursing home itself to this management company.

Now, in order to squeeze even more profit from the nursing home facility, we create a fourth company that will charge the nursing home to provide therapy services, which we call POG Therapy, L.L.C., rather than Pot of Gold Therapy, L.L.C. — again, to bury the "Pot of Gold" association in order to prevent the assets of this company from being subject to seizure to pay any verdict against the Pot of Gold nursing home. Next we create a fifth discretely named company called POG Consultants, L.L.C. to provide a variety of "consultant services," which the nursing home will again pay handsomely for.

It's important to keep in mind that the same group of people will own and profit from all of these corporate entities. Typically these entities will have many, or all, of the same corporate officers and directors (decision-makers), and frequently, even share the exact same office location. But it will certainly make it more difficult for a patient or anyone else, for that matter, to hold the nursing home operator accountable for any misconduct.

Despite the fact that Pot of Gold Healthcare Center will be housing and caring for more than 100 elderly and disabled patients, we'll locate this nursing home in one of the many states that don't require nursing home operators to purchase any type of liability insurance in order to avoid that expense. Yes, you read that correctly! States require anyone driving a car to purchase at least some minimum policy of liability insurance to protect others who may be harmed from a collision caused by negligence, yet, in most states, no such insurance requirement exists for anyone who wants to open and operate a nursing home. At the time this book went to press, it appears that only the State of Virginia has passed legislation requiring that nursing home facilities operating in that state purchase liability insurance to protect patients and their families against harms and losses resulting from neglect or abuse.

So now, what happens if a patient in Pot of Gold Healthcare Center is neglected or abused? What if a patient develops a pressure sore because staff do not turn and reposition a patient as frequently as needed and that patient's wound becomes infected (as they often do), requiring hospitalization for sepsis and surgeries to close the wound? The cost could add up to hundreds of thousands of dollars in medical bills alone, not to mention the cost of compensating the patient for the human suffering involved. After all, as you learned in Chapters 1 and 2, the known odds of neglect or abuse happening to any one patient during their stay in a nursing home are staggering.

Well, if all goes as planned by the engineers of this complex corporate structure, the patient would sue Pot of Gold Healthcare Center, L.L.C. because it's the legal entity licensed by the state to operate the Pot of Gold Healthcare Center facility. If the other companies are named as defendants, the owners will claim that only Pot of Gold Healthcare Center, L.L.C. was involved in any "direct hands-on care," so only that entity should be held responsible, even though all of the companies were certainly involved in the direct profits and facility decision-making, including on issues such as staffing, training, budgeting, etc. And if the patient prevails and a judgment is obtained, the patient will find out that Pot of Gold Healthcare Center, L.L.C. has no cash (because most of its cash is paid to POG Land, L.L.C., POG Management, L.L.C., POG Consultants, L.L.C., and POG Therapy, L.L.C.). The patient will also find out that Pot of Gold Healthcare Center, L.L.C. owns no property or other assets that can be leveraged to pay a judgment. And finally, the patient will find out that there's no liability insurance policy to pay the judgment. Pot of Gold Healthcare Center, L.L.C. can declare insolvency (bankruptcy).

A new company, Pot of Gold Healthcare Facility II, L.L.C., can be created and become the new licensee of the facility. This group of profiteers can repeat as often as necessary and laugh all the way to the bank.

Response: This is the nursing home industry game that's played in too many cities and counties across America. Can those other entities be discovered and named in the lawsuit too? The answer is yes, often they can. But it's not necessarily simple or easy, because the laws in too many states protect bad nursing homes and their continued willingness to put profits over patients.

There are a number of legal rulings and mechanisms that can be used to expose the fact that these related corporate entities are essentially collectively operating a nursing home as a sort of single business entity or joint enterprise, regardless of how the owners attempt to hide that fact on paper. The legal issues stemming from this type of scenario are beyond the scope of this book, as they can be exceedingly complicated and likely tedious reading. It's not necessary to explore all the details here, as the legal tactics vary from case to case, and state to state. All you need to know is that it can often be done.

Perhaps you're beginning to see why exposing and defeating the nursing home industry in this shell game of greed can be time-consuming and expensive for the law firm that undertakes it, but it's also extremely worthwhile and rewarding for the patient and the family that stands up and defeats these devious shenanigans to help ensure it does not happen to someone else.

But you can also see why it's important to select an attorney who has significant experience in handling nursing home cases, one who knows how to anticipate nursing home industry defense tactics, knows exactly what steps to take to find their Achilles heels, expose the sham, pierce their carefully constructed armor, and ultimately, is willing to pursue the strategies that will defeat their sophisticated schemes to avoid accountability. Taking on the nursing home industry is truly a game of chess, not checkers.

TIPS

- Do your best to attend care conferences. Take notes about what was said to help counter the facility's claim that "the family failed to attend" and to be able to dispute any misrepresentations what was actually communicated.

- Communicate any care decisions you make to the facility in writing, keeping a dated copy for yourself to eliminate the facility's ability to blame the family.

- If the patient falls or suffers any other type of injury, ask for a copy of the incident report.

- Document (dates, names, and substance of what was said) any complaints made by the patient or the patient's family to facility staff, Ombudsmen, the "corporate office," state investigators, or law enforcement to show that you didn't sit idly by when you had concerns of neglect or abuse.

- Have the nursing home verify whether they carry liability insurance to cover injuries or harm sustained by the patient while in the facility.

- When choosing an attorney, make sure they have extensive experience in handling nursing home neglect and abuse cases to ensure that they're prepared to handle and counter any excuses the nursing home may offer for their abuse or neglect.

16

FIGHTING LAWS THAT PROTECT BAD NURSING HOMES
PART I: THE ARBITRATION HURDLE

Big business can make laws as easily as it can break
them — and with as little impunity.
— **Ralph Chaplin, author and activist**

In their shameless desire to avoid accountability for neglecting and abusing patients, nursing home corporations are in too many instances actually aided and abetted by lawmakers. There are laws currently on the books in every state, along with proposed laws, that enable nursing homes to run and hide. These laws serve to help shield the industry from accountability, thus enabling bad nursing homes to continue neglecting and abusing patients. Many of the laws purporting to protect patients, improve healthcare quality and lower healthcare costs are wolves in sheep's clothing that are ultimately creating enormous hardships for patients and their families by shifting the burden from the wrongdoer to the victims — the innocent patients.

For example, in previous chapters, we've discussed laws and regulations that effectively conspire to protect bad nursing homes from accountability:

- **The corporate shell game** (perfectly legal), which allows nursing home corporations to structure their business entities in such a way that they can hide their wealth behind shell corporations that have no assets so that they can then file bankruptcy to discharge liability claims and restart business as usual with a new corporate shell.

- **Neglectful staffing policies.** To save money, nursing homes routinely understaff, and employ poorly screened and inadequately trained staff. Federal law requiring that registered nurses be available at the nursing home for only eight hours a day contribute to creating an environment that's ripe for neglect and abuse.

- **No liability insurance requirement.** Most states laws allow those licensed to operate nursing homes to do so without purchasing any type of liability insurance to protect their patients, even though those same states require anyone licensed to drive a car to purchase at least some minimum policy of liability insurance to protect others who may be harmed from a collision caused by negligence.

- **Inherent Conflict Of Interest Between Improvement vs. Enforcement In Government Inspections Of Nursing Homes.** As we discussed in Chapter 12, current federal survey policies and procedures encourage states to focus on improvement rather than punishment, which allows nursing homes to come into compliance just long enough to be re-certified, then "yo-yo" back into noncompliance.

In the next two chapters, you'll see how two of the most unjust and unconscionable legal culprits — forced arbitration and damage caps — compound the assault on patients and families impacted by nursing home neglect and abuse.

THE FORCED ARBITRATION CLAUSE

If arbitration were in any way beneficial to consumers,
it could be made an option and consumers would choose it.

— Richard Alderman,
Director, Consumer Law Center,
University of Houston Law Center

Nursing home corporations know that it's likely to be an emotionally turbulent time for families confronted with the task of admitting a loved one to a nursing home. Nursing home admissions are typically preceded by a stressful medical event, often unforeseen, that led to a hospital stay. Few families are fully prepared for this difficult time and placement decisions often have to be made quickly.

Too many nursing homes exploit this vulnerability to coerce patients and families, often unknowingly, into signing away their right to use the justice system to hold the nursing home accountable in the event that they neglect or abuse the patient. Typically, nestled somewhere within the stack of documents on which the nursing home will require signatures before admission is what's known as a *forced arbitration clause*. This clause is intended to be a binding contract between the nursing home and the patient that says if the nursing home ever abuses or neglects the patient, no one can file a lawsuit and have the matter decided by a judge or jury.

A 2009 survey of nursing-home operators by a nursing-home trade group, found that nearly 70% of residents in nursing homes had signed arbitration agreements (American Health Care Association, 2009).

These binding mandatory arbitration clauses are being forced upon patients and families pre-dispute and under the duress of having to find a facility quickly for their loved one — before there's an actual dispute or claim, before the nursing home has even begun caring for those patients. It's not a situation whereby two parties who have a dispute mutually agree to have the dispute settled in arbitration by a third party rather than go to court. The nursing home's mission is to force this arbitration agreement on the family before they even have a claim, *in case* they ever file a claim.

In a letter to Centers for Medicare and Medicaid Services (CMS), a group of 39 health and aging advocates wrote about the unfairness of this mission: "It is unreasonable to assume that residents or their loved ones are able to comprehend the likelihood of grievous harm or poor care occurring within a facility when these agreements are signed upon admission. No one should be expected to anticipate or contemplate the occurrence of such tragedies" (Bloomberg BNA, 2016).

Here's an example of a typical arbitration clause, used by one healthcare corporation:

(d) By agreeing to this Section D, Binding Arbitration, the parties are giving up and waiving their right to have any claim

decided in a court of law before a judge and/or jury. The parties
expressly agree that any dispute covered by this Section D, Binding
Arbitration, will be resolved outside of the court system except for
the limited rights of review provided under the Federal Arbitration
Act, 9 U.S.C §§ 1 et seq.

To make matters worse, the forced arbitration clause can often be slipped in near the end of the contract where you'll be less likely to notice it. When nursing home personnel walk patients and families through admission agreements, they often skip right over the page containing the arbitration clause to the signature lines at the end in order to secure signatures quickly and prevent patients and families from carefully considering this clause.

In reality, most Americans have actually consented to a wide range of forced arbitration clauses without ever knowing it. (If you don't believe it, take a closer look at the fine print in your credit card agreements!) A recent survey showed that half of all consumers never notice arbitration clauses. Eighty-eight percent still think the clause is not important, even after they experience disputes or complaints (National Roundtable on Consumer and Employment Dispute Resolution, 2013). But nothing could be farther from the truth!

Nor do most people realize that forced arbitration clauses can cover all types of harm — abuse, neglect, fraud, discrimination — and in many instances cannot be challenged in court. Unfortunately, most people don't realize just how dangerous these clauses are until they're unable to hold a corporation accountable for harm they've suffered as a result of that corporation's misconduct.

Why Forced Arbitration Is Biased Against You

Forced arbitration proliferated once corporations realized legislatures and courts would allow their use of this get-out-of-jail-free card, despite the gross unfairness of these provisions on the consumer.

An American Association for Justice report concluded: "Forced arbitration is Corporate America's Trojan Horse — a campaign to eliminate access to the courts and individual rights and replace them with big businesses' own dispute mill" (American Association for Justice, 2013). A Trojan Horse, as you probably know, has come to mean to any trick or subterfuge that causes a target to invite a foe into a protected bastion. During the Trojan War, the Greeks pretended to sail away, knowing the Trojans would pull their huge wooden horse into the city of Troy as a victory trophy. But hidden inside the horse were Greek warriors, who, that night crept out of the horse and opened the gates for the rest of the Greek army, which entered and destroyed the city of Troy, decisively ending a decade of war.

A forced arbitration clause is that Trojan horse, hidden in plain sight within that nursing home admission contract.

Why would the nursing home industry want to force patients to agree that a claim be decided by an arbitrator rather than by the public judicial system? There are several reasons, but consistent with the pattern you've seen again and again throughout this book, the strongest motivators are: secrecy and greed.

The Veil Of Secrecy

The arbitration process enables nursing home corporations to hide fraud, abuse, neglect and other misconduct, ensuring that ugly facts which may alert the public to the prevalence of abuse and neglect at a facility never come to light. They do so to protect their stream of new patient admissions and the profits those new patients will generate. Typically, nursing homes will include a clause in the agreement that serves as a gag order on the family, should they file any claim for neglect or abuse.

Here's an example of such a provision:

> **Confidentiality.** *The arbitration proceeding shall remain confidential in all respects, including all arbitration filings, deposition transcripts, documents produced or obtained in discovery, or other materials provided by and exchanged between the parties and the Arbitrator's findings of fact, conclusions of law, and award. In addition, following receipt of the Arbitrator's award, each party agrees to return to the other party within 30 days the original and all copies of documents exchanged in discovery and at the arbitration hearing.*

Forced arbitration's inherent unfairness is not just confined to the unfortunate patients who find themselves ensnared within its trap. The public at large suffers from the dangers that forced arbitration conceals. Whereas the civil justice system shines a bright light on matters of public health and safety, forced arbitration hearings are private — "secret court." Very few forced arbitration decisions are published or otherwise publicly accessible. And information regarding the corporation's prior misconduct simply never reaches the light of day.

In fact, the Consumer Financial Protection Bureau (CFPB) conducted a comprehensive study on forced arbitration clauses in 2015. Among its findings was that forced arbitration clauses shield corporate misconduct from public oversight and encourage future wrongdoing (Consumer Financial Protection Bureau, 2015).

Not only are arbitration proceedings secret, scant information is provided about the arbitrators themselves. Arbitration firms disclose precious little information about the individual arbitrators with the exception of those in California, where the legislature has required greater disclosure. Patients and families receive arbitrator names and resumés, but no information about previous cases, win-loss records, or potential conflicts of interest. Patients have no way of knowing whether the arbitrator has previously presided over proceedings involving the same nursing home corporation, nor can they learn the results of those cases — for example, cases in which the nursing home caused similar harm to other patients.

In other words, patients and families have no way of knowing whether their fate may lie in the hands of an arbitrator who's biased against them. Meanwhile, their opponent in the dispute secretly knows all about past cases and can guide itself accordingly while the patient/family is forced to negotiate in ignorance. Secrecy also ensures that the case cannot be used to set public precedent that might prevent similar harm to future victims and larger awards to patients in future cases.

Bias, Conflicts of Interest and Financial Incentives

Why should you be concerned that an arbitrator would be biased against your interests? After all, all arbitration firms claim, in their promotional materials, to be "neutral providers of alternative dispute resolution services." But in truth, the arbitration system is riddled with conflicts of interest that ultimately ensure that the game is rigged in favor of big business and against the little guy. In fact, the arbitration system bears little resemblance to what goes on inside the public legal system.

Nursing home corporations know that they'll save money and avoid accountability — or at least, be held *less* accountable — if a dispute is resolved by an arbitrator (likely biased) rather than an unbiased judge or jury. Many studies show that awards are biased in favor of corporations over consumers; for example:

- A 2009 review of 1,518 disputes between consumers and nursing homes found that the disputes subject to arbitration paid consumers awards that were, on average, 35% lower than those not subject to arbitration (American Health Care Association, 2009).

- A 2007 Public Citizen investigative report found that, in employment cases and medical malpractice cases, arbitration claimants received only about 20% of the damages they would have received in court (Public Citizen, 2007).

Arbitration firms have a strong financial incentive to establish anti-consumer rules and deliver anti-consumer rulings in order to attract and retain corporate clients, which are their bread and butter. Arbitration firms (e.g., National Arbitration Forum (NAF) and American Arbitration Association (AAA)) compete to provide arbitration services for corporations and company contracts (such as nursing home admission contracts) that often designate a specific firm to handle arbitration. Arbitration firms that rule in favor of these corporations — and at the cheapest price — naturally often win the contract.

And then there are the arbitrators themselves. For example, public judges are randomly assigned cases and have no stake in the cases they preside over. There are rules and procedures that require judges to recuse themselves from a case in which there may be a conflict of interest. By contrast, private judges (arbitrators) are chosen by one of the parties in the case, and are paid only when they're assigned cases by arbitration firms. The arbitrator gets to decide whether or not he or she has a conflict of interest and should be disqualified — it's the classic fox guarding the henhouse. Thus, it's generally the corporation contracting the arbitration firm that has the most leverage and really makes the call. This alone tips Lady Justice's balance in favor of corporate interests.

Nursing home patients and their families may not get a fair hearing in an arbitration forum because nursing homes may offer repeat business to arbitrators who tend to rule in their favor. All arbitrators hired by the arbitration firm know that those who rule in favor of the company that contracted the arbitration firm will more likely be rehired for future cases, and those who don't won't. As arbitrator Richard Hodge said in a *Los Angeles Times* interview, "You would have to be unconscious not to be aware that if you rule a certain way, you can compromise your future business" (Berkowitz, 2016).

It's no wonder that hundreds of judges have deserted the bench for their own enrichment in the private arbitration system, an arena that's largely unregulated. "Private judging is an oxymoron because those judges are businessmen — they're in this for money" says J. Anthony Kline, a state appellate justice in San Francisco.

Forced arbitration is, effectively, outsourced justice. The mission of corporate America to coerce consumers into these forced arbitration agreements seems to be part of an effort to privatize the justice system, putting our rights in the hands of business interests, rather than impartial judges and juries. Nursing home corporations drive millions of dollars in business to arbitration firms, which, in turn, hire arbitrators who issue rulings that tend to favor nursing homes, then, as you'll soon learn, pass many of the added costs of arbitration to the patients and their families.

Lack Of Due Process And Limited Discovery

But what about *due process*? After all, the Fifth Amendment to the U.S. Constitution includes the mandate that no one shall be "deprived of life, liberty or property without due process of law." The Fifth Amendment applies these same eleven words, known as the Due Process Clause, to describe a legal obligation of all states. These words have as their central promise an assurance that all levels of American government must operate within the law and provide equal protection to all citizens under the law.

So aren't we all, as U.S. citizens, entitled to due process? Not in the arbitration system.

As Peter Rutledge, Catholic University law professor, wrote, "Arbitrators do not have to follow precedent. Arbitrators also are not bound by the same rules of evidence and procedure as courts. Often there is no transcript, and arbitrators are not obligated to provide detailed findings of fact and conclusion of law in their awards" (Rutledge, 2004).

Arbitration firms are effectively allowed to set their own rules, then decide whether to follow them or break them with impunity. For example, arbitration forums have been known to simply refuse to disclose whether the arbitrator had performed legal work for corporations in the industry relevant to the dispute, even though such a history would — and should — disqualify the arbitrator.[77] Arbitration firms have also been known to accept the late filing of a document by the defendant corporation that chose the forum (even though the company didn't ask for a deadline extension), only to turn around and refuse the plaintiff-consumer's request for a filing deadline extension.[78]

Patients and their families often find it very difficult — if not impossible — to obtain information from nursing home corporations in pre-trial discovery, a fundamental legal right that would be subject to rigorously enforced rules and procedures in the court system. And the limited rights that consumers do have in the arbitration process are subject to the whims of the arbitrators. Ultimately, limiting discovery and denying due process becomes another tactic for nursing home corporations to conceal egregious acts of misconduct because critical evidence may never come to light.

---

77   Letter from Penny Hays Cauley to Kelly M. Wilen, National Arbitration Forum, Jan. 29, 2007; Letter from Kelly M. Willen to Hays Cauley P.C. Feb. 12, 2007. See also, National Arbitration Forum Code of Procedure, Rule 23, DIs.

78   "Plaintiffs' Memorandum of Points and Authorities in Support of Their Motion to Enjoin Defendants from Pursuing Arbitration Because the Arbitration Fees are Unconscionable," Paul Lewis et al. v. Jim Koons Automotive Companies, et al., Case No. 8:06-cv-1236-AW, United States District Court for the District of Maryland, Southern Division, Nov. 3, 2006.

Arbitration Is Associated With Higher Costs

Some arbitration firms have a "loser pays" rule that allows the arbitrator to assess all costs, including attorneys' fees, against the arbitration loser. When a case is filed in state or federal court, a single, nominal filing fee is usually required. Judges and juries are paid by the government (ultimately, the taxpayers) and sworn to ensure that justice is carried out. But the arbitration process includes a menu of "pay-as-you-go" fees. For example, fees can be assessed for: issuing a subpoena, filing a motion, a written explanation of an arbitrator's rationale for a decision and more. The arbitrator can charge the parties hundreds of dollars for every hour they spend reviewing the case, holding hearings, deliberating about the case, writing their opinions, etc. And worse, fees are structured on a sliding scale — the higher the dollar amount of the award sought, the higher the costs.

Corporations like to sell the idea that arbitration is a more "cost-effective" way to resolve a dispute. Well, it may be more cost effective for *them* in terms of paying pennies on the dollar (if any damages at all) to compensate victims of neglect and abuse, but it is anything but cost-effective for the patients or their families. Not only can the victims expect the private arbitration process to likely shortchange them in favor of the repeat customers (i.e., the nursing home industry), the fees associated with paying for the arbitrator can be deducted from whatever award they do recover.

Limited Right To Appeal

Challenging an arbitrator's decision is usually difficult because the right to appeal is limited and deliberately "under-communicated" to consumers. The fair rules of procedure and evidence that govern court proceedings do not apply in arbitration. While the Federal Arbitration Act gives losing parties 90 days to appeal an arbitration award, arbitration firms and their clients (such as nursing home corporations or credit card companies), generally don't advise consumers of this deadline. Instead, they wait until the 90-day appeal deadline expires, then go to court to seek judicial confirmation of the award, leaving the defendant with virtually no grounds for appeal. (All arbitration awards must be confirmed in court.)

Even if consumers meet the appeal deadline, they'll find that federal law severely limits the grounds for courts to vacate an award — typically, the consumer must prove that the arbitrator committed acts of fraud, "displayed evident partiality or corruption," or show that the corporation cannot prove that the consumer agreed to arbitration. Arbitrators can misconstrue or misapply the law, err in their findings of fact, and unlike in the public court system, the arbitration award can still be upheld. In 2001, the Supreme Court held that there would be no review of an arbitrator's decision on the merits even if the decision was "silly."[79] In 1992, the California Supreme Court held that an arbitration award can be upheld even if it would cause "substantial injustice."[80]

Clearly, until there are better consumer protection laws, unfairness — even gross injustice — may not be sufficient to overturn an arbitrator's decision.

The following chart offers a quick comparison snapshot of the consumer's rights in open public justice systems versus the secret, privatized dispute resolution system known as arbitration.

Consumer Rights In Forced Arbitration Vs. The Courts	
Court	**Forced Arbitration**
Service Of Process Required: Due Process Requires Actual Notice Through An Official Process Server To Initiate A Claim.	**Certified Mail With Signed Receipt Or By Private Carrier With Receipt Signed By "Person Of Suitable Age And Discretion"** Deemed Sufficient Notice For Arbitration Even Though Many Consumers Remain Unaware Of Cases Pending Against Them.

---

79   Major League Baseball Players Assn. v. Garvey, 532 U. S. 504 (2001) (per curiam) 532 U.S. 504, 509 (2002).

80   See Moncharsh v. Heily & Blasé, 3 Cal. 4th 1 (1992).

Neutral Decision-Maker: Jury Of Peers And/Or Impartial, Government-Employed Judge With Public Record Of Decisions.	Biased Decision-Maker With Financial Incentives: Arbitrators Chosen From A Limited Panel, Paid By An Arbitration Firm Selected And Compensated By The Company; No Public Record Of Prior Decisions Generally Available To Consumers.
Open, Public Process That May Set Precedents For Future Cases.	Closed, Secretive Proceeding Without Public Record Or Precedential Value.
Due Process Rights To Fair And Reasonable Discovery Of Information; Hearings And Motions Filed At Little Or No Cost.	Limited Right To Discovery, At Discretion Of Arbitrator. Other Due Process Rights Must Be Paid For On An À La Carte Basis.
Contingency Fee System Generally In Negligence, Malpractice, Or Product Liability Cases, Means Plaintiffs' Attorneys, Not Consumer-Plaintiffs, Assume Financial Risks For Duration Of Case.	Pay-As-You-Go Payment System Means Claimant Must Pay Costs Up-Front At Every Twist And Turn And On A Sliding Scale (E.g., For Subpoenas, Motion Filings); "Loser-Pays" Rule May Further Financially Burden Consumers.
Right To Appeal A Loss On The Merits Of The Case Or Other Grounds.	Very Limited Grounds For Appeal, Typically Limited To Fraud Or Corruption Of Arbitrator, Unconscionable Clause Or Contract, Or Failure Of Company To Prove That Consumer Agreed To Arbitration.

Who's Holding Arbitrators Accountable?

It has become clear that forced arbitration is so grossly unfair to nursing home patients and their families that the American Bar Association (ABA), American Medical Association (AMA), and even the largest and most prominent arbitration firm, American Arbitration Association (AAA), have said so and condemned pre-dispute arbitration clauses in the healthcare setting. In 1997, the AAA, in cooperation with the ABA and AMA, formed a commission on health care dispute resolution to study and make recommendations on the appropriate use of arbitration in healthcare claims (Commission on Health Care Dispute Resolution (1998).

The Commission determined that arbitration is *not* appropriate in disputes involving patients, unless the parties agree to arbitrate after the dispute arises. They developed the AAA/ABA/AMA Health Care Due Process protocol which stated that *only* voluntary agreements to arbitrate disputes between patients and HMOs should be enforceable. They concluded that "in disputes involving patients, binding forms of dispute resolution [including arbitration] should be used only where the parties agree to do so after a dispute arises" because this is the only way to guarantee that the agreement to arbitrate is both knowing and voluntary based upon equal bargaining positions and equal power.

That year, AAA publicly announced that it would stop handling pre-dispute arbitration healthcare cases. But AAA didn't keep that promise. Then, in 2002, under pressure from the California legislature and the media, AAA renewed that promise. But guess what? AAA didn't keep that promise either. And today, private corporations are increasingly replacing the American civil justice system.

Now, you'd think that the blatant unfairness of forced arbitration agreements, not to mention the devastating consequences they can have upon the accountability of this industry, would lead courts to refuse to enforce these agreements when a claim for nursing home neglect or abuse arises. In some cases, in some states, they do. For example, in 2011, a patient's son signed a contract with a forced arbitration clause when his father was admitted to the Hampton Court Nursing Center where he later suffered an eye infection that resulted in the removal of his left eye. The son filed a lawsuit on behalf of his father, but the lower courts ruled that the case must proceed to arbitration. The father died in 2013, but in an important appeal, the Florida Supreme Court ruled the arbitration agreement invalid on the grounds that the father could not be bound by an arbitration requirement that his son had signed without the father's agreement (Juan Mendez Jr. etc. v. Hampton Court Nursing Center LLC; Saunders, 2016).

However, in far too many instances, the courts side with the nursing home industry, even when the outcome seems unfathomable and contrary to common sense. Take for example, a case where the Indiana Court of Appeals ruled, incredibly, that the arbitration agreement was still enforceable, even though the Golden Living nursing facility could not produce a copy of the agreement ((*Maynard v. Golden Living*); Berklan, 2016).

Because too many courts and legislators won't act, prior to the 2016 elections, the Centers for Medicare and Medicaid Services took a huge step forward in October 2016, effectively banning pre-dispute arbitration agreements in long-term care facilities (LTCs) that receive funds from Medicare and Medicaid programs (as nearly all nursing homes do) (42 C.F.R. §483.65). The new rule, it was hoped, would ensure that arbitration agreements would no longer be a condition of admission, making it a whole lot easier for victims to sue nursing homes that harm patients through neglect and abuse.

Among the reasons cited for this rule change, CMS noted the significant power differential between LTCs and their residents, the geographical and financial restrictions that often limit choice of nursing facility, and the fact that the signing of these contracts often occurs under conditions where the residents-to-be are living with "dwindling mental acuity" and their family members are "emotionally vulnerable."

Unfortunately, as you can imagine, the nursing home industry struck back. Industry lobby groups and nursing home corporations filed a class action challenging the rule, claiming that CMS overstepped its authority. Three weeks before the new federal rule was set to go into effect on November 28, 2016, a Mississippi federal judge ruled in favor of nursing homes' right to include mandatory arbitration provisions in patient contracts, blocking the implementation of the new rule (*American Health Care Association et al. v. Sylvia Mathews Burrell, et al.*; Leonhard, 2016).

Sadly, just months after the 2017 presidential inauguration ushered in a new administration, and just eight months after publishing the consumer protection regulations banning pre-dispute arbitration agreements for nursing home residents and their families, CMS issued new industry-friendly proposed rules that rescind resident protections against these unfair provisions (CMS, 2017).

In the new proposed rule, CMS removed the requirement preventing facilities from entering into pre-dispute arbitration agreements, and also removed the provision that banned facilities from requiring these agreements as a condition of admission. This newly proposed rule also deleted the requirements from the 2016 consumer protection rule for *post*-dispute binding arbitration that required: the agreement be entered into voluntarily by the resident; a neutral arbitrator be mutually agreed upon; and the location for arbitration be convenient to both parties. Comments on this forthcoming proposed rule will be due 60 days from the date of publication in the federal register, or on or about August 7, 2017.

On the legislative front, proposed legislation, such as the *The Arbitration Fairness Act* (S.537), sponsored by Minnesota Senator Al Franken in 2017, would prohibit the use of pre-dispute forced arbitration agreements in consumer, employment, civil rights, and antitrust disputes (except in contracts between employers and labor organizations or between labor organizations). Such a bill would further require that the validity and enforceability of an agreement to arbitrate shall be determined by a court, under federal law, rather than by an arbitrator.

As of this writing, the outcome of this legislation is still pending, but is likely to meet fierce resistance by powerful industries. The prospects for passage are grim. But whether this bill passes or fails, arbitration agreements signed prior to the passage of any such legislation or regulation will likely be unaffected. Thus, it's crucial for families to carefully scrutinize all admission agreements and try to avoid agreeing to arbitration clauses if at all possible.

The nursing home industry and other related industries are, of course, closely monitoring legislative efforts to ban pre-dispute forced arbitration clauses and are motivated to get as many arbitration agreements signed as possible before the Franken bill, or some other similar legislation, is passed. So patients and families must remain vigilant.

What if you've already signed an arbitration clause which may bind you? Keep in mind that while it may negatively affect your ability to hold the nursing home fully accountable, you have *not* waived your right to seek compensation altogether. And moreover, there may still be ways in which your attorney can defeat the arbitration clause altogether. So, don't give up!

TIPS for Dealing with Forced Arbitration Clauses

Depending upon whether the Department of Health and Human Services rule banning arbitration clauses is upheld or not, you may need to take steps to avoid having your legal rights taken away. Here are some things you can do:

- Before committing to a nursing home placement, review its admission agreement to see if it includes a forced arbitration clause.

- If the nursing home agreement does include a forced arbitration clause, does it allow you to opt out of it within a certain number of days? Some agreements, for example, allow a patient to opt out within 30 days. If so, you could sign the agreement, be admitted, then opt out of the arbitration clause before the 30-day deadline.

- If the nursing home admission agreement has a forced arbitration clause that doesn't appear to allow you to opt out, ask the admissions coordinator if the facility will, in fact, insist that you agree to a forced arbitration clause before you even have a chance to experience the quality of care they provide. They may, if only out of shame or a desire to "fill a bed," agree to allow you to decline that provision of the contract. If they allow you to decline, be sure to do so in writing and secure a copy at that time. If they do require you to agree to the arbitration clause as a precondition to admission, you may want to look at other available nursing home options.

- If you've already signed an admission agreement with an arbitration clause that allows you to opt out, follow the procedures *exactly* as required by the agreement and do so in a way that you can prove that you properly opted out. For example, the agreement may require you to send the opt-out notice to a specific person, at a specific address, by a specific means (e.g., certified mail, fax, etc.) Whatever it requires, do it. Remember, you can always agree to arbitrate a case *after* you know what your claim involves. This opt-out only applies to claims that arise from events that haven't happened yet.

- If your admission agreement, including an arbitration clause, was signed under duress (e.g., you had limited time to find a facility to provide necessary healthcare to yourself or a loved one and you had few or no other options available), locate and preserve any facts and evidence which can be used to prove the agreement to arbitrate was obtained by coercion. If you hire an attorney to help you pursue your claim, the attorney may be able to use this evidence of coercion to overcome the arbitration requirement.

- Generally speaking, one must be of sound mind to enter into a binding contract, which means that a patient who signed the admission agreement containing an arbitration clause must have adequate mental capacity to understand the meaning and effect of the contract. If there is evidence that the patient lacked such capacity, it should be preserved and provided to your attorney who may be able to use this evidence to void the contract, depending on the laws of your particular state.

17

FIGHTING LAWS THAT PROTECT BAD NURSING HOMES
PART II: ARBITRARY CAPS ON DAMAGES

Liability limit has become a symbol of corporate greed in passing the risk of disaster to the U.S. government and U.S. citizens.
— **Marvin Ammori, attorney and civil liberties advocate**

When nursing home, hospital and healthcare corporations have unpaid bills, they often have no qualms about using the legal system to collect every last penny they're owed from patients and their families. And the law is on their side. After all, the law generally says that when someone does not uphold their legal responsibilities, they may be liable for the full measure of the harm they cause.

But another fundamental American legal principle is that, in order to be fair, the law should apply equally to everyone. So this should mean that when a nursing home fails to fulfill its responsibility to protect a patient from neglect and abuse and the patient is harmed as a result, the patient or the patient's family should be entitled to invoke this same legal system to hold the nursing home corporation responsible for the full measure of the harm it caused… right?

Sadly, the answer is too often *no*. The reason is that nursing homes and other powerful healthcare corporations have been able to exert extraordinary influence over lawmakers. In many jurisdictions, laws have been passed that *prejudge* and minimize the value that can be placed upon the life of a patient and the human suffering caused by nursing home neglect and abuse.

These laws are called "damage caps," and they serve to limit the amount of compensation (often referred to as "non-economic damages") patients and families can recover for the things in life that really matter.

The name "damage caps" is brutally misleading. These laws do nothing to limit the "damage" caused by the wrongdoers. Rather, the laws simply limit the *accountability* for the damage that has been caused, forcing the victims to bear the sole burden of all damages in excess of the "accountability cap," which is really the term that properly describes it. For example, Kansas has an accountability cap law that prejudges the value of a human life taken by nursing home neglect or abuse to not to exceed $250,000, no matter how much pain is caused, no matter what the injury is (including loss of life), no matter how egregious the neglect and abuse, or how profitable the nursing home corporation is (K.S.A. § 60-19a02. (2012)).

These accountability caps apply to and limit responsibility for harms such as the loss of a spouse, child or parent; loss of a limb; paralysis; horrific disfigurement; loss of sight; loss of mobility and independence, and more. In some states, such as Indiana, there are even limits placed on the amount of medical bills, lost wages, and other "economic" damages that can be recovered. So even in cases where it's proven that the nursing home provided neglectful or abusive care, the law mandates that the patient (or his/her family), rather than the nursing home, will have to pay for medical bills that exceed the accountability cap.

Consider the following example: Mildred undergoes hip replacement surgery. Because she needs physical therapy before returning home, she is admitted to a local nursing home for a stay that is anticipated to be short-term. But because there's not enough staff on duty to assist her, Mildred is allowed to fall hard, striking her head on the bed and suffering a serious subdural hematoma and traumatic brain injury. She requires many weeks of hospitalization, expensive neurological assessment and treatment, and unfortunately, due to her lingering deficits will no longer able to live on her own at home, thus requiring permanent nursing home placement. The medical bills caused by this this neglect alone totaled $1.5 million and will continue to mount until her death. These "economic damages," of course, do not even include the devastating human suffering that Mildred and her family have endured, and will continue to endure, due to this tragic act of neglect.

In Indiana and other states with similar laws, the accountability cap will limit the nursing home's responsibility to less than even the cost of the medical bills ($1.25million), and certainly won't cover the human suffering caused by the injury. Until her death, Mildred (or her family) will be responsible for all of the additional medical bills related to this negligent event. When they can no longer afford the bills, Medicaid (tax payers) will pay for the nursing home's neglect. And, while tax payers are subsidizing the harm caused by the nursing home, the nursing home can still collect the balance in unpaid bills, even though the bills resulted from the facility's own negligence. Doesn't this strike you as outrageously unfair?

And what should also concern every taxpayer is that caps like those in Indiana on total damages — including economic damages — typically mean that the taxpayers (in the form of Medicare and Medicaid) subsidize the medical bills that result from treating the patient's injuries from neglect and abuse, instead of the for-profit nursing home corporation, which caused, and could have prevented the neglect or abuse, in the first place. When a patient on Medicare files a lawsuit against a nursing home to recover for the harm that was caused by neglect or abuse, part of any recovery obtained is typically paid back to Medicare to reimburse taxpayers for the funds spent to treat the patient for the injuries caused by the nursing home. But when caps prevent the patient from obtaining a full recovery, Medicare cannot be fully reimbursed so taxpayers pay instead of the nursing home.

Ultimately, in such cases, both Medicare (the taxpayers) and the patients and families still lose. And as for the nursing home corporations, they pocket the difference between the harm they caused, and the limited accountability imposed upon them.

Elderly Patients And Their Families Are Disproportionately Impacted

One of the most insidious aspects of these "non-economic" damage cap laws is that they disproportionately harm elderly patients and their families.

Why? Because in cases of nursing home neglect or abuse, the patient is typically retired and no longer earning wages. So while the injury or death may cause horrific human suffering or even the loss of life, it doesn't result in any lost wages. Because there are no lost wages (economic damages) and because some states have granted nursing homes immunity from liability for human suffering for any amounts above the accountability cap, the nursing home corporation has limited incentive to spend money to fix the problems (e.g., intentional understaffing, lack of supplies and equipment, lack of training, hiring of convicted criminals, etc.) that caused the neglect and abuse in the first place. This places every one of their elderly patients in harm's way in the future. Thus, ultimately, caps serve to enable and protect bad nursing homes from improving the quality of care they provide.

Proof That Damage Caps Don't Work

Despite the tremendous hardship that caps can place on innocent patients and their families, and the fact that they shift compensation burdens onto others, insurers and healthcare providers argue that caps should be enacted to "combat healthcare costs."

By 2016, approximately 33 states had enacted caps on damages in healthcare negligence cases, due to special interest lobbying. Unfortunately, more and more state legislatures are being pressured by the nursing home industry and others to implement caps that will help them avoid responsibility for the full measure of harm they create. As of this writing, the United States Congress is quietly but swiftly pushing federal legislation as part of the so-called "Obamacare repeal" which would impose a federally mandated accountability cap on the value of a human life that would apply to *all* states. In other words, the citizens of all states would no longer be able to decide for themselves whether nursing homes should be fully accountable for the death, injury, and harm they cause. This philosophical turn is ironic, considering that the same factions arguing *against* federally mandated gun laws or other healthcare laws tend to be the ones advocating for federally mandated limits on the value of lives taken by nursing home abuse and neglect.

In a tragic twist of irony, insurance industry lobbyist Frank Cornelius, who helped persuade the Indiana Legislature to pass a damage cap law, later wrote about how he "rued that accomplishment" in his *New York Times* op-ed piece, "Crushed by My Own Reform." Cornelius ultimately became the victim of medical negligence that left him wheelchair-bound, on a respirator, unable to work and in constant pain. His economic damages were estimated to exceed $5 million, but he received a capped settlement of $500,000 under the law he himself had pushed as a lobbyist for the Insurance Institute of Indiana.

"All my suffering," he wrote, "might have been worthwhile, on some cosmic scale, if the law had accomplished its stated purpose. But it hasn't." Cornelius went on to point out that Indiana's national ranking in per-capita health care spending was the same in 1990 as it was in 1980. In other words, the cap on medical negligence awards had done nothing to curb healthcare spending. "The two have almost nothing to do with each other," Cornelius wrote. Less than five months after his *Times* op-ed column was published, Frank Cornelius died from an intentional morphine overdose. By then, Medicaid would no longer cover the device that administered the morphine.

But this is but one dose of the bitter irony that results from the enactment of damage caps. There are countless others.

Healthcare providers, insurers and legislators who support damage caps claim that they will deter negligent care, reduce medical errors, reduce healthcare costs, increase the number of practicing physicians, and lower doctors' malpractice premiums. But the evidence paints an entirely different picture.

In fact, several studies conducted by highly respected medical malpractice researchers have found that damage caps don't just harm injured patients and their families; they're also destroying healthcare for everyone else, and that, in fact, they serve no legitimate purpose. These studies have confirmed that, despite healthcare industry promises to the contrary, damage caps actually lead to:

- *More* medical errors
- *Higher* health care costs
- *No increase* in physicians providing patient care
- *Higher* malpractice insurance premiums

Let's take a look at the evidence…

More Medical Errors

Researchers compared five states[81] that enacted damage caps from 2003 to 2005 where Patient Safety Indicators (PSIs)[82] data was also available for at least two years before the caps laws passed to the data from no-cap control states. They found "consistent evidence that patient safety generally falls" after caps are enacted (Black et al., 2014b).

Specifically, after caps were enacted, they found:

- A gradual rise in rates for most PSIs, consistent with a gradual relaxation of care, or failure to reinforce care standards over time.

- The decline was widespread, and applied both to aspects of care that are relatively likely to lead to a malpractice suit (e.g., a foreign body left in during surgery), and aspects that are unlikely to (e.g., central-line associated bloodstream infection).

- The broad relaxation of care suggests that the fear of medical malpractice liability is a general deterrent (an incentive to be more careful in general), as well as a specific deterrent for particular actions.

- Reduced risk of medical malpractice lawsuits, as a result of caps laws, led to higher rates of preventable adverse patient safety events.

Higher Healthcare Costs

Researchers compared healthcare spending trends in nine states[83] that enacted caps from 2002 to 2005 to trends in no-cap control states (Black et al., 2014c), finding that "damage caps have *no* significant impact on Medicare Part A (hospital) spending, but lead to 4-5% *higher* Medicare Part B (physician) spending." Researchers concluded that physicians may be

---

81   Florida, Georgia, Illinois, South Carolina, Texas

82   PSIs are the "standard measures of often preventable adverse events, developed by the Agency for Healthcare Research and Quality (AHRQ)." They include: operative and post-operative errors, infections, birth-related errors and cases at risk, like hospital-acquired pneumonia.

83   Florida, Georgia, Illinois, Mississippi, Nevada, Ohio, Oklahoma, South Carolina and Texas

providing higher-risk services or procedures in cap states, which they might be deterred from practicing in no-cap states where they could potentially incur greater liability.

The study's conclusion was frank and unequivocal:

> *"There is no evidence that limiting medical malpractice lawsuits will bend the healthcare cost curve, except perhaps in the wrong direction."*

No Increase In Physicians

Researchers compared physician supply in nine states[84] that enacted caps from 2002 to 2005 to the number of physicians in 20 no-cap control states (Black et al., 2014d).

Specifically, they found:

- Cap enactment (in nine cap states) did *not* lead to an increase in the number of total patient care physicians, specialists —who face higher liability risk (with a possible exception for plastic surgeons) — nor rural physicians.

- No association between medical malpractice claim rates and physician supply at either the state or county levels from 1995 to 2011.

The study concluded:

> *"Physician supply does not seem elastic to medical malpractice risk. Thus, the states that want to attract more physicians should look elsewhere."*

Higher Malpractice Premiums

Healthcare providers, their insurers, politicians and lobbyists argue that capping compensation for injured patients will lead to reduced medical malpractice rates for doctors, or at least slower rate increases. But in reality, exactly the opposite happened in most states. And the irony is, evidence has

---

84   Florida, Georgia, Illinois, Mississippi, Nevada, Ohio, Oklahoma, South Carolina and Texas.

shown that insurance insiders know it. For example, according to Consumer Watchdog, in a 2004 filing with the Texas Department of Insurance, one insurer, GE Medical Protective, admitted that the non-economic damage cap would yield no more than a 1% drop in losses.

The forces that drive rate hikes have nothing to do with state tort laws. This is just another tired old bait-and-switch strategy used by the insurance industry to squeeze more profits at the expense of the individuals who have no organized lobby. While the insurance, nursing home and hospital industries have powerful lobbyists with cash to burn and influence to wield, there is, of course, no "future medical malpractice victims" lobby.

"Tort law reform" advocates always campaign on the promise that damage caps will help "combat the high cost of malpractice insurance," but following are highlights of what *actually* happened in various states when cap laws were passed...

- **Maryland:** $350,000 cap on non-economic damages since 1986, later increased somewhat (MD. CODE ANN., CTS. & JUD. PROC. §11.108), yet a 2005 analysis found that premiums increased by more than 70% over two years (Dao, 2005).

- **Missouri:** $350,000 cap on non-economic damages since 1986, adjusted annually for inflation, reaching $557,000 in 2003 (Missouri Department of Insurance, 2003). (This cap was struck down as unconstitutional in July 2012 (Bernard & Young, 2012).) Since 1991, total paid claims have decreased by about 30%; paid claims against physicians fell 42.3%. Yet malpractice insurance premiums rose by 121% from 2000 to 2003 (AP, 2004).

- **Florida:** Governor Jeb Bush and House Speaker Johnnie Byrd pushed through a sweeping medical malpractice overhaul bill, vowing that the bill would "reduce ever-increasing insurance premiums for Florida's physicians . . . and increase physicians' access to affordable insurance coverage." But insurers soon filed requests to increase premiums by as much as 45% (Kay, 2003).

- **Ohio:** Almost immediately after "tort reform" passed, all five major Ohio medical malpractice insurance companies announced that they would not reduce their rates; one insurer predicted a 20% rate increase (AP, 2003).

- **Oklahoma:** After caps passed in 2003, the third-largest medical malpractice insurer in the state increased premiums by 20%, followed by a 105% rate hike in 2004 (Daily Oklahoman, 2004). The largest insurer requested a staggering 83% rate hike, which was approved on the condition that it be phased in over three years (BestWire, 2003).

- **Mississippi:** Four months after a caps law passed, investigative reports revealed that surgeons still couldn't find affordable insurance, and that many Mississippi doctors were still limiting their practice or leaving the job in protest (Reed, 2003; Bryant, 2003).

- **Nevada:** Within weeks of enacting caps in 2002, two major insurance companies announced that they wouldn't reduce insurance rates for at least another year or two, if ever. The Doctor's Company, a nationwide medical malpractice insurer, filed for a 16.9% rate increase. Two other companies filed for 25% and 93% rate increases (Babula, 2002; 2003).

- **Texas:** In 2003, right after the "tort reform" referendum Prop. 12 passed, major insurers requested rate hikes as high as 35% for doctors and 65% for hospitals, despite the promises of rate cuts by the bill's supporters (Schlegel, 2003).

- **Iowa:** Iowa never had a damage cap. In the last five years examined, Iowa's premium rate dropped 6% (Bernard & Young, 2012).

A 2009 Americans for Insurance Reform investigation concludes: "States with little or no restrictions on patients' legal rights have experienced the same level of liability insurance rate changes as those states that enacted severe restrictions on patients' rights" (Americans for Insurance Reform, 2009).

Regulatory Laws vs. Caps

It's become clear that strong insurance regulatory laws are the only fair and effective way to control malpractice insurance rates. On the bright side, the harm wrought by damage caps has at least triggered a few reversals and stronger insurance regulation in few states — California and Illinois are perhaps two of the most prominent examples.

In 1975, California enacted a $250,000 cap on non-economic damages, the first in the nation, which dramatically reduced the number of *legitimate* malpractice lawsuits brought in California. Yet, even as deaths and injuries due to malpractice continued to increase between 1975 and 1988, doctors' premiums still increased by *450%,* rising faster than the national average (Balber & Heller, 2009). And of course, the reduction in malpractice suits disproportionately affected seniors, low wage earners, children and the poor, who are more likely to receive a greater percentage of awarded compensation in the form of non-economic damages. The damage cap also helped ensure that many competent plaintiffs attorneys could no longer afford to handle these malpractice cases.

As a result of the cap, California's medical malpractice insurance industry became so bloated that as little as 2 or 3 percent of premiums were used to pay claims — even the state's biggest medical malpractice insurer, The Doctors Company, spent only 10% of the $179 million it collected in premiums in 2009 to pay malpractice claims (Mohajer, 2011). In other words, the malpractice insurance company was pocketing the vast majority of the premiums. The profit motive was driving the rate increases; damage caps had nothing to do it.

Then, in 1988, California voters passed a stringent insurance regulatory law, Proposition 103, which ordered a 20% rate rollback, forced insurers to open their books and get approval for any rate change before it takes effect, and allowed the public to intervene and challenge excessive rate increases. In the twelve years after Prop. 103 (1988-2000), California malpractice premiums dropped 8%, compared to a national rate increase of 25 percent (Foundation for Taxpayer and Consumer Rights, 2005). When every other state was experiencing skyrocketing medical malpractice rate hikes in the mid-2000s, California's regulatory law led to public hearings on rate requests by medical malpractice insurers in California, which resulted in rate hikes being lowered three times in two years, saving doctors $66 million (Foundation for Taxpayer and Consumer Rights, 2005). Today, if the California medical malpractice insurance industry doesn't lower rates on its own, as the Insurance Commissioner has requested, Prop. 103 will allow the Commissioner to take action and do so.

A similar situation occurred in Illinois, which in 2005, enacted a non-economic damages cap on compensation for injured patients ($500,000 for doctors, $1,000,000 for hospitals) and a strong insurance regulatory law. In 2010, the cap was struck down as unconstitutional by the Illinois Supreme Court, but in the five years the cap was in place, it was found to not affect settlements or insurance rates.

The strong insurance regulatory reforms, however, *did* have an impact. In 2006, an Illinois malpractice insurer, Berkshire Hathaway's MedPro, reduced malpractice premiums by more than 30%. According to both state and MedPro officials, this rate cut was made possible because of the new insurance regulatory laws, *not* the cap on compensation for patients. The new regulatory law enhanced the Illinois Insurance Department's rate oversight authority and improved insurer reporting and transparency, requiring malpractice insurers to disclose data on how they set their rates (Jadhav, 2006).

One thing is certain: No state's healthcare spending or insurance problems were ever the fault of innocent, injured patients who simply tried to recover compensation for harms perpetrated upon them through malpractice. And it is deceitful, heinous and unjust for states to attempt to place the harms from neglect and abuse on the backs of injured, vulnerable patients.

ADDITIONAL RESOURCES

Since damage caps are laws, strictly enforced, recovery for damages caused by a nursing home will likely be limited by a cap if the nursing home neglect or abuse occurs in a state that caps the value of a human life. Right now, all across the country, state legislatures in the remaining 17 or so no-cap states may be gearing up for battle over legislation that would enact damage caps. And one element of the proposed repeal of the Affordable Healthcare Act would federalize caps, requiring every state to place an accountability cap on the value of a human life.

But you are not without power. You can vote for candidates who oppose damage caps. You can contact your federal and state representatives to express your concerns. And you can join forces with the following advocacy groups, for there is strength in numbers.

- **Public Citizen:** Public Citizen is a non-profit, consumer rights advocacy group and think tank based in Washington, D.C., United States, with a branch in Austin, Texas. http://www.citizen.org/

- **Consumer Voice:** The National Consumer Voice for Quality Long-Term Care was formed as NCCNHR (National Citizens' Coalition for Nursing Home Reform) in 1975 because of public concern about substandard care in nursing homes. The Consumer Voice is the outgrowth of work first achieved by advocates working for Ralph Nader and later for the National Gray Panthers. http://theconsumervoice.org/issues/for-advocates/citizen-advocacy-groups

- **California Advocates for NH Reform:** Since 1983, California Advocates for Nursing Home Reform (CANHR) has been dedicated to improving the choices, care and quality of life for California's long term care consumers. Through direct advocacy, community education, legislation and litigation it has been CANHR's goal to educate and support long term care consumers and advocates regarding the rights and remedies under the law, and to create a united voice for long term care reform and humane alternatives to institutionalization. http://www.canhr.org/

- **Long Term Care Community Coalition (LTCCC):** This New York-based activist group was first brought together in the late 1970s after a string of scandals in New York State involving long-term care facilities. In 1982, the group became a permanent watchdog for the industry; it was incorporated in 1989. LTCCC works actively with the government to improve long-term care in the state and across the country. http://www.ltccc.org. 242 West 30th Street, Suite 306. New York, NY 10001.

- **Arkansas Advocates:** http://www.aanhr.org/

- **Voices for Quality Care:** http://voicesforqualitycare.org/

- **Massachusetts Advocates:** http://www.manhr.org/

RIGHT NOW.

Right now, somewhere in this country, nursing home caregivers are committing abuses. Right now, their nursing home owners are making excuses.

Right now, a military veteran who faithfully served his country is being neglected in a U.S. nursing home. Right now, a nursing home employee who earns far too little is spending her own money to buy food and supplies for her patients because her employer won't. Right now, nursing home corporations are enjoying record profits with no limits in sight. Yet, right now, families are grieving the loss of loved ones who died needlessly from nursing home neglect and abuse because the facility's owners and operators didn't do the job they were paid to do.

Right now, a nursing home patient who is unable to communicate wants to tell someone she is being abused by her caregiver, but can't. Right now, a handsomely-paid nursing home administrator is working to reduce the facility's operating budget in order to increase his year-end bonus. Right now, a patient is developing painful pressure sores because he has gone without being turned and repositioned for far too long. Right now, a nursing home employee is doctoring a patient's medical records to conceal evidence of blatant neglect or abuse.

Right now, a nursing home aide who has no respect for a helpless patient's privacy and dignity is taking a demeaning photo to share with her friends on social media. Right now, a patient urgently needs help getting to the bathroom, but her call light is ignored and will go unanswered. Right now, a nursing home administrator is shifting the blame to the patient or the patient's family for the injuries she knows were caused by her staff's own negligence.

Right now, there are poorly paid, convicted criminal employees taking care of patients in nursing ones with deceptively beautiful landscaping and gleaming lobby floors. Right now, a nursing home corporation is creating another pyramid of shell corporations strategically linked to each other in a way that will ensure maximum profitability… and minimum liability.

But right now, there is a state investigator and nursing home ombudsman standing by, ready to help. And right now, you are armed and ready to hold that nursing home accountable. Right now, you can obtain a complete copy of your loved one's medical records. Right now, you can contact law enforcement if you believe a crime may have been committed against your loved one. Right now, you can take steps to allow a civil jury to send a powerful message to those responsible for the atrocities associated with this industry.

In the introduction to this book, I proposed that nursing home neglect and abuse is one of the largest, most dangerous, and preventable health threats in the United States today. I asked you to read the chapters that followed, consider the facts, and decide for yourself. Since you've made it to the end of this book, I suspect that you now agree.

But convincing you of this regrettable fact is not the goal of this book.

Rather, the goal is to convince you that you can do something about it. Now, you probably didn't choose to read this book because you imagined that you could transform the entire industry. Probably your concern, quite rightly, was to learn how you can protect yourself or someone you love. You can do that. And you *should* do that.

And granted, it may be unlikely that you alone can defeat the devastating dynamics at play in this industry that, collectively, create perfect storms for neglect and abuse. But as President Barack Obama once said: "Change will not come if we wait for some other person or some other time. We are the ones we've been waiting for." And make no mistake, you now have the knowledge and the tools to hold the nursing home that's being paid to care for you or your loved one accountable.

You can take comfort in knowing when you do take steps, even small ones, to force a nursing home to do the job they're supposed to do, you help ensure that this facility will behave more responsibly in the future not only towards you or your loved one, but also towards others in your community.

For as President Obama also said: "Each one of us can make a difference, and all of us ought to try."

ABOUT THE AUTHOR

Jeff is a trial attorney, author, and speaker who was born and raised in Indiana. He is passionate about sharing strategies and insights that help patients and their families hold the nursing home industry accountable for abuse and neglect. Over the last two decades, Jeff has built a distinguished record as lead trial counsel representing hundreds of victims of nursing home abuse and medical malpractice in Indiana and Texas. He began his career as an attorney representing people who developed serious illnesses as a result of having been unknowingly exposed to dangerous levels of toxic chemicals in soil and drinking water. He is the recipient of various national and state legal achievement awards, such as lifetime admittance into the Multi-Million Dollar Advocates Forum™ and Elite Lawyers of America©. As a vigorous advocate for victims of nursing home abuse and medical negligence, Jeff has been an invited speaker at legal education seminars on the topics of nursing home neglect and abuse and litigation technology.

In his spare time, Jeff enjoys spending time with his family, playing basketball, and coaching youth athletics.

BIBLIOGRAPHY

BEGIN HERE: MAKING A DIFFERENCE

Annual Nursing Home Data Compendium, Centers for Medicare & Medicaid Services' (CMS), 2015.

CHAPTER 1: WHY BOTHER?

Annual Nursing Home Data Compendium, Centers for Medicare & Medicaid Services' (CMS), 2015.

Atlanta Long-Term Care Ombudsman Program. (2000) The Silenced Voice Speaks Out: A Study of Abuse and Neglect of Nursing Home Residents." Atlanta, GA: Atlanta Legal Aide Society, and Washington, DC: National Citizens Coalition for Nursing Home Reform.

Ben Natan, M., & Lowenstein, A. (2010). Study of factors that affect abuse of older people in nursing homes. Nursing Management, 17(8), 20-24.

Broyles, K. (2000). The silenced voice speaks out: A study of abuse and neglect of nursing home residents. Atlanta, GA: A report from the Atlanta Long Term Care Ombudsman Program and Atlanta Legal Aide Society to the National Citizens Coalition for Nursing Home Reform.

Center for Disease Control and Prevention. (1993) National Mortality Followback Survey With Death Certificate, Proxy Respondent, and Medical Examiner/Coroner Abstract Data File Description. 1993.

Gibbs, Lisa M., MD (2004) Annals of Long-Term Care: Clinical Care and Aging;12[4]:30-35).

Hawes C. Elder (2003) Abuse in Residential Long-Term Care Settings: What Is Known and What Information Is Needed? In: National Research Council (US) Panel to Review Risk and Prevalence of Elder Abuse and Neglect; Bonnie RJ, Wallace RB, editors. Elder Mistreatment: Abuse, Neglect, and Exploitation in an Aging America. Washington (DC): National Academies Press (US). 14.

Levinson, Office of Inspector General, *Adverse Events in Skilled Nursing Facilities: National Incidence Among Medicare Beneficiaries*, OEI-06-11-00370 (Feb. 2014).

MacDonald P. Make a Difference: Abuse/neglect Pilot Project. Danvers, MA: North Shore Elder Services; 2000. Project report to the National Citizens' Coalition for Nursing Home Reform, Washington, DC.

Pillemer K, Hudson B .(1993) A model abuse prevention program for nursing assistants. The Gerontologist. 1993;33:128–131.

Pillemer, K. & Moore, D. (1989). Abuse of patients in nursing homes: findings from a survey of staff. *Gerontologist,* 29(3), 314-320.

CHAPTER 2: TIP OF THE ICEBERG

Abt Associates, Inc., Colorado Foundation for Medical Care. (2013). Five-Star Quality Rating System: Annual Report 2012. Prepared for Centers for Medicare & Medicaid Services (CMS), AGG/Research Contracts & Grants Division. June 7, 2013.

AHCA (American Health Care Association), 2013 Quality Report.

Annual Nursing Home Data Compendium, Centers for Medicare & Medicaid Services' (CMS), 2015.

Atlanta Long-Term Care Ombudsman Program. (2000) The Silenced Voice Speaks Out: A Study of Abuse and Neglect of Nursing Home Residents." Atlanta, GA: Atlanta Legal Aide Society, and Washington, DC: National Citizens Coalition for Nursing Home Reform.

Blakely BE, Dolon R. (1991) The relative contributions of occupation groups in the discovery and treatment of elder abuse and neglect. Journal of Gerontological Social Work. 1991;1(17):183–199.

Bowers B, Hawes C, Burger S. (2001) Focus group interviews with family members of nursing home residents and individual interviews with residents about the complaint process. 2001. Conducted for the Complaint Investigation Improvement Project (CIP). Working papers at the School of Nursing, University of Wisconsin at Madison (Bowers) and the School of Rural Public Health, Texas A&M University System Health Science Center, College Station, TX.

Burgess AW, Dowdell EB, Prentky RA. (2000) Sexual abuse of nursing home residents. Journal of Psychosocial Nursing & Mental Health Services. Jun;38(6):10-8.

Clark-Daniels CL, Daniels RS, Baumhover LA. (1990) Abuse and neglect of the elderly: Are emergency department personnel aware of mandatory reporting laws? Annals of Emergency Medicine. 1990;19:970–977.

CMS, "Minimum Data Set (MDS) 3.0 Discharge Assessments that Have Not Been Completed and/or Submitted," S&C: 1-56-NH (Aug. 23, 2013),

Hawes C. Elder (2003) Abuse in Residential Long-Term Care Settings: What Is Known and What Information Is Needed? In: National Research Council (US) Panel to Review Risk and Prevalence of Elder Abuse and Neglect; Bonnie RJ, Wallace RB, editors. Elder Mistreatment: Abuse, Neglect, and Exploitation in an Aging America. Washington (DC): National Academies Press (US). 14.

Hawes C, Blevins D, Shanley L. (2001) Preventing Abuse and Neglect in Nursing Homes: The Role of the Nurse Aide Registries. 2001. Report to the Centers for Medicare and Medicaid Services (formerly HCFA) from the School of Rural Public Health, Texas A&M University System Health Science Center, College Station, TX.

Hawes C, Blevins D. (2001) The Role of the Ombudsman in Nursing Home Complaint Investigations; Presentation prepared for the annual meeting of the National Citizens Coalition for Nursing Home Reform; Arlington, DC. September 30 to October 3, 2001; College Station, TX: Texas A&M.

Huber R, Borders K, Netting FE, Nelson HW. (2001) Data from long-term care ombudsman programs in six states—The implications of collecting resident demographics. The Gerontologist. 2001;41:61–68.

Huber R, Netting FE, Kautz JR. (1996) Differences in types of complaints and how they are resolved by local ombudsmen operating in/not in Area Agencies on Aging. Journal of Applied Gerontology. 1996;15(1):87–101.

Kleinschmidt KC, Krueger P, Patterson C. (1997) Elder abuse: A review. Annals of Emergency Medicine. 1997;30(4):463–472.

Lachs MS, Pillemer K. (1995) Abuse and neglect of elderly persons. New England Journal of Medicine. 1995;333(7):437.

Levinson, Office of Inspector General, Adverse Events in Skilled Nursing Facilities: National Incidence Among Medicare Beneficiaries, OEI-06-11-00370 (Feb. 2014).

McNamara RM, Rousseau E, Sanders AB. (1992) Geriatric emergency medicine: A survey of practicing emergency physicians. Annals of Emergency Medicine. 1992;21:796–801.

National Center on Elder Abuse. The National Elder Abuse Incidence Study. Washington, DC: Author; 1998. Report prepared for the Administration on Aging and Administration for Children and Families in collaboration with Westat, Inc.

Pettee EJ. (1997) Elder abuse: Implications for staff development. Journal of Nursing Staff Development. 1997;13(1):7–12.

Pillemer K, Bachman-Prehn R. (1991) Helping and hurting: Predictors of maltreatment of patients in nursing homes. Research on Aging 1991; 13:74-95.

Pillemer K, Finkelhor D. (1998) The prevalence of elder abuse: A random sample survey. The Gerontologist. 1988;28(10):51.

Reynolds E, Stanton S. Elder abuse: (1983) A nursing perspective. In: Kosberg JI, editor. Abuse and Maltreatment of the Elderly: Causes and Interventions. Boston: John Wright; 1983.

Tatara T. (1990) Elder Abuse in the United States: An Issue Paper. Washington, DC: National Aging Resource Center; 1990.

U.S. Department of Health and Human Services, (1990) Office of the Inspector General. Resident Abuse in Nursing Homes: Understanding and Preventing Abuse. Washington, DC: U.S. Government Printing Office; 1990.

U.S. Department of Health and Human Services, (1990) Office of the Inspector General. Resident Abuse in Nursing Homes: Resolving

Physical Abuse Complaints. Washington, DC: U.S. Government Printing Office; 1990.

U.S. Government Accounting Office. (2008). Nursing Homes: Federal Monitoring Surveys Demonstrate Continued Understatement of Serious Care Problems and CMS Oversight Weaknesses.

Wolf, RS. (1988) Elder abuse: Ten years later. Journal of the American Geriatrics Society. 1988;36:758–762.

U.S. House of Representatives, Committee on Government Reform, Special Investigations Division, Minority Staff. (2001) Abuse of residents is a major problem in U.S. nursing homes, prepared for rep. Henry A. Waxman.

CHAPTER 3: A PERFECT STORM IN THE MAKING

Aaronson W E, Zinn J S, Rosko M D. "Do For-Profit and Not-For-Profit Nursing Facilities Behave Differently?" Gerontologist. 1994;34(6):775–86.

Bliesmer M M, Smayling M, Kane R, Shannon I. "The Relationship between Nursing Staffing Levels and Nursing Home Outcomes" Journal of Aging and Health. 1998;10(3):351–71.

Bureau of Labor Statistics, U.S. Department of Labor, Occupational Outlook Handbook, 2016-17 Edition, Nursing Assistants and Orderlies, (last pulled July 22, 2016).

Burgess AW, Dowdell EB, Prentky RA. (2000) Sexual abuse of nursing home residents. Journal of Psychosocial Nursing & Mental Health Services. Jun;38(6):10-8.

Department of Health and Human Services, Report to Congress: Appropriateness of Minimum Nurse Staffing Ratios and Nursing Home, Phase II Final Report, 2-21, 22 (December 2001),

Family Caregiver Alliance, National Center on Caregiving. (2016) Selected Long-Term Care Statistics. https://www.caregiver.org/selected-long-term-care-statistics

Goldmier, Dr. Harold. (2015) Nursing Home Care Industry Is A Solid Investment. May 28, 2015. http://seekingalpha.com/ article/3220236-nursing-home-care-industry-is-a-solid-investment.

Harrington, C. (2005a). Nurse staffing in nursing homes in the United States. Journal of gerontological nursing, 31(2), 18-23.

Harrington, C. (2005b). Nurse staffing in nursing homes in the United States: Part II. Journal of gerontological nursing, 31(3), 9-15.

Harrington, C. (2008). Nursing Home Staffing Standards in State Statutes and Regulations. San Francisco, CA: Department of Social and Behavioral Science, University of California, San Francisco.

Harrington, C., Granda, B., Carrillo, H., Chang, J., Woleslagle, B., Swan, J. H., Dreyer, K., Woodford, B., Orakpo, W., & Gill, J. (2008). State Data Book On Long Term Care, 2007 142 Program And Market Characteristics. San Francisco, CA: Department of Social and Behavioral Science, University of California, San Francisco.

Harrington, C., Kovner, C., Mezey, M., Kayser-Jones, J., Burger, S., Mohler, M., Burke, R., & Zimmerman, D. (2000). Experts recommend minimum nurse staffing standards for nursing facilities in the United States. The Gerontologist, 40(1), 5-16.

Harrington, C., & Swan, J. H. (2003). Nursing home staffing, turnover, and case mix. Medical care research and review : MCRR, 60(3), 366-392; discussion 393-369.

Harrington, C., Swan, J. H., & Carrillo, H. (2007). Nurse staffing levels and Medicaid reimbursement rates in nursing facilities. Health services research, 42(3 Pt 1), 1105-1129.

Harrington, C., Woolhandler, S., Mullan, J., Carrillo, H., & Himmelstein, D. U. (2001). Does investor ownership of nursing homes compromise the quality of care? American journal of public health, 91(9), 1452-1455.

Harrington, C., Zimmerman, D., Karon, S. L., Robinson, J., & Beutel, P. (2000). Nursing home staffing and its relationship to deficiencies. The journals of gerontology. Series B, Psychological sciences and social sciences, 55(5), S278-287.

Harrington, C., Kovner, C., Mezey, M., Kayser-Jones, J., Burger, S., Mohler, M., Burke, R., & Zimmerman, D. (2000). Experts recommend minimum nurse staffing standards for nursing facilities in the United States. The Geronologist, 40(1), 5-16.

Harrington, C., Carrillo, H., Mullan, J., & Swan, J. H. (1998). Nursing facility staffing in the states: the 1991 to 1995 period. Medical care research and review : MCRR, 55(3), 334- 363.

Hawes C. Elder (2003) Abuse in Residential Long-Term Care Settings: What Is Known and What Information Is Needed? In: National Research Council (US) Panel to Review Risk and Prevalence of Elder Abuse and Neglect; Bonnie RJ, Wallace RB, editors. Elder Mistreatment: Abuse, Neglect, and Exploitation in an Aging America. Washington (DC): National Academies Press (US). 14.

Hawes C, Blevins D, Shanley L. (2001) Preventing Abuse and Neglect in Nursing Homes: The Role of the Nurse Aide Registries. 2001. Report to the Centers for Medicare and Medicaid Services (formerly HCFA) from the School of Rural Public Health, Texas A&M University System Health Science Center, College Station, TX.

Institute of Medicine (US) Committee on the Adequacy of Nursing Staff in Hospitals and Nursing Homes; Wunderlich GS, Sloan F, Davis CK, editors. Nursing Staff in Hospitals and Nursing Homes: Is It Adequate? Washington (DC): National Academies Press (US); 1996. 6, Staffing and Quality of Care in Nursing Homes.

Levinson, Daniel R., Office of the Inspector General, DHHS. (2014) Nursing facility's compliance with federal regulations for reporting allegations of abuse or neglect. August 2014.

Levinson, Daniel R., Office of the Inspector General, DHHS. (2011) Nursing Facilities' Employment of Individuals with Criminal Convictions. March 2011.

Mueller, C., Arling, G., Kane, R., Bershadsky, J., Holland, D., & Joy, A. (2006). Nursing home staffing standards: their relationship to nurse staffing levels. The Gerontologist, 46(1), 74-80.

National Health Policy Forum (2014) The Basics: National Spending for Long-Term Services and Supports. Retrieved (January 2016) from http://www.nhpf.org/library/the-basics/Basics_LTSS_03-27-14.pdf.

Pillemer K, Bachman-Prehn R. (1991) Helping and hurting: Predictors of maltreatment of patients in nursing homes. Research on Aging 1991; 13:74-95.

Shekelle PG. Effect of Nurse-to-Patient Staffing Ratios on Patient Morbidity and Mortality. In: Making Health Care Safer II: An Updated Critical Analysis of the Evidence for Patient Safety Practices. Rockville (MD): Agency for Healthcare Research and Quality (US); 2013 Mar. (Evidence Reports/Technology Assessments, No. 211.)

Schnelle, J. F., Simmons, S. F., Harrington, C., Cadogan, M., Garcia, E., & B, M. B.-J. (2004). Relationship of nursing home staffing to quality of care. Health services research, 39(2), 225-250.

Schnelle J F, Bates-Jensen B M, Levy-Storms L, Grbic V, Yoshii J, Cadogan M P, Simmons S F. (2004) "The Minimum Data Set Prevalence of Restraint Quality Indicator: Does It Reflect Differences in Care?" Gerontologist. 2004;44(2)

Unruh L, Wan TT. (2004) A systems framework for evaluating nursing care quality in nursing homes, Journal of Medical Systems , 2004, vol. 28 (pg. 197-214).

U.S. Centers for Medicare and Medicaid Services (CMS). (2000). Report to Congress: Appropriateness of Minium Nurse Staffing Ratio in Nursing Homes Phase I Report. Washington, D.C.: Prepared by Abt Associates Inc.

U.S. Centers for Medicare and Medicaid Services (CMS). (2001). Report to Congress: Appropriateness of Minimum Nurse Staffing Ratio in Nursing Homes Phase II Final Report. Washington, D.C.: Prepared by Abt Associates Inc.

Zinn, J. S., Mor, V., Feng, Z., & Intrator, O. (2007). Doing better to do good: the impact of strategic adaptation on nursing home performance. Health services research, 42(3 Pt 1), 1200-1218.

CHAPTER 4: PRESSURE SORES

American Medical Directors Association. Pressure Ulcers in the Long-Term Care Setting: Clinical Practice Guideline. (2008).

Institute for Healthcare Improvement. (2007). Relieve the pressure and reduce harm. http://www.ihi.org/resources/Pages/ ImprovementStories/RelievethePressureandReduceHarm.aspx. Retrieved August 4, 2016.

Lyman, V. (2009). Successful heel pressure sore prevention program in a long-term care setting. Journal of Wound, Ostomy and Continence Nursing, 36(6), 616-621.

Minnesota Evidence-Based Practice Center. (2007) The High Cost of Poor Care: The Financial Case for Prevention in America's Nursing Homes. Rockville, MD. The National Consumer Voice for Quality Long-Term Care.

National Center for Health Statistics. (2004) Eunice Park-Lee & Christine Caffrey, Division of Health Care Statistics. U.S. Department of Health and Human Services, Centers for Disease Control. Pressure Ulcers Among Nursing Home Residents, United States, 2004.

Russo, A., Steiner, C., & Spector, W. (2008). Hospitalizations related to pressure sores among adults 18 years and older, 2006. Statistical Brief #64. Agency for Healthcare Research and Quality.

Tippet, A. W. (2009). Reducing the incidence of pressure sores in nursing home residents: A prospective 6-year evaluation. Ostomy Wound Management, 55(11), 52-58.

CHAPTER 5: FALLS

Alexander BH, Rivara FP, Wolf ME. (1992) The cost and frequency of hospitalization for fall–related injuries in older adults. American Journal of Public Health 1992;82(7):1020–3.

American Geriatrics Society, British Geriatrics Society, and American Academy of Orthopaedic Surgeons Panel on Falls Prevention. (2001) (Guideline for the prevention of falls in older persons. J Am Geriatr Soc. 2001;49:664-672.

Becker, C., & Rapp, K. (2010). Fall prevention in nursing homes. Clinics in Geriatric Medicine, 26(4), 693-704.

Carroll, N. V., Slattum, P. W., & Cox, F. M. (2005). The cost of falls among the community-dwelling elderly. J Manag Care Pharm, 11(4), 307-16.

Centers for Disease Control and Prevention, National Center for Injury Prevention and Control. (2013) Web–based Injury Statistics Query and Reporting System (WISQARS) [online]. Accessed August 6, 2016.

Findorff, M. J., Wyman, J. F., Nyman, J. A., & Croghan, C. F. (2007). Measuring the direct healthcare costs of a fall injury event. Nursing Research, 56(4), 283-287.

Hayes WC, Myers ER, Morris JN, Gerhart TN, Yett HS, Lipsitz LA. (1993) Impact near the hip dominates fracture risk in elderly nursing home residents who fall. Calcif Tissue Int 1993;52:192-198.

Jager TE, Weiss HB, Coben JH, Pepe PE. (1994)Traumatic brain injuries evaluated in U.S. emergency departments, 1992–1994. Academic Emergency Medicine 2000&359;7(2):134–40.

Kannus P, Parkkari J, Niem S, Pasanen M, Palvanen M, Jarvinen M, Vuori I. (2000) Prevention of hip fractures in elderly people with use of a hip protector. New England Journal of Medicine 2000;343(21):1506–13.

Lyman, V. (2009). Successful heel pressure ulcer prevention program in a long-term care setting. Journal of Wound, Ostomy and Continence Nursing, 36(6), 616-621.

Mustard CA, Mayer T. (1997) Case-control study of exposure to medication and the risk of injurious falls requiring hospitalization among nursing home residents. American Journal of Epidemiology 1997;145:738–45.

Neyens JCL, Dijcks BPJ, Twisk J, et al. (2009) A multifactorial intervention for the prevention of falls in psychogeriatric nursing home patients, a randomized controlled trial (RCT). Age and Ageing 2009;38:194-199.

Nowalk MP, Prendergast JM, Bayles CM, D'Amico MJ, Colvin GC. A randomized trial of exercise programs among older individuals living in two long-term care facilities: the FallsFREE program. Journal of the American Geriatrics Society 2001;49:859–65.

Rapp, K., Cameron, I. D., Kurrle, S., Klenk, J., Kleiner, A., Heinrich, S., et al. (2010). Excess mortality after pelvic fractures in institutionalized older people. Osteoporosis International, 21(11), 1835-1839.

Ray WA, Thapa PB, Gideon P. (2000) Benzodiazepenes and the risk of falls in nursing home residents. Journal of the American Geriatrics Society 2000;48(6):682–5.

Ray WA, Taylor JA, Meador KG, Thapa PB, Brown AK, Kajihara HK, et al. (1997) A randomized trial of consultation service to reduce falls in nursing homes. Journal of the American Medical Association 1997;278(7):557–62.

Rubenstein LZ. (1997) Preventing falls in the nursing home. Journal of the American Medical Association 1997;278(7):595–6.

Rubenstein LZ, Robbins AS, Josephson KR, Schulman BL, Osterweil D. (1990) The value of assessing falls in an elderly population. A randomized clinical trial. Annals of Internal Medicine 1990;113(4):308–16.

Rubenstein LZ, Robbins AS, Schulman BL, Rosado J, Osterweil D, Josephson KR. (1988) Falls and instability in the elderly. Journal of the American Geriatrics Society 1988;36:266–78.

Sorensen, S. V., De Lissovoy, G., Kunaprayoon, D., Resnick, B., Rupnow, M. F. T., & Studenski, S. (2006). A taxonomy and economic consequences of nursing home falls. Drugs and Aging, 23(3), 251-262.

Sorock GS, Quigley PA, Rutledge MK et al. (2009) Central nervous system medication changes and falls in nursing home residents. Geriatr Nurs 2009;30:334-340.

Sterling DA, O'Connor JA, Bonadies J. (2001) Geriatric falls: injury severity is high and disproportionate to mechanism. Journal of Trauma–Injury, Infection and Critical Care 2001;50(1):116–9.

Stevens JA, Corso PS, Finkelstein EA, Miller TR. (2006) The costs of fatal and nonfatal falls among older adults. Injury Prevention 2006;12:290–5.

Thapa PB, Brockman KG, Gideon P, Fought RL, Ray WA. (1996) Injurious falls in nonambulatory nursing home residents: a comparative study of circumstances, incidence and risk factors. Journal of the American Geriatrics Society 1996;44:273–8.

Tinetti ME. (1987) Factors associated with serious injury during falls by ambulatory nursing home residents. Journal of the American Geriatrics Society 1987;35:644–8.

Vellas BJ, Wayne SJ, Romero LJ, Baumgartner RN, Garry PJ. (1997) Fear of falling and restriction of mobility in elderly fallers. Age and Ageing 1997;26:189–193.

Vu MQ, Weintraub N, Rubenstein LZ. Falls in the nursing home: are they preventable? Journal of the American Medical Directors Association 2005;6:S82–7.

CHAPTER 6: MEDICATION "ERRORS"

Avorn J, Gurwitz JH (1995). Drug use in the nursing home. Annals of Internal Medicine, 123, 195 204).

Barker KN, Flynn EA, Pepper GA, et al. (2002) Medication errors observed in 36 health care facilities. Arch Internal Med. 2002;163:1897–903.

Barker K.N. et al., (1992) American Journal of Hospital Pharmacy. 39:987-997. 1992.

Bates DW. (1996) Medication errors — how common are they and what can be done to prevent them? Drug Saf.1996;15:303–10.

Bates DW, Boyle DL, Vander Vliet MB, et al. (1995) Relationship between medication errors and adverse drug events. J Gen Intern Med 1995;10:199-205.

Beyea SC, Hicks RW, Becker SC. (2003a) Medication errors in the OR—a secondary analysis of MEDMARX. AORN Jr. 2003;77(1):122–34.

Beyea SC, Hicks RW, Becker SC. (2003b) Medication errors in the day surgery setting. Surgical Services Mgmt. 2003;9:65–76.; 93.

Daniel S. Budnitz, M.D., M.P.H., Maribeth C. Lovegrove, M.P.H., Nadine Shehab, Pharm.D., M.P.H., and Chesley L. Richards, M.D., M.P.H.. (2011) Emergency Hospitalizations for Adverse Drug Events in Older Americans. N Engl J Med 2011; 365:2002-2012.

Dlott JS1, George RA, Huang X, Odeh M, Kaufman HW, Ansell J, Hylek EM. (2014) National assessment of warfarin anticoagulation therapy for stroke prevention in atrial fibrillation. 2014 Apr 1;129(13):1407-14.

Cooper JW. (1996). Probable adverse drug reactions in a rural geriatric nursing home population: a 4-year study, Journal of the American Geriatrics Society, 44, 194 197.

Jerry H. Gurwitz, MD, Terry S. Field, DSc, Martha J. Radford, MD, Leslie R. Harrold, MD, MPH, Richard Becker, MD, George Reed, PhD, Kristin DeBellis, PharmD, Jason Moldoff, BA, Nancy Verzier, MSN, RN. (2007) The Safety of Warfarin Therapy in the Nursing Home Setting. The American Journal of Medicine (2007) 120, 539-544.

Gurwitz J.H. et al., (2005) American Journal of Medicine. 118(3):251-258. 2005.

Hicks R, Becker S, Krenzischeck D, et al. Medication errors in the PACU: a secondary analysis of MEDMARX findings. J PeriAnesth Nurs. 2004;19(1):18–28.

Institute of Medicine. (2007) Preventing medication errors. Washington, DC: National Academy Press; 2007.

Kesselheim AS, Avorn J, Sarpatwari A. (2016) The High Cost of Prescription Drugs in the United States: Origins and Prospects for Reform. JAMA. 2016;316(8):858-871.

Levinson, Office of Inspector General, Adverse Events in Skilled Nursing Facilities: National Incidence Among Medicare Beneficiaries, OEI-06-11-00370 (Feb. 2014).

Lindley CM, Tully MP, Paramsothy V, Tallis R. C. (1992). Inappropriate medication is a major cause of adverse drug reactions in elderly patients, age and aging, 21, 294 300).

Mannesse CK, Derk FHM, de Ridder MAJ, et al. (1997). Adverse drug reactions in elderly patients as contributing factor for hospital admission: Cross Sectional study. British Medical Journal, 7116 (315), 1057-1058.

Murphy S, Roberts R. (2006) "Black box" 101: how the Food and Drug Administration evaluates, communicates, and manages drug benefit/risk. J Allergy Clin Immunol 2006;117:34-9.

National Center for Health Statistics. Health, United States, 2015: With Special Feature on Racial and Ethnic Health Disparities. Hyattsville, MD. 2016.

Ornstein, Charles. (2015) Popular Blood Thinner Causing Deaths, Injuries at Nursing Homes. ProPublica, July 12, 2015. Last retrieved August 30, 2016.

Pepper G. (1995) Errors in drug administration by nurses. Am J Health Syst Pharm. 1995;52:390–5.

Phillips J, Beam S, Brinker A, et al. (2001) Retrospective analysis of mortalities associated with medication errors. Am J Health Syst Pharm. 2001;58:1835–41.

Raju TN, Kecskes S, Thorton JP, et al. (1989) Medication errors in neonatal and paediatric intensive care units. Lancet. 1989;2:374–6.

Rogers AE, Hwang WT, Scott LD, et al. (2004) The working hours of hospital staff nurses and patient safety. Health Aff. 2004;23(4):202–12.

Stratton KM, Blegen MA, Pepper C, et al. (2004) Reporting of medication errors by pediatric nurses. J Pediatr Nurs. 2004;19(6):385–392.

Tang FI, Sheu SJ, Yu S, et al. (2007) Nurses relate the contributing factors involved in medication errors. J Clin Nurs. 2007 Mar;16(3):447–57.

Wagner AK, Chan KA, Dashevsky I, et al. (2006) FDA drug prescribing warnings: is the black box half empty or half full? Pharmacoepidemiol Drug Saf. 2006 Jun;15(6):369–86.

Walsh KE, Kaushal R, Chessare JB. (2005) How to avoid paediatric medication errors: a user's guide to the literature. Arch Dis Child. 2005;90:698–702.

Williams CE, Greene SB, Hansen RA , Pierson S, and Desai, R. NC Nursing Home Medication Error Quality Initiative (MEQI), Annual Report FY2012, October 1, 2011 to September 30, 2012. Chapel Hill, NC. The Cecil G. Sheps Center for Health Services Research at the University of North Carolina at Chapel Hill.

Wolf ZR, Hicks R, Serembus JF. (2006) Characteristics of medication errors made by students during the administration phase: a descriptive study. J Prof Nurs. 2006;22(1):39–51.

CHAPTER 7: PHYSICAL, SEXUAL AND PSYCHOLOGICAL ABUSE

Burgess, A.W. (2000) Sexual Abuse of Nursing Home Residents. 36 J. Psychosocial Nursing & Mental Health Serv. 10 (2000). CBS News. Report: Tracking Abuse In Nursing Homes. January 31, 2002.

Capezuti, Elizabeth A. & Swedlow, Deborah J.. (2000) Sexual Abuse in Nursing Homes, 2 Elder's Advisor 51, 54 (2000).

CMF Memorandum to State Survey Agency Directors, S&C-05-09, clarification of nursing home reporting requirements for alleged violations of mistreatment, neglect, and abuse, including injuries of unknown source, and misappropriation of resident property, December 16, 2004.

Hawks, Robert A. (2006) "Grandparent Molesting: Sexual Abuse of Elderly Nursing Home Residents and its Prevention," Marquette Elder's Advisor: Volume 8: Issue 1, Article 8.

Institute of Medicine (1986). Improving the Quality of Care in Nursing Homes. Washington, D.C.: National Academy Press.

Jennifer Hagerty Lingler, Ethical Issues in Distinguishing Sexual Activity from Sexual Maltreatment among Women with Dementia, 15 J. ELDER ABUSE & NEGLECT 85, 92 (2003) (quoting Bonnie Brandl & Tess Meuer, Domestic Abuse in Later Life, 8 ELDER L.J. 297, 301 (2000)).

Kemper P, Murtaugh CM (1991). Lifetime Use of Nursing Home Care. New England Journal of Medicine, 324, 595-600.

Levinson, Daniel R., Office of the Inspector General, DHHS. (2014) Nursing facility's compliance with federal regulations for reporting allegations of abuse or neglect. August 2014.

Payne, Brian K. & Cikovic, Richard. An Empirical Examination of the Characteristics, Consequences, and Causes of Elder Abuse in Nursing Homes, 7 J. Elder Abuse & Neglect 61, 66 (1995).

Teaster, Pamela B. et al., "The 2004 Survey of State Adult Protective Services: Abuse of Adults 60 Years of Age and Older," (Washington, DC: National Center on Elder Abuse, 2006), 5.

Teaster, Pamela B. & Roberto, Karen A.. When Elders Are Molested: Sexual Abuse of Nursing Home Residents Too Often Goes Unreported, LEGAL TIMES, June 27, 2005. (This article is based on a five-year study by the authors of APS cases in Virginia from 1996-2001.)

Teaster, Pamela B. & Roberto, Karen A.. (2004) Sexual Abuse of Older Adults: APS Cases and Outcomes, 44 The Gerontologist 788, 794, 2004.

U.S. House of Representatives, Committee on Government Reform, Special Investigations Division, Minority Staff. (2001) Abuse of residents is a major problem in U.S. nursing homes, prepared for rep. Henry A. Waxman.

CHAPTER 8: THE LIST GOES ON: EXAMPLES OF OTHER HARMS

Aud, Myra A. (2004) Dangerous wandering: Elopements of older patients with dementia from long-term care facilities. American Journal of Alzheimer's Disease and Other Dementias. Vol. 19: Issue 6. November 1, 2004.

American Medical Directors Association. (2009) Dehydration and Fluid Maintenance in the Long-Term Care Setting, Clinical Practice Guideline. Columbia, MD: AMDA 2009. http://www.paltc.org/sample-dehydration-and-fluid-maintenance-cpg

Atlanta Long-Term Care Ombudsman Program. (2000) The Silenced Voice Speaks Out: A Study of Abuse and Neglect of Nursing Home

Patients. Atlanta, GA: Atlanta Legal Aid Society; Washington, DC: National Citizens Coalition for Nursing Home Reform; 2000.

Basler, B. "(2004) Undercover Patient." September 2004. AARP Bulletin.

Boltz, M. (2003). Litigation Issues Related To Wandering and Elopement. The John A. Hartford Foundation Institute for Geriatric Nursing, New York University, The Steinhardt School of Education, Division of Nursing.

Brahm, Phil. State laws complicate social media abuse cases in nursing homes. McKnights, July 14, 2016.

Burger, Sarah Greene, Kayser-Jones, Jeanie, and Bell, Julie Prince. (2000) Malnutrition and Dehydration in Nursing Homes: Key Issues In Prevention and Treatment. National Citizens' Coalition for Nursing Home Reform. June 2000.

Butterworth, C.E. (1974) "The Skeleton in the Hospital Closet," Nutrition Today 9 (1974):4–8.

Centers for Medicare & Medicaid Services. CMS Manual System. Pub. 100-07 State Operations Provider Certification. Transmittal 168. March 8, 2017. https://www.cms.gov/Medicare/Provider-Enrollment-and-Certification/GuidanceforLawsAndRegulations/Downloads/Appendix-PP-03-08-2017.pdf

Davis KM., Minaker KL, Hazzard W, Andres R, Bierman EL, Blass JP (EDS). (1998) Principles of Geriatric Medicine and Gerontology, 2nd ed. New York: McGraw Hill 1998: chapter 110, 1079-1083.=

Department of Health and Human Services, Centers for Medicare & Medicaid Services. (2006). Federal Register, 42 CFR Part 482, Medicare and Medicaid Programs; Hospitals Conditions of Participation: Patient's Rights; Final Rule retrieved August 11, 2007 from http://www.cms.hhs.gov/quarterlyproviderup- dates/downloads/CMS3018N.pdf.

Hall GR, Buckwalter KC, Stolley JM, et al. Standardized care plan. Managing Alzheimer's patients at home. J Gerontol Nurs. 1995;21(1):37-47.

Hawes C. (1997) The Prevalence of Undernutrition Among Nursing Home Patients. Testimony before the U.S. Senate Special Committee on Aging–Forum on the Risk of Malnutrition in Nursing Homes; Washington, DC. October 22, 1997.

Health Care Financing Administration. National restraint reduction newsletter. Winter 1999. Available at: http://www.hcfa.gov/publications/newsletters/restraint/1999/rrwin99.htm.

Lai CK, Arthur DG. (2003) Wandering behaviour in people with dementia. J Adv Nurs. 2003;44(2):173-182.

Lester PE, Garite A, Kohen I. Wandering and elopement in nursing homes. Annals of Long-Term Care: Clinical Care and Aging. 2012;20(3):32-36.

Neufeld RR, Libow LS, Foley WJ, Dunbar JM, Cohen C, Breuer B. Restraint reduction reduces serious injuries among nursing home patients. J Am Geriatr Soc 1999;47:1202-1207.

Ornstein, Charles and Huseman, Jessica. (2016a) Inappropriate Social Media Posts by Nursing Home Workers, Detailed. Last updated Aug. 8, 2016. https://www.propublica.org/article/inappropriate-social-media-posts-by-nursing-home-workers-detailed.

Ornstein, Charles. (2016b) Senator demands stop to abuse of nursing home patients on social media. SeniorJournal.com.March 11, 2016. http://seniorjournal.com/NEWS/Politics/2016/20160311_Senator-demands-stop-to-abuse-of-nursing-home-patients-on-social-media.htm.

Ornstein, Charles. Policing Patient Privacy. (2015) Nursing Home Workers Share Explicit Photos of Patients on Snapchat. ProPublica, December 21, 2015. https://www.propublica.org/article/nursing-home-workers-share-explicit-photos-of-patients-on-snapchat.

Rodriguez J. Patient falls and elopement: costs and controls. Nurs Homes. 1993; 42(4):16-17. http://findarticles.com/p/articles/mi_m3830/is_n4_v42/ai_14041236/.

Shaver HJ, Loper JA, Lutes RA. (1980) Nutritional status of nursing home patients. J Parenter Enteral Nutr. 1980;4:367–370.

Silver AJ, Morley JE, Strome LS, Jones D, Vickers L. (1988)s Nutritional status in an academic nursing home. J Am Geriatr Soc. 1988;36:487–491.

Smith, M., Schultz, S. (2009) Great Escapes: The Wandering Dilemma. The University of Iowa Geriatric Education, University of Iowa, Iowa City, Iowa.

Taber, C. W., & Thomas, C. L. (1997). Taber's cyclopedic medical dictionary. Philadelphia: F.A. Davis.

Thomas DR, Ashman W, Morley JE, Evans WJ and Council for Nutritional Strategies in Long-Term Care. (2000) Nutritional management in long-term care:development of a clinical guideline. Journal of Gerontology, 55A, M725-M734.

Thomas DR, Verdery RB, Gardner L, Kant AK, Lindsay J. A. (1991) prospective study of outcome from protein-energy malnutrition in nursing home patients. J Parenter Enteral Nutr. 1991;15:400–404.

Wick JY, Zanni GR. (2006) Aimless excursions: wandering in the elderly. Consult Pharm. 2006;21(8):608-612, 615-618.

CHAPTER 10: ENGAGING AN OMBUDSMAN

Administration for Community Living. Administration on Aging. Long-Term Care Ombudsman Program (OAA, Title VII, Chapter 2, Sections 711/712). 2013. Last retrieved November 29, 2016. http://www.aoa.acl.gov/AoA_Programs/Elder_Rights/Ombudsman/index.aspx#data

Long-Term Care Ombudsman Program: Overview of the History, Role and Responsibilities. National Long-Term Care Ombudsman Resource Center. 2016.

LTCO Services of San Luis Obispo County, CA, http://ombudsmanslo.org/success-stories. Last retrieved November 29, 2016.

Tennessee Commission on Aging & Disability, Tennessee Association of Human Resource Agencies (TAHRA). https://www.tn.gov/aging/topic/long-term-care-ombudsman. Last retrieved November 29, 2016.

CHAPTER 11: YOUR RIGHT TO A STATE INVESTIGATION: FILING A COMPLAINT

Institute of Medicine, Committee on Nursing Home Regulation. December 1984. Case Studies of Nursing Home Regulation in Six States. Unpublished Reports.

National Association of Attorneys General. February 1978. Enforcing Quality of Care in Nursing Homes. Committee on the Office of Attorney General.

U.S. Senate. February 9, 1970. Medicare and Medicaid: Problems, Issues, and Alternatives. Report of the staff to the Senate Committee on Finance, 91st Congress, 2d Session. Committee print.

Casper, S. K., and R. E. Burke. February 1985. Policy Recommendations for the Survey Process. Prepared for the Institute of Medicine Committee on Nursing Home Regulation.

Jost, Timothy S. December 1984. Enforcement of Quality Nursing Home Care in the Legal System. Prepared for the Institute of Medicine Committee on Nursing Home Regulation.

Mathematica Policy Research, Inc. January 1985. Evaluation of the State Demonstrations in Nursing Home Quality Assurance Processes. Final report.

CHAPTER 12: RESEARCHING NURSING HOMES

Institute of Medicine (US) Committee on Nursing Home Regulation. Improving the Quality of Care in Nursing Homes. Washington (DC): National Academies Press (US); 1986. 5, Enforcing Compliance with Federal Standards. Available from: https://www.ncbi.nlm.nih.gov/books/NBK217546/

Health Care Financing Administration. 1981. Provider Certification State Operations Manual. Unpublished manual.

CHAPTER 13: FILING A CRIMINAL COMPLAINT

Andrews, Greg. Defendant in American Senior Communities probe agrees to plead guilty. Indianapolis Business Journal. December 17, 2016.

Ellis, Blake & Hicken, Melanie. (2017a) Sick, Dying and Raped in America's Nursing Homes. CNN Investigations, February 2017. http://www.cnn.com/interactive/2017/02/health/nursing-home-sex-abuse-investigation/

Ellis, Blake & Hicken, Melanie. (2017b) Six Women. Three Nursing Homes. And the Man Accused of Rape. CNN Investigations, February 2017. http://www.cnn.com/interactive/2017/02/health/nursing-home-aide-rape-charges/

Krieg, Sheryl. Man charged with raping disabled nursing home resident. News-Sentinel. July 28, 2016. http://www.news-sentinel.com/news/local/crime/Man-charged-with-raping-disabled-nursing-home-resident.

Ladwig, Boris. Former nursing home employee defrauded elderly. Daily News. Jun 13, 2015.

Lenhoff, Alyssa & Livingston, Doug. Nursing homes, administrators escape criminal charges. The Vindicator. December 3, 2012. http://www.thenewsoutlet.org/nursing-homes-administrators-escape-criminal-charges-2/.

Maddux, Stan. (2016) Michigan City nurse's aide charged with posting shower video of woman, 85. South Bend Tribune. Feb 19, 2016.

Maryland Health Care Commission – Certificate of Need for the Closure of the Nursing Facility at University Specialty Hospital; March 19, 2004.

Mullaney, Tim. (2014) Woman gets 27-year prison sentence for stealing nursing home residents' identities. McKnight's: January 24, 2014.

Norwalk Reflector. Former nursing home business office manager sentenced to prison for theft from residents. May 17, 2017.

U. S. Attorney's Office, Southern District of Indiana — U.S. Department of Justice. Press Release: Former American Senior Communities executives indicted. Wednesday, October 12, 2016. https://www.justice.gov/usao-sdin/pr/former-american-senior-communities-executives-indicted

CHAPTER 14: FILING A CIVIL LAWSUIT

Campbell v. Pitt County Memorial Hospital, Inc., 84 N.C. App. 314 (1987).

Chipps v. Humana Health Insurance Co. of Florida, Inc., No. CL 96-00423 AE (Fla., Palm Beach County Cir. Ct. Jan. 4, 2000).

Grimshaw v. Ford Motor Co., 1 19 Cal.App.3d 757, 174 Cal. Rptr. 348 (1981).

Harris, Gardiner, Koli, Eric, (2005) "Lucrative Drug, Danger Signals and the F.D.A.," New York Times, June 10, 2005; MDL-1355.

Lakey v. Sta-Rite Industries Inc., 93 CVS 00425 (Wake County Super. Ct., N.C., settlement January 14, 1997).

Lawrence Chimerine and Ross Eisenbrey. The Frivolous Case for Tort Law Change. Opponents of the legal system exaggerate its costs, ignore its benefits. Briefing Paper #157. May 16, 2005. http://www.epi.org/publication/bp157/

Leggett, Christopher. (1999) The Ford Pinto Case: The Valuation Of Life As It Applies To The Negligence-Efficiency Argument. Spring, 1999. https://users.wfu.edu/palmitar/Law&Valuation/Papers/1999/Leggett-pinto.html#Text.

Moore, T.J., Weiss, SR, Kaplan, S, Blaisdell, CJ. (2002) Reported Adverse Drug Events in Infants and Children under 2 Years of Age, PEDIATRICS 2002 Nov; 110(5):e53).

National Bank of Commerce v. HCA Health Services of Midwest, Inc., No. 84-160 (Saline County Cir. Ct., Ark., verdict October 6, 1986).

Nader R. "Unsafe at any speed: the designed-in dangers of the American automobile. 1965". Am J Public Health. 101: 254–6.

Nader v. General Motors Corp. Court of Appeals of New York, 1970).

Sweet et al v. Rose Art Industries Inc et al, 2:06-cv-00527.

United States ex rel. Beaujon v. Hebrew Homes Health Network, Inc., et al., Case No. 12-20951 CIV (S.D. Fla.).

United States ex rel. Lovvorn v. EHSI, et. al. C.A. 10-1580 (E.D. Pa).

United States ex rel. Gallick et al., v. EHSI et al., C.A. 2:13cv-092 (S.D. Ohio).

United States vs. Vanguard, et al., CA 3:16 -cv-02380 (M.D.Tenn 2016).

U.S. v. Toyota Motor Corp, U.S. District Court, Southern District of New York, No. 14-cr-00186.

Winerip, Michael. (2001) "Ford and Firestone Settle Suit Over Explorer Crash," New York Times, January 9, 2001.

CHAPTER 16: FIGHTING LAWS THAT PROTECT BAD NURSING HOMES — PART I: THE ARBITRATION HURDLE

American Association for Justice. License to Steal: How the U.S. Chamber Forced Arbitration on America. October 2013.

American Health Care Association. Special Study on Arbitration in the Long Term Care Industry. June 16, 2009.

American Health Care Association et al. v. Sylvia Mathews Burrell, et al., CIVIL ACTION NO. 3:16-CV-00233. In the United States District Court for the Northern District of Mississippi Oxford Division, Order dated 11/7/2016.

Berklan, James M. ed. (2016) Court: Arbitration agreement still enforceable even though SNF doesn't have copy of it. McKnight's. July 24, 2016.

Berkowitz, Eric. (2016) "Is Justice Served? Los Angeles Times. October 22, 2016.

Centers for Medicare & Medicaid Services. (CMS) 42 CFR, Part 483. FR Doc. 2017-11883 Filed: 6/5/2017 4:15 pm; Publication Date: 6/8/2017. https://www.federalregister.gov/documents/2017/06/08/2017-11883/medicare-and-medicaid-programs-long-term-care-facilities--arbitration-agreements.

Commission on Health Care Dispute Resolution. (1998) Healthcare Due Process Protocol. Final Report July 27, 1998.

Consumer Financial Protection Bureau. (2015) Arbitration Study: Report to Congress, pursuant to Dodd–Frank Wall Street Reform and Consumer Protection Act § 1028(a). Consumer Financial Protection Bureau. March 2015.

Leonhard, Megan. (2016) "Nursing Home Patients Lose Round on Forced Arbitration." Money. Nov 08, 2016.

Maynard v. Golden Living, 56 N.E.3d 1232 (Ind. App. 2016)

Juan Mendez Jr. etc. v. Hampton Court Nursing Center LLC, case number SC14-1349, in the Supreme Court of Florida.

National Roundtable on Consumer and Employment Dispute Resolution. (2012) Consumer Arbitration Roundtable Summary Report. April 17, 2012, at 54. http://law.psu.edu/ file/YAM/YAM_National_Roundtable_Summary_Report.pdf.

Public Citizen. (2007) How Credit Card Companies Ensnare Customers. September 2007.

Peter B. Rutledge. (2004) Toward a Contractual Approach to Arbitral Immunity.

Saunders, Jim. (2016) Florida Supreme Court rejects arbitration in nursing-home injury case. September 22, 2016.

CHAPTER 17: FIGHTING LAWS THAT PROTECT BAD NURSING HOMES — PART II: ARBITRARY CAPS ON DAMAGE

Americans for Insurance Reform, True Risk: Medical Liability, Malpractice Insurance And Health Care (July 2009) at 17-18.

Associated Press. "Despite New Law, Insurance Companies Won't Lower Rates Right Away," Associated Press. Jan. 9, 2003.

Associated Press. "State report says malpractice claims fell." Associated Press. November 5, 2004.

Babula, Joelle. "Medical Liability Company Requests Premium Increase," Las Vegas Review-Journal, Feb. 11, 2003;

Babula, "State Insurance Program Holds Off on Lowering Rates," Las Vegas Review-Journal, Aug. 14, 2002.

Balber, Carmen & Heller, Doug. (2009) "Insurance Rate Regulation, Not Medical Liability Limits, Lowered California Malpractice Insurance Premiums," http://www.consumerwatchdog.org/newsrelease/house-republicans-have-their- talking-points-california-backwards-insurance-rate-regulati.

Blythe Bernard and Virginia Young. (2012) "Medical malpractice cap is struck down by Missouri Supreme Court," St. Louis Post-Dispatch, August 1, 2012.

BestWire. "Oklahoma's Largest Medical-Liability Company Gets 83% Rate Increase Over Three Years." Dec. 2, 2003.

Bernard S. Black, David A. Hyman and Myungho Paik. (2014a) "Do Doctors Practice Defensive Medicine, Revisited," Northwestern University Law & Economics Research Paper No. 13-20; Illinois Program in Law, Behavior and Social Science Paper No. LBSS14-21 (October 2014).

Bernard S. Black and Zenon Zabinski. (2014b) "The Deterrent Effect of Tort Law: Evidence from Medical Malpractice Reform," Northwestern University Law & Economics Research Paper No. 13-09 (July 2014).

Bernard S. Black, David A. Hyman and Myungho Paik. (2014c) "Do Doctors Practice Defensive Medicine, Revisited," Northwestern University Law & Economics Research Paper No. 13-20; Illinois Program in Law, Behavior and Social Science Paper No. LBSS14-21 (October 2014).

Bernard S. Black, David A. Hyman and Myungho Paik. (2014d) "Does Medical Malpractice Reform Increase Physician Supply? Evidence from the Third Reform Wave," Northwestern University Law & Economics Research Paper No. 14- 11; University of Illinois Program in Law, Behavior and Social Science Research Paper No. LBSS 14-36 (July 2014).

Branson, Reed. "Doctors In Oxford Shut, Cite Insurance," Commercial Appeal, Feb. 14, 2003;

Bryant, Ben. "Tort Reform Has Done Little to Ease Malpractice Crisis," Biloxi Sun-Herald, Feb. 2, 2003.

Commercial Appeal. "Miss. Tort Reform Effort Falls Short." Commercial Appeal. Feb. 18, 2003.

Cornelius, Frank. (1994) "Crushed by My Own Reform." New York Times. October 7, 1994.

Dao, James. (2005) "A Push in States to Curb Malpractice Costs," New York Times, Jan. 14, 2005.

Daily Oklahoman. "Hike Approved for Premiums." Daily Oklahoman. April 8, 2004.

Foundation for Taxpayer and Consumer Rights,. (2005) Insurance Regulation, Not Malpractice Caps, Stabilize Doctors' Premiums, http://www.ftcr.org/healthcare/fs/fs003013.php3 (last visited Feb. 16, 2005).

Foundation for Taxpayer and Consumer Rights. "California Group Successfully Challenges 29.2% Rate Hike Proposed by California's Ninth Largest Medical Malpractice Insurer; Proposition 103 Invoked to Slash Medical Protective Company's Requested Increase by 60%," Sep 16, 2004. http://consumerwatchdog.org/insurance/pr/pr004625.php3.

Jadhav, Adam. "Minor insurer is cutting malpractice rates for doctors," St. Louis Post-Dispatch, October 13, 2006.

Kay, Julie. (2003) "Medical Malpractice; Despite Legislation that Promised to Rein in Physicians' Insurance Premiums, Three Firms File for Big Rate Increases." Palm Beach Daily Business Review, Nov. 20, 2003.

Missouri Department of Insurance. (2003) Medical Malpractice Insurance in Missouri; The Current Difficulties in Perspective 7.

Mohajer, Shaya Tayefe. "Calif regulator: Malpractice insurance too pricey," Associated Press, February 17, 2011; http://www.mercurynews.com/news/ci_17414760?nclick_check=1

Schlegel, Darrin. (2003) "Some Malpractice Rates to Rise Despite Prop. 12," Houston Chronicle, Nov. 19, 2003; Darrin Schlegel, "Malpractice Insurer Fails in Bid for Rate Hike," Houston Chronicle, Nov. 21, 2003; (Oct. 2003 rate filing from Texas Medical Liability Insurance Assoc. (JUA) to Texas Department of Insurance).